P.MES. Harrow High School.

EUROPE

BY THE SAME AUTHOR

An 'Over-deepened' Valley in Switzerland

EUROPE

BY

THOMAS PICKLES, B.Sc.

ILLUSTRATED WITH
25 PHOTOGRAPHS
AND 87 MAPS & CHARTS

REVISED EDITION

J. M. DENT AND SONS LTD.
BEDFORD ST. LONDON W.C.2

© Revised edition, J. M. Dent & Sons Ltd, 1963
All rights reserved
Made in Great Britain
at the
Aldine Press · Letchworth · Herts
for
J. M. DENT & SONS LTD
Aldine House · Bedford Street · London
First published 1932
Revised 1960
Revised edition 1963

PREFACE

THIS book is intended primarily for pupils in middle and upper forms of Grammar and Technical Secondary Schools. While keeping constantly in mind the claims of the examinations in these schools the writer has also presented a somewhat wider view of the subject than is usual in such textbooks.

On the one hand some account is given of the historical background without which it is impossible to understand the peoples and problems of modern Europe. On the other hand, attempt is made to provide an adequate geographical basis for the study of present - day social conditions in the various countries.

The writer holds, too, that the story of the formation and deformation of the land surface is of such unique cultural value that some brief outline must be included in the school course. Consequently, certain episodes in the geological history of the Continent have been included, and suggestions made as to the effects of geological processes upon the history and present-day activities of the people of Europe.

Care has been taken, however, not to present a 'deterministic' view of geography. Throughout emphasis is laid on the way in which man has overcome the difficulties or utilized the opportunities presented by nature. 'There are no necessities, but everywhere possibilities' (Febvre).

Considerable space has also been given to descriptions of the life and work of the people in the various countries. Experience shows that while pupils in Grammar Schools are capable of grasping fundamental geographical principles and of appreciating something of the complex interplay between nature and man, they need a background of local colour to make their studies 'live' and interesting. Many quotations are therefore included from official handbooks, and from recently written 'travel' books, to which acknowledgment is made in the text. In this new edition the text has been modified in accordance with the changes brought about by the Second World War; in particular, the sections on the U.S.S.R. and Germany have been largely rewritten, and the Rhine Basin has been treated as a unit.

In redrawing some of the sketch-maps, a 'pictorial' method of representing relief has been adopted (e.g. Figs. 24, 25, and 34). Expressions of opinion by teachers as to the suitability of this method would be welcomed.

Special thanks are also due to J. D. Meale, Esq., B.Sc., and the late A. Heathcote, Esq., B.A., who kindly read the proofs; to G. W. Pym, Esq., M.A., who has given assistance in checking the historical data; to J. Rushby, Esq., B.A., who has helped in the preparation of this new edition, and to H. W. Marsh, Esq., for his expert assistance in the preparation of reprints.

                                                  T. PICKLES.

CONTENTS

PHOTOGRAPHS

MAPS AND CHARTS

INTRODUCTORY STUDIES

Europe's Place in the World

OUR continent is but a small corner of the world, embracing less than one-twentieth of its surface. Yet it contains a quarter of the world's people and nearly half the great cities of the world; it conducts more than a quarter of the world's trade, and owns more than half of the world's shipping; its farm land is the most productive in the world, and its factories produce more manufactured goods than those of any other continent.

Moreover, the European has not been content merely to develop his own lands. 'With the exception of the Far East —China and Japan—and parts of South America the white man has with the irresistible " drive " of his energetic expansion discovered for himself, opened up, and then taken under his control, all the continents of the world.

'By the technical miracles of modern science of transport of goods and of ideas, the cable and the "wireless," the giant liner and the trans-continental railways, and those children of the internal combustion engine and the electric spark—the motor car, the lorry, the aeroplane, and the motor plough—the white man has carried his control into the secret recesses of every continent. He has farmed the world by controlling the labour of men of every race under the sun. The hands of Africans, Asiatics, and Islanders produce the rubber and the gold, the cotton and the oils, the foods and fabrics of every land, and pour this gathered wealth into the lap of the West.'— Basil Mathews, *The Clash of Colour*.

Though Europeans and their descendants in America, the Dominions, and other regions took the lead in the industrial and economic development of the world's resources, this does not imply that other races are 'inferior.' On the contrary, the study of geography and the changes which have taken place in all the continents in recent years show that though each race has its own special characteristics none possesses all-round inherent superiority.

While being careful, then, not to assume that Europe is the only part of the world where great things have been achieved, we may reasonably ask ourselves how our small continent was able to gain its outstanding position. Geography can supply *part* of the answer by showing how Nature has fitted Europe to be the cradle of great civilizations, and the scene of great industrial and commercial development. Among the special advantages possessed by our continent we may note the following:

(1) Europe is in the temperate zone, where man must work hard in order to live, but where the climate is neither so hot as to sap all his energies, nor so cold as to prevent high mental development.

(2) There are few parts of the world where there is such a variety of land surface—hills, plains, fertile valleys, semi-enclosed basins, and coasts broken by long inlets which penetrate far into the land. The development of navigation was also favoured by the fact that western Europe has milder winters than any other part of the world in the same latitude, so that nearly all her coasts are ice-free at all times.

(3) Nature has endowed our continent with fertile soils and varied climates, which enable man to produce not only essential foodstuffs, but also a surplus of particular products which he can exchange for those of neighbouring areas.

(4) Europe has great stores of coal, metals, and other minerals in sufficiently close proximity to favour the development of manufacturing industries.

(5) Europe is in the centre of the land-mass of the world, and is, therefore, favourably situated for the development of world trade.

(6) Europe is but a peninsular extension of Asia. From the latter continent wave after wave of people have surged onward into Europe. The resultant mixing of related races helps to account for the vigour and vitality of European peoples.

How Nature Built Europe

Hundreds of millions of years ago a continent stretched over the region now occupied by the North Atlantic and north-western Europe. Near the southern edge of this continent was the great *Caledonian* range of mountains, remnants of which still appear as the Scottish Highlands and the Scandinavian Highlands. As this Atlantic continent was worn away, rivers carried away the waste material, and laid it down as sediment in a sea which stretched across central Europe. Gradually this sea was filled up with deposits of sand, clay, and lime, and on the swampy flats thus formed grew the dense forests whose decay formed the coal on which our modern life so closely depends.

Some millions of years later the rocks of the earth's crust were crumpled up in enormous folds, to form a range of mountains to which we give the name *Hercynian range*—although it no longer exists. This range ran across the middle of what is now Europe, and included southern Britain, France, Spain, and Germany. Later still came a period of submergence, during which a great part of the coast was under the sea; great rivers flowing from the Caledonian and Hercynian ranges brought down a vast quantity of sediment, which was deposited in the seas to form the rocks which now cover the lowlands of Europe.

The last great continent-forming movement was another series of crumplings which formed the Alps and other 'new' mountain chains of Europe. In comparatively recent times (say five hundred thousand years ago!) the climate of Europe, which had been for a long period nearly tropical, began to get colder and colder. More and more snow fell in winter, and soon accumulated to such great depths that the summer sunshine could not melt it all. Great snow-fields formed on all the highlands of Europe—particularly in Scandinavia. The snow was compressed to form glaciers and ice sheets; great tongues of ice pressed southward over the plains, and a great part of northern Europe was submerged beneath a mass of ice several hundreds of feet thick.   (See Fig. 1.)   As we shall see in later chapters, this last episode in the long and eventful geological history of our continent has had very great effects on the form of the land, and on the life and work of the people.

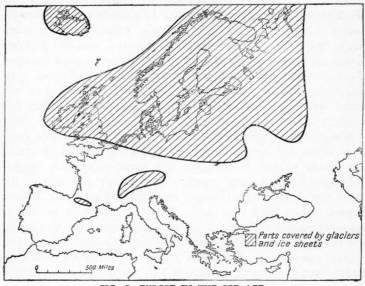

FIG. 1. EUROPE IN THE ICE AGE

About the beginning of the Ice Age man made his appearance in Europe; but it was not until the ice-sheet had finally disappeared that he could make much progress.   Even then his advance was very slow at first, and history can tell us nothing of what happened more than a few thousand years ago.

If the width of this page represents the time Nature took to build Europe, the smallest dot you can make would represent the time that man has occupied its surface, while the period over which history stretches would be only one-twentieth of that dot.   What has man accomplished in that small period? How has he fitted himself into the framework Nature prepared for him? How has he used the opportunities presented to him by Nature? How has he overcome the obstacles Nature placed in his path? To answer such questions we must look fairly closely at the various parts of Europe, for we shall find that the response of man to his environment has varied greatly in different parts of Europe. One thing, at least, may be said at the outset: Geography is not like a problem in arithmetic, to which there is only one correct answer. Man has found many answers to his problems, and some of these answers we read when we study the geography of Europe. What the answers are depends very largely on the men themselves. We can never say: 'Men were *compelled* to do certain things; in this place they were bound to become fishermen, in that place workers in wood or metal, in some other place great sailors and traders.' But we can learn *how* men live and work, and in some cases *why* they lead a particular kind of life.

THE SURFACE OF THE LAND

The long geological processes so briefly described above have produced a continent which, though almost the smallest in the world, is yet the most varied. In the north-west are the Scandinavian and Scottish Highlands, representing the remnants of one of the oldest mountain ranges in the world. South of these is the Great Plain of Europe, shaped like a triangle, with its base on the Urals and its apex in England. Central and southern Europe is a complex region of plateaus, mountain chains, valleys and plains, peninsulas and semi-inland seas. Intricate as is the relief of this portion of Europe, its chief features may easily be memorized if they are grouped according to their mode of origin. (See Fig. 2.)

The key to the whole area is the system of fold mountains. The Alps, the Apennines, the Atlas Mountains, and the Sierra Nevada are all detached portions of one great S-shaped loop; the Carpathians and the Balkans form a similar, though reversed, loop; between these two loops there is the line of the

Illyrian Alps and the Pindus, which is continued through the islands of Crete and Cyprus to Asia Minor; at the extreme western and eastern ends of the system of folds are the Pyrenees and the Caucasus, each running roughly from west to east.

FIG. 2 EUROPE: STRUCTURAL DIVISIONS

In the angles between these ranges are certain plateaus, formed of hard rocks, which are remnants of the old Hercynian Range. Among these are the Meseta of Spain, between the Sierra Nevada and the Pyrenees; the Central Plateau of France, between the Pyrenees and the Alps; the Bohemian Block, between the Alps and the Carpathians; and the Rhodope Block, between the Balkans and the Pindus Mountains.

Within the loops of the fold mountains are certain fertile plains, which were formed by the subsidence of the land, e.g. the basin of the Po and the plain of Hungary; and on the outer edges of the folds are smaller valleys, which were formed by the land sinking between faults, e.g. the Rhine valley between Basle and Mainz, the Rhône valley in south-eastern France, and the plain of Andalusia in southern Spain.

The mountains of central and southern Europe do not form a continuous barrier; on the contrary there are many gaps or gateways which have always facilitated communication. Among these are the Rhône-Saône valley, which provides the shortest route from the Mediterranean to the English Channel; the Burgundian Gate, between the Vosges and the Jura; and the Moravian Gate, between the Bohemian Block and the Carpathians.

The rivers, too, have been of great importance in the historical and economic development of the continent. It is a striking fact that the largest rivers are arranged in pairs, each pair forming a diagonal route across the continent from the northern to the southern coasts. Thus the Rhône-Saône and the Seine form an almost continuous waterway across France; the Rhine and the Danube almost link the North Sea with the Black Sea; the Dniester and Vistula, the Dnieper and Dvina form similar diagonals from the Baltic Sea to the Black Sea; and the Volga and the Northern Dvina almost span the continent at its greatest width between the White Sea and the Caspian Sea.

THE TRANS-CONTINENTAL RAILWAYS OF EUROPE

The course of the great 'through' railway routes of Europe has been very largely determined by the physical features, and one of the most interesting ways of grasping the broad outlines of the relief of the continent is to follow on the physical

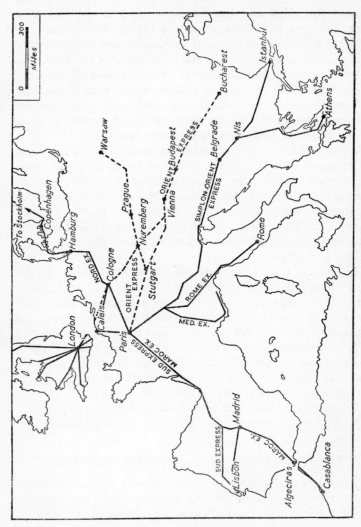

FIG. 3. CHIEF EXPRESS RAILWAY ROUTES OF EUROPE
(N.B. In 1962 the Orient Express ceased to run beyond Vienna)

map the course of some of the chief express routes. Using Fig. 3, an atlas, and a continental time-table as guides, the pupil should make a strip-map of each main route, showing the towns passed through and the physical features for some distance on each side of the route.

THE CLIMATE OF EUROPE

Everybody is interested in the weather, because it plays such an important part in our everyday lives; but the mention of the climate of a country does not usually rouse any special interest. Certainly there is no great interest in the mere statistics of the rainfall and temperature of a place, or, at first sight, in the rainfall or isotherm map. Such statistics and maps are convenient ways of summing up the weather experienced in various districts at various times of the year; and when we consider the ways in which the weather influences the work of the people, the houses they build, the clothes they wear, the food they grow and eat, and even their habits and their national characteristics, we realize that the formerly dry facts about climate become full of significance and interest.

Let us, for example, 'take a walk' across the January isotherm map of Europe. Beginning at home we find that Britain is crossed by the 40° F. isotherm. We know quite well that the temperature is not always 40° F. in January; sometimes we have long spells of frost when the thermometer does not rise above 32° F., and at other times the thermometer may rise above 50° F. What the isotherm means is not that the temperature is always 40° F., but that the average of all the days and all the nights for all the Januaries of about thirty years has been 40° F.

Now suppose our object is to get as quickly as possible to a very cold place. Which way should we have to go from Britain? The map shows us that instead of going northward as we might expect, we must go a little north of east, for the coldest part of Europe is in the north-east of Russia. If we go five hundred miles northward from London we shall find the climate there slightly warmer; but if we go the same distance eastward we shall find the average temperature to be

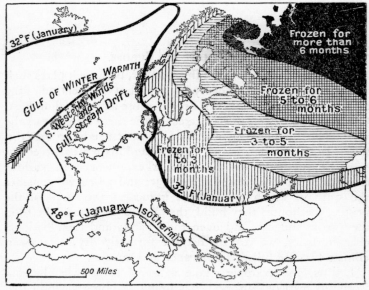

FIG. 4. EUROPE: WINTER TEMPERATURE

below freezing point, while in central Russia, on the same latitude as London, we find that on the average they have more than 20° of frost, and the land is frost-bound for three to five months. (See Fig. 4.)

If we could take a 'magic carpet' flight across Europe we should see what the low winter temperatures of the interior mean to the people. In the extreme west of Europe the winters are so mild that some work on the land is possible in nearly every month; in the east all outdoor farm work must cease for several months, and the farmer must work fourteen or fifteen hours a day in the summer to make up for his forced inactivity in the winter. In the west small open fires suffice to heat our living-rooms, and we do not usually heat our bedrooms; but in Russia a large portion of the living-room is occupied by a great closed stove, upon which the beds are often laid in winter. The farther east we go the colder become the winters. While our rivers are seldom frozen, the lower Rhine is ice-bound for twenty days in an average year, the Vistula for seventy days, and the Volga for one hundred and fifty days. Ice never interferes with the movements of ships in the North Sea, but it is a serious impediment in the western Baltic, and regular postal services are established across the Gulf of Bothnia in winter. Even the Black Sea has its northern shore ice-bound, and the northern half of the Caspian Sea, some five hundred miles nearer the Equator than Britain, is frozen across for several months.

Not only is the winter more severe as we go farther east, but spring begins later and autumn earlier, and the changes from winter to summer, and vice versa, are much more rapid. In our country we can hardly say when winter begins and summer ends, but in Russia the change comes with startling rapidity, and in a few days the dominant colour of the landscape changes from white to green and brown.

In summer also there are great differences between the coastal margins and the continental interior. As we go northward from Britain the climate becomes colder, while as we go eastward it becomes warmer. In July Moscow is warmer than London on the average, while south-eastern Russia, which was much colder than Iceland in winter, is now nearly as warm as the Equator.

Turning to the rainfall maps we see that all the mountainous districts have heavy rainfall, since there the air currents are forced to ascend and the consequent cooling causes condensation of water vapour; but the only lowlands with heavy rain all the year round are those near the north-west coast. All central and eastern Europe has more rain in summer than in winter.   (On the rainfall maps the amount of snow which falls is represented by the equivalent amount of rain, one foot of snow being roughly equal to an inch of rain.)   The greater part of the Mediterranean region has fairly heavy rain in the winter half of the year, and very little in the long hot summer. This must create serious problems for the farmers, and it

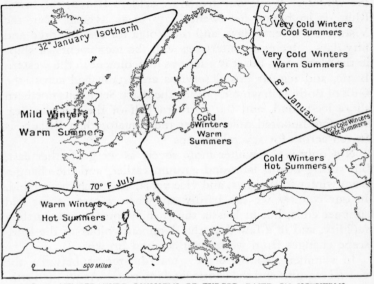

FIG. 5. TEMPERATURE DIVISIONS OF EUROPE, BASED ON ISOTHERMS

will be interesting to see, when studying the Mediterranean countries, how the people overcome this difficulty.   Certain portions of the margins of Europe—south-eastern Russia, south-eastern Spain, and the White Sea district—have little rain at any time.   In the last-named district the drought matters little, for the climate is too cold for much to grow in any case; but the two former districts have hot summers, which make the land very productive where water can be supplied.

All such climatic characteristics have a very great influence on the life and work of the people, and must be carefully considered if we are to understand the varied human activities in Europe. But the inquiring mind will desire not only to work forward from the climatic facts to their effects on the life of the people, but also backward to the reasons why there are such great climatic differences between the various parts of Europe. (See Figs. 5 and 6.)

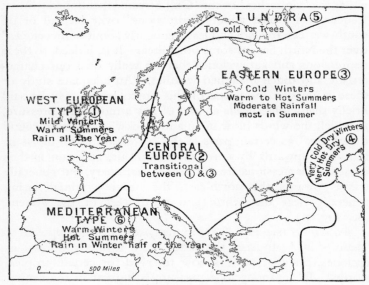

FIG. 6. CLIMATIC DIVISIONS

(1) Let us think of our own weather first, as an example of the **North-west European type** of climate.

In the first place all the land included within this division is near the sea; as the sea heats slowly in summer and cools slowly in winter, and as our prevailing winds in both summer and winter come from the south-west, over the Atlantic Ocean, we have mild winters, cool summers, and ample rain at all times. Another important factor in our climate is the Gulf Stream, which transfers a great deal of heat from equatorial regions to north-western Europe. It must be remembered, however, that the Gulf Stream could have little effect if the prevailing winds were from the east; the beneficial effect of the current is due mainly to the westerly winds which carry inland the air which has been warmed by the current.

Although the foregoing are important factors in our climate, those who listen to the 'weather forecasts' will never hear either the 'westerlies' or the 'Gulf Stream' mentioned. Most frequently we hear about 'depressions' over Iceland or off south-western Ireland, and less frequently about 'anticyclones' over the North Sea, or some other area. It is, indeed, to these depressions and anticyclones that we really owe our characteristic and much maligned weather. An adequate study of these is outside the scope of this book, but it may be said briefly that a *depression* is an area of low atmospheric pressure, in which the winds blow in an anti-clockwise direction round the centre. In certain parts of the depression warm moist air is forced upwards by currents of cool air, and rain is thus caused. Depressions are not usually stationary, but generally travel towards the north-east, the heaviest rainfall being generally near the centre and north-west of the system. (See Fig. 7.)

Anticyclones (see Fig. 8) are in many respects the opposite of 'depressions.' Indeed, the latter were formerly known as cyclones, but that term is now reserved for certain tropical storms. In an anticyclone pressure is highest in the centre, the winds are usually light, circulation of the air is in a clockwise direction, there is little upward thrusting of one wind-current over another, and so there is little rain. Moreover, anticyclones frequently remain stationary for several days, or even weeks; in summer they cause long spells of dry hot weather; in winter long spells of dry frosty weather or fog.

North-western Europe is said to have an *equable* climate, since its range of temperature (i.e. the difference between summer and winter temperatures) is not very great. (See Fig. 9.)

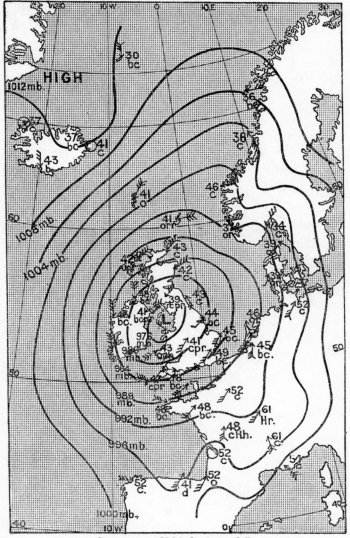

By courtesy of H.M. Stationery Office

FIG. 7. TYPICAL DEPRESSION

Pressure in millibars (1,000 m.b. = 29.53 in.)

The strength of the *wind* is indicated by the number of barbs on the arrows

Weather symbols:— b = blue sky   c = cloud   p = passing showers
r = rain   o = overcast   d = drizzle

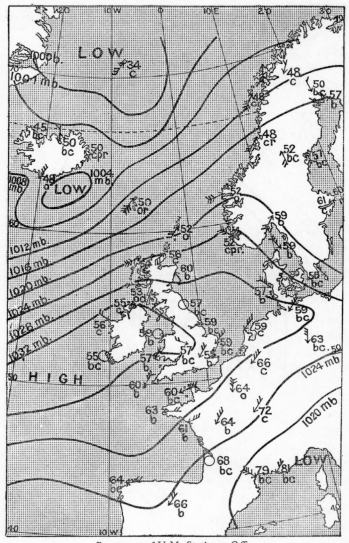

By *courtesy of H.M. Stationery Office*
FIG. 8. TYPICAL ANTICYCLONE
Pressure in millibars (1,000 m.b. = 29·53 in.)

The strength of the *wind* is indicated by the number of **barbs on the** arrows

Weather symbols:—b = blue sky   c = cloud   p = passing showers
r = rain   o = overcast   d = drizzle

(2) and (3) **Central and Eastern Europe,** on the other hand, have an *extreme* climate, since the range of temperatures is high. The region is colder in winter and warmer in summer than our own country, because the great land-mass heats relatively quickly in summer and cools relatively quickly in winter. It

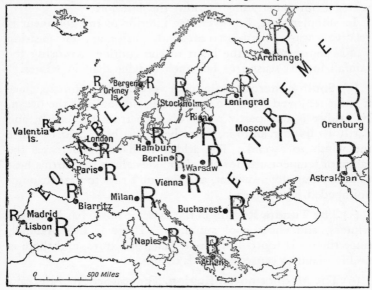

FIG. 9. RANGE OF TEMPERATURE
(The height of the R is proportional to the range of temperature)

is also less subject to the moderating influences of winds from the sea, and is exposed to winds from the interior of Asia, which are very cold in winter and hot in summer. It will be noticed from the isotherm maps, however, that the difference between the winter temperatures of eastern and western Europe is greater than the difference between the summer temperatures of the two regions, showing that the moderating influence of the sea is much more effective in winter than in summer.

One obvious reason why this region has less rain than the

north-western coast lands is that it is farther from the sea, and the winds have been robbed of their moisture by the time they reach the interior. Again, in winter the low temperatures cause relatively high atmospheric pressure, which seems to have the effect of preventing the 'depressions' and westerly winds from penetrating far into the interior.

In summer time, however, the interior of the continent is relatively warm, the heated air tends to rise, and rain-bearing winds penetrate into the heart of the continent, causing the rainfall in this season to be much heavier than in winter.

(4) **South-eastern Russia** has a very extreme climate, since it is far removed from the moderating influence of the ocean. Its aridity is due partly to its distance from the ocean, and partly to its low altitude, there being no high land to cause the winds to ascend. The aridity in its turn increases the range of temperature, for the clear skies allow the earth's heat to radiate rapidly in winter, and the sun's rays to pass through unimpeded in summer.

(5) **The Tundra Region** in the extreme north has long cold winters, and short cool summers. There is little rainfall, since the air is too cold to hold much moisture, and there is no high land to cause the winds to rise.

(6) **The Mediterranean Region.** The restriction of the rain to the winter half of the year over the greater part of this region may be explained in two ways. One explanation emphasizes the fact that the Mediterranean is situated between the two great wind belts of the northern hemisphere—the westerlies and the trades. As the vertical sun moves northward in summer and southward in winter it causes these wind-belts to move north and south also, so that the rain-bearing westerlies blow over the Mediterranean in winter, and the trades, which are dry since they blow from the land and from cooler to warmer regions, blow over the region in summer. Wind maps show, however, that there are no definite belts of westerlies and trades over the Mediterranean in

winter and summer respectively; and a simpler explanation of the winter rain and summer drought is to be found in the fact that in winter the air over the Mediterranean is warmer than that over the neighbouring lands, while in summer the reverse is true. Consequently in winter the pressure over the Mediterranean is relatively low, and depressions from the Atlantic are drawn in, causing frequent rain. In summer, on the contrary, the pressure is relatively high, depressions do not pass over the region, and dry winds blow from the north towards the over-heated Sahara.

Natural Vegetation and Zones of Cultivation

Although over the greater part of Europe man has replaced the natural vegetation by cultivated plants, it is still possible to gain a fairly accurate idea of the types of vegetation which originally flourished in various parts of the continent.

(1) **The Tundra.** In the extreme north, around the White Sea, the land is frost-bound for eight months, and though the top foot or so thaws in the brief summer, the subsoil is permanently frozen. These conditions prevent the growth of trees and hinder the development of cultivation. Moss and lichen, which live through the winter, take the place of edible grasses, and support herds of reindeer. Dwarf willows and birches are also found, and in the short summer the ground is carpeted with a profusion of brightly coloured flowers.

(2) **Coniferous Forest** covers nearly all the surface of northern Russia, Finland, and Scandinavia. On account of the low temperatures the roots of the trees cannot take in much moisture; hence broad-leaved trees cannot live in this region, since such leaves would give out moisture more quickly than the roots could supply it. The needle-like, varnished leaves of the pine, however, present little surface to the air, and so lose little moisture. Lumbering and hunting are the principal occupations of the inhabitants, though here and there are

small clearings on which such cool-weather crops as potatoes and rye are grown.

(3) Southward again, and extending over the European Plain and up the lower slopes of the central highlands, are remnants of the formerly continuous belt of **Deciduous Forest.** Though this has been largely cleared and replaced by intensively cultivated fields, surviving woodlands give the clue to its former character.

In western and central Europe the beech is the characteristic tree, but as we go northward beech is replaced by oak, and on the northern fringe the ash becomes the dominant tree.

(4) **The Mediterranean Region.** Here winter is the growing season, since then the weather is warm and sunny, and there is adequate rainfall.   The summers, on the other hand, are so hot and dry, that the only plants which can survive are such as have special means of combating the drought, e.g. narrow leaves, which are covered with hairs and turn edgeways to the sun; low wide-spreading branches, which do not expose the leaves to as much wind as do higher trees; long roots, which go deep into the ground in search of the moisture which is retained in the subsoil.   The agriculturist, too, has to adapt his methods to suit the climate.   Wheat is grown through the winter, and harvested at the beginning of the hot dry summer; the olive and the vine, whose fruits ripen best in warm, dry weather, are widely grown; and in well-cultivated districts every drop of water is carefully conserved for irrigation purposes.

(5) **The Steppe Lands of South-eastern Russia** are not favourable to the growth of trees since the winters are long and cold, and the summers hot and dry, while the soil is too porous to retain much of the moisture provided by the melting snow.   Certain types of grasses, however, manage to thrive under these conditions.   Some have wide-spreading wiry roots which are not easily killed by frost or drought; others hurry through their life-cycle in the first three months of summer

before the sun has attained its maximum power, then scatter seeds which remain dormant in the soil until the following spring; and nearly all are characterized by tubular or wiry shoots which have the 'breathing' pores inside, so that moisture is conserved. Near the watercourses willows and poplars are frequently found.

THE PEOPLES OF EUROPE

A political map of Europe shows us a patchwork of colours, each representing a country inhabited by people who have so much in common that they are not only content to live under one government, but are passionately determined so to live. Each 'nation' is, however, composed of people with various physical characteristics, and a study of these has shown that most of the inhabitants of Europe are descended from one or more of three chief types of people.

These are, in order of their entry into Europe:

(1) **The Mediterranean Type,** characterized by long skulls, dark hair, darkish skins, and rather short stature. People of this group inhabit mainly the lands around the western Mediterranean (Italy, Corsica, southern France, Portugal, and southern and central Spain). Isolated 'fragments' of this racial type are, strangely enough, found in the extreme north-west of Spain and in western Ireland.

(2) **The Alpine Peoples,** broad skulled and of medium stature and complexion, whose descendants are to be found mainly in the mountainous portions of central Europe, France, and Great Britain.

The Slavs are a branch of this Alpine group who have pushed eastward into the European plain. From them the peoples of European Russia, Poland, Czechoslovakia, and Yugoslavia are mainly descended.

(3) **The Nordic Type,** tall, light complexioned, fair haired, and blue eyed. Their descendants are to be found chiefly in

B   E

Scandinavia, Britain, north Germany, Denmark, Belgium, and northern France.

In addition to these three chief types are others who came from Asia. From one such group are descended the Lapps and the Magyars, and (in part) the Finns, the Estonians, and the Bulgars. From another stock, known as the Turki, came the Tartars of southern Russia and the Turks.

The nationalities of Europe do not coincide with these 'racial' groups. Especially in western Europe the nations are composed of a mixture of races, and some of the characteristics of two or more types are usually combined in one individual.

THE DEVELOPMENT OF CIVILIZATION IN EUROPE

Though western Europe is to-day the most highly developed corner of the world, it is only comparatively recently that man has been able to make use of the opportunities which Nature afforded in this region. The earliest civilizations in the world arose in the fertile river valleys of China, India, Mesopotamia, and Egypt, where the warm climate, fertile soil, absence of forest, protection by encircling mountains and deserts, and facilities for irrigation and communication afforded by the rivers, made it relatively easy for man to develop. The vast period during which such regions were the centre of civilization is known as the **Valley Phase.** Later, as man learnt the art of sea navigation, the Mediterranean became the centre of the civilized world. This **Inland Sea Phase** of civilization lasted from about 2500 years B.C. to about A.D. 1500.

The Mediterranean was well suited to be a 'cradle of civilization' because:

(a) Its coasts are diversified by many peninsulas and islands, which guided the early navigators from point to point, and by many harbours which are accessible at all times, since the sea is practically tideless.

(b) On its shores are many small and fertile plains, each protected by mountains on the landward side, so that they

form semi-isolated basins within which the people were able
to develop in safety.

(c) The Mediterranean type of climate, with its hot, dry
summers, does not favour the growth of dense forest; hence
the early inhabitants could cultivate the soil without having
first to clear the ground of forest.　The warm, rather wet
winters make the region suitable for the cultivation of wheat,
while the dry summers suit the vine and the olive; thus the

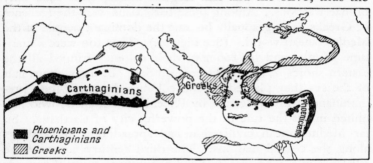

FIG. 10. THE MEDITERRANEAN 'CRADLE OF CIVILIZATION'

early inhabitants could provide themselves with the necessary
foodstuffs, and small groups of people could easily become
self-supporting.

(d) Irrigation is, however, necessary in most Mediterranean
areas if the land is to be fully utilized in the hot, dry summer;
but as irrigation can only be carried on where the people work
together for the common good, they soon learnt to obey the
laws framed for the good of the community.

The first European civilization arose on the island of Crete
some 2500 years B.C., and spread across the 'land bridges' of
the Aegean islands to the coast-lands of Greece.　A thousand
years later the Phoenicians, a nation of traders whose home
was on the coast of Syria, had established themselves as the
chief sea-power of the world.　From such rich cities as Tyre
and Sidon their ships went out to every part of the Mediterranean; chains of sister cities and colonies were established

all along the coast (see Fig. 10), and overland routes were organized by which tin was transported from Brittany to the mouth of the Rhône, and amber from the Baltic to the Black Sea.

While the Phoenicians were at the height of their power barbarian tribes swept southward into the Balkan peninsula. Armed with iron weapons they easily defeated the more civilized inhabitants of the Aegean coasts, who used only bronze weapons. Among these barbarians were the Hellenes or Greeks, who gradually became the dominant people of the Mediterranean world. (See Fig. 10.) They too were a maritime people, and by 800 B.C. their colonies fringed all the eastern shores of the Mediterranean Sea. In the western half of the sea they planted several colonies, but here their predominance was challenged by Phoenician colonists, who had united under the rule of the powerful city of Carthage. So far Mediterranean civilization had spread only by seaways along the coastal margins. The third century B.C. saw the rise of Rome, who was destined not only to unify the whole Mediterranean world, but also to extend her dominions far beyond the borders of the inland sea.

Stronger at sea than either the Greeks or the Carthaginians, the Romans also discovered the secret of subjugating inland people. Wherever they went they built roads which linked the remotest parts of their empire to the central city.

At the beginning of the Christian era the Roman Empire was a great quadrilateral, bounded on the south by the Sahara, on the north by the line of the Rhine and the Danube, on the west by the Atlantic, and on the east by the deserts of Arabia and Persia. (See Fig. 11.) For four hundred years this region enjoyed the 'Pax Romana'; commerce and industry flourished, the people learnt new and better ways of living, and there was a greater degree of unity than ever before or since.

Rome, as the central city of the central peninsula of the Mediterranean, was well fitted to be the controlling centre of the Empire. But such control could only be exercised by strong rulers; under weaker government the Empire tended to fall apart, and it eventually became necessary to divide it into two sections—a western half, centred on Rome, and an eastern half, with Constantinople as its capital. Just about the time when the Empire was weakened by such divisions, its

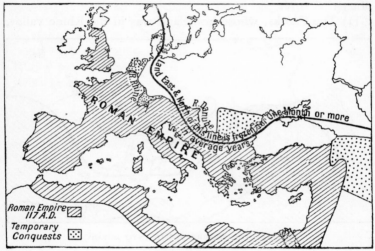

FIG. 11

long north-eastern frontier was being attacked by barbarian tribes, such as the Goths, the Vandals, and the Huns.

This last-named people were fierce nomads, who had left the steppes of central Asia, possibly during a period of unusual drought, and surged in an irresistible flood westward. The less savage peoples of central Europe fled before them in terror, and so began the migrations which resulted in the final downfall of Rome.

During the Dark Ages which followed this disruption of the the Roman Empire, European civilization was at a low ebb, but the teaching and training of the Romans were never entirely forgotten, and the conquering barbarians gradually learnt the arts of civilization from their subject peoples. The

Popes too had great power, and the Church, in spite of much
corruption among the clergy, was a great civilizing and
unifying influence.

It is impossible here to follow all the stages in the development of modern Europe, but the following points should be
noted:

(1) The Franks, whose homeland was in the Rhine valley,

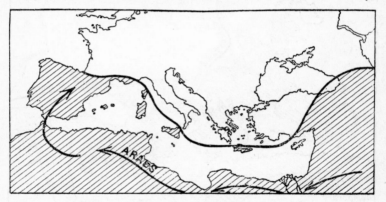

FIG. 12. THE DESERT ROUTE INTO EUROPE

near the present city of Frankfurt, soon became the dominant
power in western Europe. After the death of Charlemagne
(A.D. 814) the Frankish dominions fell apart; the western half,
which had formerly been under Roman rule, eventually became the Kingdom of France, while the eastern half, which
had never been conquered by Rome, formed the basis from
which Germany eventually developed. (See Fig. 58.)

The Italian peninsula, no longer the home of a great unifying
power, was divided between rival rulers, and so remained
until the middle of last century.

(2) In the eighth century Arabs or 'Moors' advanced westward along the northern coast of Africa, crossed into Spain,
and established a civilization which was unsurpassed in
Europe for many centuries. (Fig. 12.)

(3) In the ninth century the Magyars, an Asiatic people who had settled on the steppes of southern Russia, were driven westward by other nomadic invaders, and settled on the plains of Hungary. (Fig. 13.)

In the thirteenth century the Tartars, another nomadic tribe from central Asia, advanced into southern Russia.

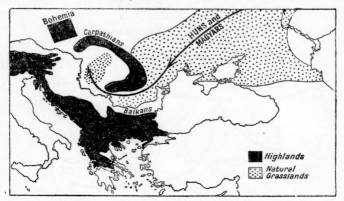

FIG. 13. THE GRASSLAND GATEWAY INTO EUROPE

(4) During the ninth and tenth centuries, Norsemen from the lands around the Baltic and the mouth of the Rhine pushed outwards in all directions; in western Europe they settled in Britain and northern France; in eastern Europe they followed the rivers from the Baltic to the Black Sea, and their chieftains made themselves rulers of what is now known as Russia.

(5) Slavonic tribes were gradually pushed eastward by advancing waves of German colonists. (Fig. 59.)

(6) Up to the end of the fifteenth century civilization was still in the Inland Sea Phase. The Mediterranean was still the main highway of commerce, and such cities as Venice, Genoa, and Florence gained great wealth by conducting the trade between Europe and the East. In north-western Europe the Hanseatic League, a confederation of trading cities, controlled the trade of the Baltic and the North Sea, the chief link between

the Hansa ports and the Mediterranean being the Rhine
valley. (See Fig. 14.)

(7) With the discovery of America civilization entered the
Atlantic Phase. The Mediterranean now became but a back-

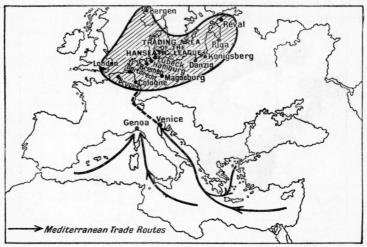

FIG. 14. THE RHINE AS THE LINK BETWEEN TWO 'INLAND SEA' TRADING
REGIONS

water of commerce, while countries with an Atlantic coast like
Spain, Portugal, the Netherlands, and Britain, rose rapidly to
power. The modern history of Europe is largely the story of
the struggles of these countries for the supremacy on land
and sea which would ensure their supremacy in commerce
and industry.

THE SCANDINAVIAN PENINSULA

THIS peninsula, which comprises the countries of Norway and Sweden, is one of the oldest bits of land in the world. As we have seen, it was once part of the great Caledonian Range which extended across the North Sea, through Scotland, and perhaps into North America. During the course of millions of years these mountains were worn away, until the whole land was nearly at sea-level. Uplift then took place, forming a great tilted block with a steep slope westward, and a more gentle slope to the east. The weather and rivers then began to wear away the surface of this tilted block, carving it into mountains and valleys. During the Great Ice Age glaciers and ice-sheets further modified the surface, scraping the soil off the high land, and gouging out the valleys so that they became U-shaped. One of the most recent episodes in this eventful history was the sinking of the land to form the 'drowned' fiord coast, which is so characteristic of Norway. In the south the sinking of the land formed a great sea channel running from the Kattegat to the White Sea. Remnants of this strait are still to be seen in the depression which includes lakes Vener, Vetter, and Malar, the Gulf of Finland, and lakes Ladoga and Onega. The mud which was deposited in this strait now forms the most fertile farming belt of Sweden.

This brief story of the method of formation of the Scandinavian Peninsula helps us to understand many things about its present-day geography. If we look only at a political map we may think it strange that there are two countries in such a narrow peninsula. But either a physical map or a population map shows us that this is quite to be expected; for the broad belt of high land between the two countries forms one of the best boundaries in the world, as it is not only difficult to cross, but is also practically unpeopled, and must always have kept the Norwegians and the Swedes from close contact.   Indeed, communication has always been easier between Norway and Denmark than between Norway and Sweden, and the two former countries were united under one government from the fourteenth century to the beginning of the nineteenth.   So close was the union that Norway was for centuries merely a province of Denmark, and the languages of the two countries became almost identical.

Again, since the block from which the plateau was carved had its highest ridge near the Atlantic, Norway is comparatively narrow, and consists almost entirely of high land, while Sweden occupies much more than half the peninsula, and has a wide coastal plain.   One consequence of the unequal distribution of lowland is that farming is of much greater importance in Sweden, while the people of Norway have been led to depend more on the harvest of the sea.   Though Nature has been so niggardly in the matter of cultivable land, she has given Norway special climatic advantages.   The prevailing south-westerly winds not only bring much rain to Norway, but also help to give her remarkably mild winters; Sweden, on the contrary, is in the rain shadow of the mountains, is shut off from the mild westerly winds, and is open to cold winter winds from the continent.   Norway, too, derives great benefit from the Gulf Stream Drift, which washes her shores and helps to keep her harbours from freezing.   The Gulf of Bothnia, on the other hand, is ice-bound for four or five months in the year, and ice is a hindrance to navigation on all the Baltic coasts.

NORWAY

THE most interesting feature of Norway is its magnificent fiord coast, which, if stretched out in a straight line, would reach nearly half-way round the world.   Fortunate indeed are those who can spend a summer holiday cruising about these fiords. Let us, at least, take an imaginary trip along such a fiord as that shown in Fig. 15. We will begin high up on the barren plateau or 'fjeld,' which constitutes about nine-tenths of the surface of Norway. Above us (at *A* in Fig. 16) are jagged peaks and pinnacles of rock, sculptured into fantastic shapes by the action of frost and ice, and still surrounded even in summer by a great expanse of snow. Below these, at *B*, are rounded slopes and bare rocks, from which the soil was scraped by the glaciers of the Ice Age; the scanty vegetation consists only of moss and a few dwarf shrubs; nowhere is there sign of human habitation or possibility of human occupation.

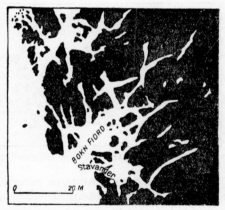

FIG. 15. PART OF NORWAY'S FIORD COAST

As we descend, however, we begin to see tufts of coarse grass, heather, and bilberries, while below, at *C*, is a group of wooden huts, called a 'saeter.' In Norway, as in Switzerland and other mountainous countries, the farmers drive their cattle and goats to the upland pastures in summer time, thus setting free the valley lands for the production of hay and other crops. This seasonal movement of flocks and herds is called *transhumance*. In Norway the herds begin to move up to the mountains about the end of June, and stay there for two or three months.

The summer pastures may be two or three days' journey from the village, and in some cases the cattle have to be transported across the fiord by boat. The men usually remain at work on the valley farm while the herd-boys and dairymaids accompany the cattle, and live in the log huts which form the saeter. Butter and cheese are made from the milk, and the hay from one or two small meadows is stored in one of

the huts, ready to be transported by sledges to the valley in
winter.

Below the saeters are the valleys which were 'over-deepened'
by the scouring action of the glaciers of the Ice Age, so that
they are U-shaped in cross-section.   Over the steep sides the

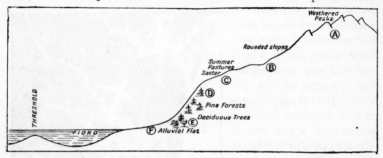

FIG. 16. DIAGRAMMATIC SECTION FROM FJELD TO FIORD

mountain streams plunge in picturesque waterfalls, some of
which make a single leap of five hundred feet or more to the
fiord below.   As we are descending the main valley leading to
the head of the fiord, our path, though steep, is not precipitous,
and we pass through pine forests (*D*) and deciduous woods
(*E*) to the delta or alluvial flat (*F*).   This has been built up
at the head of the fiord by the sediment swept down by swift
streams, such as that whose course we have followed from
the fjeld.   Here, at the meeting of land-routes and water-
routes, and on the largest stretch of fertile land to be found
near the fiord, has grown up the principal settlement.

The characteristic occupations of the Norwegians can be
observed as we pass through the farm lands to the village, and
then to the shore.   Each farm consists largely of permanent
pasture or meadow, stretching up the lower slopes to the foot
of the forest.   If it is August we may see the farm workers
drying the hay by hanging it on poles or wooden fences.   Hay
is the chief winter food of the cattle, and so no effort is spared
to get as much of it as possible, and to cure it before it is

spoilt by the heavy rains to which Norway is subject. On the alluvial lands near the wooden farm-houses we shall see small fields of barley, oats, potatoes, and roots, but no wheat, as the climate is too damp for it to ripen with certainty.

Another characteristic occupation of the Norwegians, lumbering, may be brought to our notice by the buzzing of saws in a near-by sawmill. The logs are cut in winter, dragged by horses to the steep slopes at the edge of the valley, and floated down the swollen rivers in early summer. Electricity derived from the waterfalls is largely used for driving the machinery. Passing down to the beach, through a village composed mainly of wooden houses, we shall probably see evidence of the fishing industry in the platforms on which cod-fish are being dried for export.

Embarking now on one of the many fishing boats which lie drawn up on the beach we shall have the opportunity of observing the characteristics which distinguish the fiords from other inlets, viz.: (1) The sides are high and steep; indeed, where the fiords run from west to east the southern side may be completely shut off from the direct rays of the sun, and consequently be practically devoid of farm land and human settlements. (2) Cultivable land is scarce, even on the sunny slopes, and is restricted to narrow ledges just above the high tide, or to small deltas where tributary streams enter the fiord. (3) The fiords are very deep since the steep slopes of the mountain sides are continued below the water level. We may even see a great Atlantic liner, carrying tourists on a cruise of the fiords, steaming within a few hundred yards of the shore. If, however, we took soundings near the mouth of the fiord we should find that there the water is shallower, the fiord being separated from the open sea by a submerged ledge or threshold. (See Fig. 16.) This threshold prevents the cold water of the ocean depths from entering the fiord and lets in only the warm surface water from the Gulf Stream Drift; consequently the fiords do not freeze even in the coldest winters. (4) There are many tributary fiords, which enter the main fiord at unexpected angles.   Notice on the map (Fig. 15) how these follow two or three main directions.   This is because the fiords were formed originally by great cracks or faults, which have since been widened and deepened by rivers and glaciers, and then partially submerged so that they became arms of the sea.   (5) At the mouth of the fiord, beyond the threshold, are groups of rocky islands called *skerries*.   These stretch for hundreds of miles parallel to the main coast, and act as a breakwater, forming a stretch of calm water near the shore.   This *Inner Lead*, as it is called, forms a sheltered highway for coastal steamers and fishing boats all the way from Stavanger to the North Cape.

How the Fiords have influenced the Norwegian People

We have seen that the mountainous character of the country and the steepness of the coasts restrict farming to the small lowlands near the fiords.   The farms cannot support large numbers of people, and so the Norwegians, shut off from expansion inland by the barren fjeld and invited seaward by the calm waters of the fiords, have become seafaring people. Fishing and farming have always been the principal occupations, but they do not provide for all the needs of the people, and other ways of making a living must be found.   In former times the Vikings, unable to earn a livelihood at home, sallied forth to plunder the richer lands of western Europe and the Mediterranean.   At first they would return home every winter with the booty they had gained, but later they began to settle in the new lands over the seas, e.g. the Normans in France, and the Danes in England and Iceland.   In modern times, instead of plundering, the Norwegians build tramp steamers, which ply between foreign ports, picking up cargo where they can, and thus earning money which is sent home to Norway.   Norway to-day has, in proportion to her population, the largest mercantile marine in the world.   Again, instead of taking the land belonging to other people, many Norwegians, unable to find a living at home, have emigrated to other countries, especially to the United States of America and Canada.

THE INDUSTRIES OF NORWAY

The industries we observed in our imaginary journey along the fiord—forestry, fishing, and farming—are the means of livelihood of the majority of the Norwegian people. Often one man will be both farmer and fisherman, or farmer and lumberman, while a family may share all these occupations, and so be almost self-supporting.

Forestry and the Timber Industries occupy about one-quarter of the workmen of Norway, and provide one-third of the total value of the exports. The chief lumbering districts are the valleys converging on Oslo Fiord and on Trondheim. Norway formerly exported much timber, but nowadays almost all that can be spared from constructional work within the country is regarded as a valuable raw material for the manufacture of pulp and paper. These commodities command prices which include, not only the raw material, but also the hydro-electricity, and the labour and skill used in their manufacture.

Fishing provides work for almost as many people as the timber industries. The chief fish caught are cod, herring, and brisling (for 'sardines'), while whaling and sealing are also of considerable importance. Cod fishing is carried on chiefly in the northern seas around the Lofoten Isles and off the north coast. Each year thirty to forty thousand fishermen from the whole length of the coast gather at these fishing grounds. Fishing begins in January at the Lofoten Isles, when the cod come in from the depths of the Atlantic to spawn. By April the fish are to be found off the north coast, and fishing is continued there until the middle of June. In an average season about sixty million cod-fish are landed.

Formerly the fishing was carried on in open sailing boats, and the men returned at night to the islands or to the mainland, where they sheltered in log huts which were sometimes so overcrowded that the men had to sleep standing up in their wet clothes. Though in recent years conditions have been much improved, and decked motor boats with proper living accommodation have been introduced, cod fishing is still an arduous and dangerous occupation.

The fish are preserved for export in two forms. Stock fish (so called because they look like sticks) are those which are cured whole; and klip fish is cod which has been cut open, salted, and dried. Both types are exported, the klip fish in particular finding a ready market in Spain, Portugal, West Africa, and South America. Large quantities of cod are also packed in ice and exported as fresh fish or frozen fillets to other countries in western Europe. Oil is extracted from the liver, and the fish-refuse is used for the manufacture of fish meal and fertilizer. Dried heads of cod-fish are also used locally for cattle food.

The two chief centres of the cod-fishing industry are Tromsö and Hammerfest. Both these towns are situated north of the Arctic Circle, and therefore experience the midnight sun. At Tromsö there are nine weeks, and at Hammerfest eleven weeks, during which the sun never sets, and for the same periods in winter the sun never rises. Hammerfest has the distinction of being the most northerly town in the world, but its harbour is never closed by ice, largely on account of the warm Gulf Stream Drift and the mild west winds from the Atlantic. It exports cod-fish, cod-liver oil, and whale oil, and is an important centre for the collection of eiderdown, furs, and reindeer skins.

Tromsö, situated on the island of that name, is the largest town of the Lofoten Isles. It is the chief cod-fishing and sealing port of Norway, and is the headquarters of the colliery company which works the coal mines of the Norwegian islands of Spitsbergen.

The herring fisheries are centred in the more southerly seas, off Trondheim, Bergen, and Stavanger. Part of the catch is exported, fresh or salted, but most of it is used for making fish oil and fish meal. Even the herring scales are sold—to the manufacturers of artificial pearls. Brisling are caught

COD-DRYING IN NORWAY

chiefly off the southern coasts, where Stavanger is the most important canning station.

Whaling is now carried on mainly in the Antarctic Ocean, but the experience gained by the Norwegian whalers in the Arctic Seas enabled them to take the lead in this new field. Two types of vessels take part in the whaling industry: small 'whale-catchers,' equipped with guns for firing the explosive harpoons, and with air pumps for expanding the body of the whale so that it does not sink; and 'floating factories,' on which the whales that are brought by the whale-catchers are cut up, and the blubber boiled to extract the oil. Usually the bones and other refuse are taken to land stations to be turned into bone meal and fertilizers, but some of the modern floating factories are capable of carrying out every process while still at sea.

Farming. Of the total area of Norway only 3 per cent is cultivated, and less than a quarter of this is arable land. Oats, barley, and rye are the chief cereals, but the country cannot produce sufficient grain for her own needs, and has to import nearly all the wheat she uses. On the other hand, relatively large numbers of cattle are kept—on the average, one cow for every two people. There is, therefore, a considerable surplus of milk, and this is exported, mainly in condensed form. The chief farming region is, naturally, around the Oslo Fiord, where there is the largest area of low, fertile ground.

Manufactures. The chief industries are such as depend on local supplies of raw material and on cheap hydro-electricity. Timber and timber products form the greater part of the industrial output, but many people are employed in the food industries, such as fish preserving, and the manufacture of condensed milk and butter. Electrical furnaces are used for the smelting of ores of iron, copper, zinc, and aluminium, and for the production of the fertilizer known as cyanamide. To make this latter substance carbon, generally in the form of anthracite, is heated with limestone in an electrical furnace to form calcium carbide; from this cyanamide is produced by allowing it to absorb nitrogen obtained from liquid air.

C   E

An interesting feature of Norwegian industries is that the
majority of them use hydro-electricity in place of coal.   Consequently, instead of being concentrated in smoky cities they
have largely developed in small centres near sources of hydro-
electricity.   Indeed, nearly half the factory workers live in
rural districts.

THE TOWNS OF NORWAY

Oslo, with a population of 440,000, is the only large town in
Norway.   Of the rest, only Bergen has more than 100,000
people, and only Trondheim and Stavanger exceed 50,000.

Oslo (Christiania), the capital of Norway, lies at the head of
the Christiania Fiord, in the centre of the only large area of
fertile lowland, and at the focus of the routes which follow
the coastal plains and the Glommen valley.   Though ice often
forms in its harbour in winter, ice breakers keep it open to
the largest vessels throughout the year, and it is by far the
most important port of Norway.

Bergen is situated on an isthmus within a landlocked harbour,
practically at the western extremity of the country, midway
between the Hardanger and Sogne Fiords, and between Trondheim and Oslo.   In the Middle Ages it was one of the chief
trading stations of the Hanseatic League (see Fig. 14), and was
the chief port of Norway.   At the present day its trade consists
chiefly in the exportation of timber, fish, and fish products.
It formerly suffered as a port by lack of railway connection
with the interior, but early in this century a railway was constructed over the Hardanger Fjeld to Oslo.   This Highland
Railway has opened up many formerly isolated valleys, and
done much to encourage the development of winter sports
for tourists.

Trondheim is situated at the head of the Trondheim Fiord,
from which a lowland gateway leads southward by the Glommen valley to Oslo.   It was formerly the capital of the country,
and the name Trondheim, which is sometimes replaced by the
yet older name of Nidaros, means 'throne-home.'   The

coronation ceremonies of the Norwegian kings are still conducted in its cathedral, which is the finest in Norway.

THE FOREIGN TRADE OF NORWAY

It will be obvious from the foregoing account of the industries of Norway that her exports must consist mainly of metals, wood pulp, paper, fish, and fish products. With the money she obtains for these she has to buy oil, coal, textiles, wheat, tropical foodstuffs, and miscellaneous manufactured goods. The most interesting fact, however, concerning Norway's trade is that every year she appears to buy more than she sells. In a recent year, for example, she spent £450,000,000 on imports, but sold only £290,000,000 worth of goods. How can Norway keep on doing this from year to year and not be bankrupt? The answer is, that she has other sources of income besides her export of *goods*; her merchant ships earn money which is paid to Norwegian sailors and shipowners, and used by them to buy things they and their families need. Other 'hidden' sources of income for Norway are her emigrants, who send money home to their relatives, and tourists who spend money in the country.

SWEDEN

A JOURNEY through Sweden from south to north would show that the country may be divided into four roughly parallel belts which vary considerably in their fertility, mineral wealth, natural vegetation, and occupations of the people. (See Fig. 17.)

(1) In the extreme south is the province of Scania, which gave its name to the Scandinavian peninsula. This province is composed of soft rocks, similar to those of Denmark, and very different from those of the rest of Sweden. It is the most

fertile and most densely peopled part of the country, and grows so much of her grain that it is often called 'the Granary of

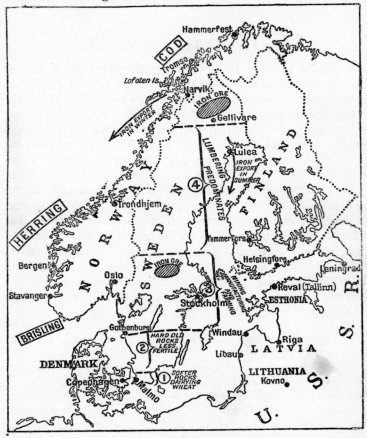

FIG. 17. SCANDINAVIA AND THE BALTIC

Sweden.' Wheat, barley, oats, and rye are cultivated, and sugar beet is the most important root crop. This is also the chief dairying region of Sweden, and in normal times considerable quantities of butter, bacon, and eggs are exported to Britain and other European countries.

Except on the coast there are no large towns and few villages, each white-walled farm-house being situated in the midst of its own fields. *Malmö*, the third city and third port of Sweden, stands on an artificial harbour near the southern extremity of the peninsula. The harbour is kept open by ice-breakers throughout the year, and ferry-steamers run daily to Copenhagen and Lübeck. The port exports much dairy produce from the surrounding lowlands, and has miscellaneous industries such as the manufacture of cotton goods, soap, shoes, and tobacco. *Helsingborg* is situated on the narrowest portion of the Sound, and from it train-ferries run to Helsingör in Denmark. It is an important agricultural centre, and its industries are concerned chiefly with the manufacture of agricultural products.

(2) Between Scania and the lakes Vener and Vetter lies a belt of hilly wooded country, composed of hard old rocks similar to those forming the Scandinavian Highlands. The rather scanty population is concentrated in the more fertile valleys which produce good pasture for dairy cattle. The farm-houses, in contrast to those of Scania, are usually built of timber, and smeared with red clay to prevent dry rot.

(3) To the north of this hilly tract is the fertile central trough which contains the great lakes Vener, Vetter, and Malar, as well as innumerable smaller sheets of water. The two chief ports of Sweden—Gothenburg and Stockholm—are situated respectively at the western and eastern ends of this trough. *Gothenburg*, situated at the mouth of the Gota River, which flows from Lake Vener, is the chief port of Sweden. It is an example of the towns which owe their origin to the will and foresight of individuals. It was founded early in the seventeenth century by Gustavus Adolphus, under whose rule Sweden became a great continental power. At this period the combined countries of Norway and Denmark owned all the Atlantic coast of Scandinavia, with the exception of a

narrow strip at the mouth of the Gota River; so Gustavus
built there a great fortress to ensure Sweden a gateway to the
sea. Tradition says that an eagle showed him where to build
this fortress, but we may be sure that he chose the position
after very careful consideration of its geographical advantages, for a great strategist must be a good geographer. Its

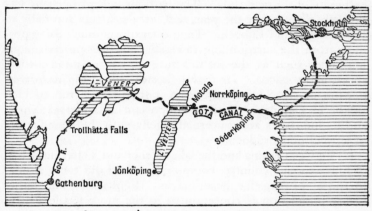

FIG. 18. SWEDEN'S LAKE-BELT AND THE GOTA CANAL

modern importance, too, is due to the decision of individuals,
for early in the present century it was chosen, after careful
consideration of alternatives, as the most suitable Swedish port
for ocean trade; the harbour was modernized, great shipping
companies made it their headquarters, and electricity generated
at the Trollhätta Falls on the Gota River provided the basis
for industrial development.

From Gothenburg we may sail right across the country to
Stockholm by the *Gota Canal*. (See Fig. 18.) Ascending the
River Gota, the first feature of interest is the Trollhätta
Falls, which besides providing electricity for Gothenburg and
the surrounding region supply a surplus which is 'exported'
via the Sound to Denmark. Avoiding the falls by means of a
ship-canal, we proceed through lakes Vener and Vetter. At

the southern end of the latter lake is *Jönköping*, the centre of the
match industry, and the birthplace of the inventor of safety
matches. The canal leaves Lake Vetter at *Motala*, notable for
its radio station, and passes a little south of *Norrköping*, famous
for its textile industries, which are run by hydro-electricity
derived from falls on the Motala River. Beyond Norrköping
the canal runs out to sea, and passes through an archipelago
of small islands to enter Stockholm through the 'back door'
of Lake Malar. The combined river, lake, and sea route,
known as the Gota Canal, is 347 miles long, but the actual
canal occupies only 56 miles. In this distance there are 65
locks, which so delay the traffic as to detract considerably
from the commercial value of the route.

Stockholm, the capital of Sweden, is situated on the channel
which joins Lake Malar to the sea. In this channel are a
number of islands, on the central one of which the Vikings
built a fortress to guard the entrance to their chief base,
Lake Malar. The town which grew up around this fortress
gradually spread over these islands, and on to both banks of
the mainland. The city is intersected by so many channels
that it has been called 'the Venice of the North.'

The harbour of Stockholm, though sometimes impeded by
ice, is practically always kept open by ice-breakers. As a port
it has the advantage of being situated near supplies of timber
and minerals, and in the centre of the chief industrial area of
Sweden. Hence, though it suffers somewhat from its remoteness from the great trade routes, it conducts a large share of
the trade of the country.

North of Stockholm is a belt of country about one hundred
miles wide, in which may be observed all the characteristic
industries of Sweden—lumbering, mining, farming, and manufacturing. The dense coniferous forests which stretch from
latitude 60° N. to beyond the Arctic Circle, form one of the
chief sources of wealth in Sweden, and the logs cut in a normal
year would, if placed end to end, go twice round the Equator.
The trees are felled in winter, dragged over snow-ways to the

frozen rivers, and floated down to the sawmills in spring and summer. Here the logs are cut up into pit props, boards, and planks for export. Much timber is manufactured into doors, window-frames, and cheap furniture, and Sweden also leads the world in the production of wood pulp. Among the advantages which Sweden possesses as a lumber-producing country are: (*a*) the great extent of her forests, which are carefully supervised by the government to prevent their exhaustion; (*b*) the cold winters which cause the timber to be close-grained, and the heavy snowfall which facilitates transport in winter; (*c*) numerous streams which, swollen in spring and summer by the melting snows, assist in the transport of the logs, and provide abundant hydro-electrical power to drive the sawmills and pulp factories. The fact that the main streams flow in separate parallel courses to the sea, instead of being gathered together in one or two great river basins, prevents too great a concentration of logs at the mouth of any one river.

Mining. The *Bergslagen* district of central Sweden is one of the chief iron-mining districts in Europe. The ore is of excellent quality, and most of it is smelted within the country, some of it by the use of charcoal, some in electrical furnaces, and some with imported coal. The steel produced is of very high quality, and most of it is used locally in the manufacture of such specialities as roller bearings, cutting tools, etc.

Manufacturing. Sweden, like Norway, is handicapped as a manufacturing country by her lack of coal. She has, however, certain advantages, viz., raw materials, such as iron ore and timber; abundant and cheap hydro-electricity; and, what is perhaps of greater importance than these, people with a mechanical turn of mind, and a determination to overcome difficulties.

It is interesting to notice how many Swedish industries are based on Swedish inventions, many of which had for their object either economy in the use of fuel, or the substitution of electricity or oil for coal. Among such industries may be mentioned the electrical smelting of iron, the making of electrical machinery, and the manufacture of fertilizers by the use of powerful electric currents. The match-making industry, in which Sweden holds first place in the world, was based on Swedish inventions of safety matches and of match-making machinery. Sweden's pre-eminence in the wood-pulp industry is also due in large measure to the inventive genius of her people, many of the processes having been first discovered in Sweden. Minor specialities, which owe their origin, in part at least, to Swedish inventions, are the manufacture of ball-bearings, cream separators, lighthouse lamps, and primus stoves. Perhaps the best known Swedish inventor was Alfred Nobel, who invented dynamite and smokeless gunpowder. By his will he left a large sum of money to provide annual prizes for the most striking discoveries in physics, chemistry, and medicine, for the best literary production, and for the greatest contribution to world peace.

Among the towns of this section the most notable are *Dannemora*, the chief centre for the mining, smelting, and steel-manufacturing industries, and *Falun*, formerly noted for its 'copper mountain,' which was worked from A.D. 1220 until recent times.

(4) The province of Norrland is nearly all covered with coniferous forests, and lumbering is the chief occupation of the people in all but the part north of the Arctic Circle. Here, around *Gellivare* and *Kirunavare*, is the second great iron-mining district of Sweden. Nearly all the ore from this region is exported, chiefly to Great Britain and Germany. In summer much of the ore is sent out from the port of Luleå, on the Gulf of Bothnia, but in winter this port is closed by ice for several months. Consequently a railway has been constructed northwards to the Norwegian port of Narvik, which, though two hundred miles farther north, is ice-free at all times. This railway is noteworthy as the most northerly electric railway in the world. The hydro-electric stations of Porjus and Hare's Leap Fall, from which the railway receives its electricity, are among the largest in the world.

*C   E

THE LAPPS

These interesting people inhabit the northern part of Sweden, and the adjoining districts of Norway and Finland. They are of small stature, and their flat noses and prominent cheek bones give them a Mongolian appearance. The adults have very dark complexions, but this may be due to their dislike of washing; it is said, indeed, that a Lapp can effectively disguise himself by washing his face!

They are divided into three main classes according to their mode of life. The *Sea Lapps* live on the Norwegian coast, and are occupied mainly in fishing and cattle rearing. Many of them are quite prosperous, and have adopted the modes of life of the Norwegians, but others still lead a primitive exist-ence, and dwell in mud huts which are shared by the cattle. The *River Lapps* live mainly on the fish they catch in the rivers, though many of them are now taking up dairy farming. The *Nomad Lapps*, though the least numerous, are the most interesting. They depend almost entirely on reindeer, which provide them with milk, meat, clothing, and means of trans-port. The people are grouped in small tribes, and though the reindeer are owned by individuals, they are pastured together in great herds which may number two or three thousand. The essential food of the reindeer is a particular type of moss which grows only in the snowy regions. The animals seem able to smell this moss through the snow, for they often dig down several feet in order to reach it. The nomadic life of the Lapps is due to the frequent movements in search of fresh pastures, the herds being driven to the snow-covered uplands in summer and to the sheltered valleys in winter. A most interesting account of the nomadic Lapps is given by Miss E. B. Nord-strom in her book, *Tent Folk of the Far North*. She was appointed by the Swedish Government to teach the Lapp children in one of their summer encampments, and to reach her 'school' she had to travel over the high fells with the Lapps and their reindeer. The main herd had already been driven

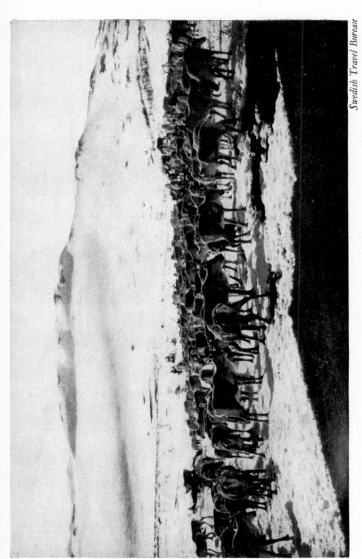

REINDEER IN LAPLAND

over the mountains, and the party with which Miss Nordstrom travelled consisted of only a score of men, women, and children under the leadership of the head of the tribe. Eight or ten sledges, each drawn by a reindeer, which was also tied to the sledge ahead, formed the caravan which transported the tents and household goods of the tribe. For nine hours, without rest, the party marched through blinding snow and bitter cold, until some of the reindeer could travel no longer and fell exhausted in the snow, to be dragged along by those in front until their weight brought the whole train to a standstill. Then the sledges were unpacked, while the reindeer scraped through many feet of snow to uncover the succulent moss on which they fed. Men set up a tent, consisting of poles over which two pieces of cloth were stretched, while the women cut down dwarf birches for firewood. Soon a fire was burning inside the tent, coffee was made, the party tucked themselves up in furs, and lay down to sleep on the floor of birch boughs, oblivious of the snow which drifted through the smoke hole in the top of the tent.

During the summer Miss Nordstrom taught the Lapp children to read and write; but the Lapps taught her many things too, and every one who reads the fascinating account of her life with these simple nomads must admire their courage and fortitude no less than the skill with which they gain a livelihood in the most difficult circumstances. In autumn the men return from the upland pastures with the main herd of reindeer. Then the young calves are branded, each with its owner's mark, reindeer meat is set to dry in the sun, milk is evaporated, and cheese prepared to provide sufficient food for the winter. Nowadays many Lapp families send their children to be educated in boarding-schools established by the Government, while they themselves earn a substantial money income by the sale of reindeer meat and craftwork in wool, wood, bone, and leather.

DENMARK

WHEN we think of Denmark we usually think also of dairy produce—Danish bacon, Danish butter, Danish eggs—for Denmark sends us very large quantities of these products. Dairy farming and the preparation and sale of dairy produce are the only means of livelihood of the great majority of the Danish people, who depend on the exports of these commodities for the money with which they buy food, clothing, and manufactured goods from other countries.

Why has Denmark specialized to such an extent in dairy farming? and how is it that this small, yet densely peopled country, can produce such a large surplus of food?

Certainly, her mild moist climate is suitable for cattle; much of the country is very fertile; and she is well situated for trade with other countries; but in none of these respects has she any advantage over many parts of eastern England. Perhaps the chief reason why Denmark developed her dairying industries to such a great extent is that there was hardly any other way in which she could provide for her increasing population. Though her soil is excellent for growing wheat, and Denmark leads the world in the yield of wheat per acre, she is such a small country that she could not hope to export sufficient wheat to enable her to buy all the things she needs. Unlike Norway and Sweden, she has no large areas of forest, and though fishing is of some importance, it could never provide for more than a fraction of the people. Neither could she easily develop great manufacturing industries, for she lacks coal, minerals, raw materials, and water power. So in the last quarter of the nineteenth century Denmark began in earnest to develop her dairy-farming industry, and soon took the lead in dairy-farming methods.

If we visited Denmark we should be struck by several differences between their dairy farms and ours. Perhaps the first thing we should notice in the fields would be that the cows are not allowed to roam at will, but are tied to stakes, and compelled to eat the grass within the circle of their rope, before they are moved on to the next stake. Of course this means extra trouble for the farmer, but the Danes maintain that this method gives a much greater yield of grass.

Another difference between Danish dairy-farming land and our own is that in Denmark there are relatively few fields of permanent grass. Whereas in England only 50 per cent of the cultivated land is ploughed, in Denmark the percentage is 85. This does not mean that very little grass is grown in Denmark; on the contrary special grasses are sown as part of the system of rotation of crops, and either eaten by the cows as described above, or made into hay for winter use. A large proportion of the land is also devoted to the production of root crops and cereals for animal food. The use of arable land in place of permanent grassland for feeding cattle is one of the chief reasons for Denmark's great milk production, for her farmers maintain that they can keep more cattle on a given area of arable land than is possible on the same area of grassland.

Another feature we should notice would be the great subdivision of the land. A tiny farm of six acres may be divided into seven or eight strips, each growing a different crop. This is because the Danish farmers adopt a rotation system spreading over seven or eight years, in place of our three- or four-year system. The order of the crops varies from place to place, but the following crops will usually be found growing on any farm: rye, barley, mangolds, clover, wheat, oats, peas or beans, potatoes.

Again, if we were to compare the number of farm-houses seen on a given area of ground we should find that there are far more in Denmark than in a typical farming district of Britain. This is, of course, because the farms themselves are smaller. Only one farm in forty is over 150 acres, nearly half of them are less than forty acres, and one-fifth of them are less than eight acres. As even a small holding of six or eight acres is made to keep a family, the land has to be very carefully cultivated so as to make it produce as much as possible. When, as in Denmark, a great deal of labour is expended on small plots of ground in order to make them yield the maximum produce, the cultivation is said to be *intensive*.

If we were to inspect the farm buildings and observe the work of the farmer and his wife, we should see several other differences between Danish methods and our own. For example, on most of the larger farms milking is done by machines; and everywhere the cows are milked three times a day, instead of twice as in England. The Danish farmer claims that he thus obtains an extra yield of milk, which more than compensates for the extra labour involved.

We should, however, see no churns or cream separators; for the Danish farmer's wife does not make her own butter. Instead, motor lorries collect the milk from all the farms in a given district, and take it to a central creamery or butter factory. Here it is tested for purity and quality, the cream is taken out to be made into butter, and the farmer receives back his skimmed milk to feed his calves and pigs.

Most of these creameries are run by the farmers themselves on co-operative lines. Co-operation is, indeed, a great feature of Danish life. In addition to the societies which run the creameries there are societies for collecting and marketing eggs, for curing bacon, and for buying seeds, fertilizers, and other things the farmers require. Since these societies deal in large quantities they are able to buy, sell, or manufacture more economically than the small farmer could do.

The export of bacon is vital to the prosperity of the Danish people, and every effort is made by the Government and the co-operatives to ensure that each farmer produces the highest quality bacon at the lowest possible price. Scientific breeding has produced the type of pig which adds the greatest weight for a given quantity of food in a given period of time. The farmer is told exactly how much food each animal must be given, and makes regular checks on growth so that he can deliver to the co-operative bacon factory the pigs of standard weight and quality. The farmers receive similar expert guidance in the production of eggs and butter for export.

The success of this highly scientific farming is due in large measure to the system of voluntary adult education not only in technical and farm schools, but also in the Folk High Schools which provide a general cultural education.

The Land Surface and Chief Towns

Though Denmark nowhere rises above six hundred feet, there is considerable diversity in the land surface. The islands of Funen, Zealand, and Laaland are among the most fertile regions of Europe; and here are the sunken lanes, leafy hedges, and picturesque farm-houses similar to those of rural England.

The western half of the peninsula of Jutland, however, is of a very different character; much of the land was originally sandy and infertile heath and marsh, and has only been made productive by the expenditure of much money and labour. All along the west coast is a line of sand dunes, backed by lakes and marshes. Formerly the sand was blown inland by every storm, thus defeating any attempts at cultivation of the region behind the coast. In modern times, however, the dunes have been anchored by planting special grasses which held the sand together, so that pine-trees could eventually be planted on it. Many of the marshes have been drained; canals have been dug to irrigate land which was too dry; and barren, sandy tracts have been fertilized by the addition of marl and manures. By these methods over 2,000 square miles of land have been reclaimed and transformed from useless waste into productive forest or arable land.

Although dairy farming is the basis of Denmark's prosperity, little more than a quarter of the workers of the country are engaged in farming. Most of the rest are engaged in the preparation and sale of the dairy produce, and in the importation and distribution of the foodstuffs and manufactured goods. Some manufacturing is also carried on, the chief products being margarine, agricultural machinery, electrical equipment, and Diesel oil engines.

Copenhagen, with a population of 980,000, contains one-fifth of all the people in the country. It is larger than Stockholm, though Sweden has nearly three times as many people as Denmark. One reason for this is that nearly all the trade of Denmark is concentrated at Copenhagen, while Sweden's commerce is shared between the three ports of Stockholm, Gothenburg, and Malmö. Again, Copenhagen conducts a good deal of trade for other countries, since the Sound on which it is situated is the chief entrance to the Baltic. In former times the port gained much wealth by imposing levies on ships entering or leaving the Baltic; and though the Sound is now free to all ships, and Copenhagen is a free port, it still has a good deal more trade than could be provided by Denmark alone. Large vessels, with goods consigned to various Baltic ports, often unload at Copenhagen, the goods being re-shipped in smaller vessels. In the same way Copenhagen collects articles of export from the surrounding ports. Such trade is called *transit* or *entrepôt trade*, and Copenhagen is known as an *entrepôt*.

The only other port of importance in Denmark is *Esbjerg*. Situated on the west coast, it is the chief fishing port, and exports much dairy produce to Britain. From Esbjerg a railway runs right across Jutland and the islands, with connecting train-ferries, to Copenhagen and to Helsingör. Thence another train-ferry runs to Helsingborg in Sweden, thus giving in effect unbroken rail connection between Esbjerg and Stockholm.

In 1937 Europe's longest bridge, connecting the Danish islands of Masnedo and Falster, was completed. It has 50 spans of about 200 feet each, and cost over £2,000,000.

NATURE AND MAN IN SCANDINAVIA

ALTHOUGH, as we have seen, there are great differences between the three Scandinavian countries, they are all alike in one respect: all have had to contend with great natural disadvantages; yet each nation has had the will and energy to find means of overcoming these obstacles. Norway, denied a plentiful harvest on land, has turned to the sea; Sweden relies to a great extent on the industries built up by the inventive genius of her people; Denmark has shown the world how farming may be made the basis of prosperity in a temperate country denied other sources of wealth. Had these countries been inhabited by people lacking in initiative and enterprise, they would never have attained their present prosperity. Geographical conditions alone do not decide the way in which a people shall develop; a very great deal depends on the people themselves, and the extent to which they possess the energy and ability to overcome natural obstacles, or to use natural advantages.

SCANDINAVIA IN HISTORY

THE Scandinavian peoples, like the Germans and the English, belong to the Teutonic group. The Norwegian, Swedish, and Danish languages are merely local developments from the speech which was common to all the Scandinavian people about a thousand years ago, so there is still a great similarity between them.

The Scandinavians first appear in history as raiders by sea and by land—the Vikings from Norway and Denmark, and the Varangians from Sweden. The Vikings (Norsemen or Danes) not only settled in Britain and in Normandy, but also penetrated up the estuaries of the Elbe, the Scheldt, the Loire, and the Garonne, and even reached the shores of Italy and northern Africa, while in the year A.D. 1000 Eric the Red sailed past Iceland and Greenland to 'Vineland' (Nova Scotia). The Swedes, on the other hand, were naturally attracted by the lands across the Baltic. In the ninth century groups of them penetrated along the rivers into the heart of Russia, and even as far as the Caspian and Black Sea. As we shall see later, their chieftains (the Rus) eventually became rulers of Russia.

The 'Viking Age,' which was characterized by these immigrations, ended about the year A.D. 1000. Though for short periods during the succeeding centuries the three countries were ruled by one king, there was never any real unity between them.

The remote 'geological accident' which tilted and uplifted the Scandinavian block ensured that its two sides should have different climates and products, and that peoples of Norway and Sweden should differ in occupations and world outlook.

ICELAND

THIS sub-arctic island was first peopled by settlers from Norway in the ninth century. From the thirteenth century it was subject to Denmark until in 1944 it became a completely independent republic.

The land surface has been built up by the outpourings of lava from Hecla and a score of other volcanoes, and moulded to its present form by glaciers which still occupy one-eighth of its surface. Some farming is carried on in the milder areas near the south coast, and in some districts steam water from the numerous geysers is used to heat greenhouses in which fruit and flowers are grown. Fishing is, however, the mainstay of the island, and it is on the exports of cod and other fish that the Icelanders depend for their livelihood.

Reykyavik, the capital and chief port, is situated on the ice-free south coast.

THE FAROE ISLANDS

This archipelago of small, rocky islands situated between Scotland and Iceland is a dependency of Denmark. The few thousand inhabitants of the islands depend almost entirely on fishing. The chief town is *Thorshavn*.

EXERCISES

1. Draw simplified sketch-maps to show that:
(a) The Norwegian coast is warmer than the Baltic coast of Sweden in winter.
(b) Norway has more rain than Sweden.
(c) Sweden has a larger proportion of its area occupied by coniferous forest than has Norway.
State briefly the cause of these differences between the two countries.

2. Make lists of the products of Norway, Sweden, and Denmark which may come to your notice from time to time. (Advertisements and trade labels are useful sources of information.)

3. How would you travel to Oslo? To Copenhagen? To Stockholm? How long would it take you to reach these places from your own home?

4. Do you consider that Nature *compelled* the Vikings to become raiders? Has she *compelled* the Norwegians in modern times to become fishermen and merchant seamen?

5. Wages of working-men in Sweden are about the highest of all continental countries. Can you think of any *climatic* reason why a Swedish workman may *need* higher wages than, say, a Belgian workman?

6. Among Sweden's important imports are motor-vehicles, oil, coffee, and fruit.
Consider each commodity in turn, say why it is needed in Sweden, where it is likely to come from, and what light it throws on the life and work of the people.

7. Consider the following table for a typical recent year:

FOREIGN TRADE PER HEAD OF THE POPULATION

Country	Exports	Imports	Total
Norway .	£130	£80	£210
Sweden .	£110	£120	£330
Denmark .	£90	£100	£190

Say what are the chief items of export by each of the three countries, and explain why Norway can import far more than she exports.

8. For every 1,000 people Norway has the equivalent of a 1,800-ton steamer, Sweden a 300-ton steamer, and Denmark a 320-ton steamer. What geographical explanation can you give of the differences in these figures?

FINLAND

THE most striking surface feature of Finland is the great number of lakes. A good atlas shows a bewildering maze of lakes and connecting waterways which occupy quite a quarter of the surface of the southern half of the country. These lakes owe their origin to the ice-sheet which covered the land in the Glacial Period, leaving an irregular deposit, called moraine, in the hollows of which the lakes have formed. Running across the land, generally from north-west to south-east, are long sandy ridges, thought to have been deposited by rivers which ran underneath the ice. These 'eskers,' as they are called, form a marked feature of the landscape, the roads often follow their crests, and the dry sandy soil has encouraged the growth of towns and villages.

The lakes and the rivers are the chief lines of communication, for even in winter they provide easy routes for the sledges which run over the ice and snow.

Although Finland does not stretch quite so far north as Norway, it is the most northerly country in Europe, for nearly the whole of it is north of latitude 60°. It is in roughly the same latitude as Iceland, Greenland, and Alaska, and the mental association of Finns, Lapps, and reindeer gives many people the quite erroneous impression that Finland is a land of snow and ice. It is unfortunate that the Lapps are sometimes called Finns, for they are two quite different races, and there are only about 1,300 of the former in Finland. It is true, of course, that Finland's northerly position, and her distance from the open Atlantic, give her long and severe winters. The country is ice-bound for five months; and regular mail services to Sweden are established over the ice on the Gulf of Bothnia. The Gulf of Finland is also frozen for four months, but in the extreme north the country formerly had a narrow corridor to the ice-free Arctic shores. This strip of territory, together with the valuable nickel mines around Petsamo, was, however, ceded to the U.S.S.R. in 1940.

Summer comes suddenly and brings a remarkable change. 'Suddenly there is a loosening of the chains of ice. The rivers become roaring cataracts of ice blocks. The "isgang," or ice rush, has commenced. First the dripping trees and then the streaming earth appear. Then the summer comes rushing over the land like a tidal wave of green leaves and delicate scents. The long winter nights are succeeded by the long summer days. The earth has not time to cool, and vegetation grows at hothouse pace. Under the stimulus of continuous sunlight the leaves of the trees grow to double the size with which we are familiar. . . . By night everything is quite distinct, but all the tones of nature have been softened to a delicate, opalescent glow. These are the white nights of the north, full of magic and enchantment, laying a spell upon the earth.'—*Suomi, the Land of the Finns*, A. MacCullam Scott.

Lumbering. As nearly two-thirds of the country is covered with forests, mainly of the coniferous type, lumbering is one of the chief occupations of the people. Logging is carried on in winter, when the frozen snow facilitates transport to the rivers. In spring and summer the logs are floated down the swollen rivers or carried by motor lorries to electrically driven saw-mills and pulp factories. Timber alone provides nearly a third of the exports, while wood pulp and paper account for another 50 per cent. Other articles made from the timber are artificial silk, matches, plywood, veneers, and bobbins.

Farming. Although forestry provides such a large pro-portion of the exports, agriculture is the chief occupation of the people. Forestry and agriculture are largely supplementary to each other, men working in the forests in winter and on their farms in summer. Even in the south of the country, where most of the cultivated land is situated, wheat does not grow well, and the chief crops are hay, rye, barley, oats, and potatoes. In 1920 the land was redistributed, so as to enable as many people as possible to earn their living from the soil, and more than three-quarters of the farms are less than twenty-five acres in extent.   In spite of careful cultivation the country cannot produce sufficient food for her people, and much grain has to be imported.   On the other hand, dairy farming is a growing industry, and in normal years Finland exports considerable quantities of butter, cheese, eggs, and bacon to Britain and other manufacturing countries of Europe.

Industries. Like Norway and Sweden, Finland is handicapped as a manufacturing country by lack of coal, and by the absence of raw materials other than timber.   Aided by electricity generated at rapids where the rivers leave the lakes, she has, however, developed some textile and metal industries, while her manufactures of pulp and paper are among the largest in the world.

Tammerfors (Tampere), the 'Manchester of Finland,' is situated on an esker at the exit from one of the largest lakes.   It is the chief industrial centre of Finland, but factories are as inconspicuous as in every other Finnish city.   'Tampere is not only one of the most beautifully situated industrial cities in the world, but also the cleanest.   Here is no smoke, no grime, no dirt.   "White coal," the power generated by the rapids which run through the business quarter of the town, is the fuel of the factories.'—*Finland*, Kay Gilmour.   The textile industry of the city was founded by a Scotsman, who, when visiting the city early in the nineteenth century, was so impressed by the abundance of available water power that he established a factory there.

Helsingfors (Helsinki) is the capital of the country, and a finely built modern city.   It is the chief port of the country, and is situated on a magnificent harbour, divided in two by a promontory, and sheltered from storms by a group of islands. Though the sea is frozen for four months in winter, a channel to the port is usually kept open by ice breakers.

Abo (Turku), the ancient capital, is the most picturesque city of Finland, and one of its chief manufacturing centres.

The Aaland Islands, situated between the coasts of Finland

and Sweden, were claimed after the First World War by both these countries. The Finns based their claim on the undoubted fact that the islands are geographically much more a part of Finland than of Sweden, the sea between the largest islands and the coast of Finland being thickly strewn with innumerable wooded islets, which form 'land-bridges' to the mainland. Sweden, with equal justice, claimed that the population of the islands is Swedish by race and language; in addition, she pointed out, they were a potential danger to Sweden if they were in the hands of another country, as Stockholm could be bombarded from them. Trivial as this dispute may seem to us, its settlement was of importance, as it was the first quarrel between nations to be settled by the League of Nations. As a result of inquiries by a commission appointed by the League, the islands became a part of Finland, but the inhabitants were allowed a large measure of self-government.

Brief as is the foregoing account of Finland, it should suffice to dispel any lingering idea that it is a desolate country in a primitive stage of development. On the contrary, it is in many respects one of the most advanced countries in the world. There are practically no class distinctions, no slums, no smoke, no dirt. There is an excellent system of education, practically every one can read and write, and a large proportion of the people take a keen and intelligent interest in the affairs of their own country and of the outside world. The equality of the sexes is a great feature of Finnish life; Finland was the first country in the world to grant women the same political status as men, and even before the Second World War women were often engaged in many occupations which in other countries were usually reserved for men, and they are often to be seen working as tram conductors, railway clerks, road sweepers, window cleaners, etc. The equality of women with men is due in some measure to the fact that women have always had to take a large share in keeping the home going, and even now are frequently left to look after the farms while the men go out to earn money in the lumbering industry.

RUSSIA

THE most impressive thing about Russia, as seen on a map of the world, is its size. The 'Union of Soviet Socialist Republics,' as it is called, stretches from the Baltic Sea to the Pacific Ocean, and from the Arctic Ocean almost halfway to the Equator. Its area is approximately one-sixth of the total land surface of the world, while Russia in Europe occupies nearly half of the surface of our continent.

Geography furnishes one important reason why Russia has become such an enormous country : most of it is one vast plain, and there are no well-marked physical barriers. In European Russia, which we are to consider, the Caucasus and the Urals are the only ranges of mountains. The former constitute the physical (though not the political) boundary of Europe; and the latter, although they look impressive on the map, have such gentle slopes that they present no serious obstacle to the movement of people. The highest part of the Russian plain is the Valdai Hills, between Moscow and Leningrad; but the gradients even there are almost imperceptible. Indeed, if we represent the Valdai Hills by a brick nine inches high, and the gradient by a plank supported at one end by the brick, our plank would have to be over three hundred yards long ! Little wonder that the rivers of Russia are long, and slow-flowing, so that they have always been the chief means of communication within the country. The river-ways, too, have helped the Russians to expand in all directions, though, as we shall see, they also afforded routes by which the land could be invaded.

RUSSIA THROUGH THE CENTURIES

In its natural condition practically the whole of central and northern Russia was covered with forest, while the south was a great steppe - land. Neither of these types of country was favourable to the early development of a great nation, for the forests favoured the development of isolated settlements, while the steppes were a broad highway along which hordes of barbarians passed from Asia to central Europe. (See Fig. 13.) It is not surprising, therefore, that Russian history does not begin so early as that of western and Mediterranean Europe.

About the time of Alfred the Great a large part of the country was inhabited by people belonging to the Slav race. An old story says that three Viking brothers were invited by these Slavs to help to restore order in their country, and that having carried out their task, the brothers seized the reins of government and established themselves as rulers of the country. Whatever the truth of this story, we know that towards the end of the ninth century numerous bands of Norsemen invaded the country, using the rivers as highways, and eventually established themselves in various centres, from which they dominated the country. The Slavs called these Norsemen *Rus*, or seafarers, and it is from that term that the name of the country is derived, although the Norsemen were never more than a small ruling caste. Like the Anglo-Saxons in England, the various sections of the Rus did not readily combine under one supreme chieftain, and under their rule the country was frequently split up into many little principalities, whose jealousies were to prove a source of fatal weakness in the face of fresh invasions. In the thirteenth century southern Russia was attacked by the Golden Horde, fierce nomadic Tartars from central Asia. These invaders laid waste the whole of southern Russia, and reduced the nation to servitude. But the Tartars were men of the open plains, and their hold over the forest lands of the centre and north was never very strong. There the spirit of nationality was kept alive, and the little principality of Moscow, which embraced the forest land between the Volga and its tributary the Oka, was the centre round which modern Russia grew up. Her princes gradually extended their dominions at the expense of the Tartars, and eventually threw off the rule of the Tartars, who were weakened by inter-tribal quarrels.

Towards the end of the fifteenth century the Tartars were finally driven from the country, and for the next three hundred years the history of Russia is concerned chiefly with the almost continuous expansion of the power of the Muscovy princes.

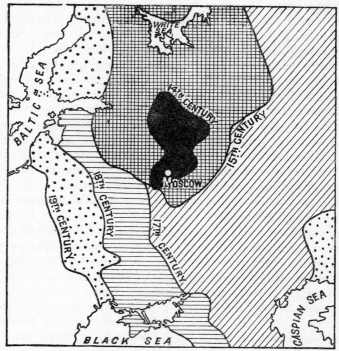

FIG. 19. STAGES IN THE GROWTH OF RUSSIA

(See Fig. 19.) Near the end of the sixteenth century a robber chieftain, named Yermak, placed himself at the head of a band of Cossacks, and conquered western Siberia by a series of amazing marches hardly surpassed in the history of discovery. In return for a free pardon for former crimes he gave the lands he had conquered to Ivan the Terrible, who was the first Muscovite prince to be crowned tsar. In this region, too, Russia first began to use the White Sea as an outlet towards the west, the practicability of the route having been proved by Richard Chancellor, an English captain, who had set out in 1553 with Sir Hugh Willoughby in an attempt to find a north-east passage to China. The ships were blown out of their course, Willoughby and the crew of two ships were lost, and Chancellor had to seek safety in the White Sea. There he made friends with Russian traders, and eventually made his way to Moscow, where he was cordially received by the tsar. As a result of this visit commercial relations with England were established via the White Sea.

Russia, was, however, still hemmed in on the west by the Poles, and shut off from the Black Sea by the Turks and the Cossacks. These latter were groups of nomadic herdsmen and raiders who occupied the grasslands of south-eastern Russia. Bit by bit Russian colonists pushed forward the limits of the cultivated lands at the expense of the Cossack pastures, building great walls of wood or earth to protect the lands they had won. These 'watch-lines,' as they were called, extended for nearly three thousand miles from the valley of the Dnieper to the mountains of central Asia. Peter the Great, who was the strongest ruler Russia has ever known, greatly reduced the power of the Cossacks, but failed to subjugate them completely. Unable to gain an outlet by the Black Sea, Peter turned his attention to the Baltic, and wrested from Sweden lands south of the Gulf of Finland. In 1703 he built the port of St. Petersburg (now Leningrad) to give Russia a 'window to the west,' and make it possible for Russia to take her place as one of the Great Powers of Europe. Some eighty years later Catherine the Great finally conquered the Cossack territories, thus giving Russia her long-desired outlet via the Black Sea.

Less than a century ago the vast majority of the Russian people were serfs, who owned no land, but were bound to work on the estates of the great landowners and nobles. In 1861, however, the Government bought large areas of land from the landowners, and turned it over to the peasants, who agreed to pay for it in annual instalments. The serfs thus became peasant proprietors, and were free to earn their living on their own land. Unfortunately, the hopes of prosperity roused by this emancipation of the serfs did not materialize. Primitive methods of farming, lack of capital, the small size of the original holdings, and subdivision of the land in successive generations soon caused the peasants to be as badly off as before, and great numbers had to go to work in the towns, or on those estates which remained in the hands of the nobles. In spite of further grants of land the lot of the peasants grew steadily worse, and the country was always on the verge of starvation. The Government was despotic and tyrannical, and though a Duma or Parliament was established after an attempted revolution in 1905, its powers were so restricted that it was practically useless. The country was again on the brink of revolution when the First World War broke out in 1914, and three years later the war-weary soldiers and the discontented, suffering people combined to destroy the autocracy which had lasted for three hundred years.

The tsar, Nicholas II, was forced from the throne in March 1917, and for a time the Duma took over the task of government; but they were unable to control the revolutionary forces, and within a few months the Bolsheviks, led by Lenin and Trotsky, had established themselves as masters of the country. They set to work to establish a system of Communism, in which there was to be no private property, and everything was to belong to the State. The Union of Socialist Soviet Republics (U.S.S.R.), as Russia is now called, is made up of sixteen republics, some of which include other 'autonomous' republics.

The Natural Divisions of Russia

Though Russia in Europe is one great plain, there are great differences in the temperature, rainfall, soil, vegetation, cultivated crops, and modes of life of the people in various parts.

Temperature maps show us that the whole of Russia has an extreme climate; but while western Russia is frost-bound for three months in an average year, the north-east is frost-bound for more than six months (see Fig. 4); and while southern Russia has long hot summers, northern Russia has short cool summers. These facts alone suffice to account for many of the differences between the various parts of Russia.

When we consider the rainfall we find that, while no part of Russia has much precipitation of moisture (i.e. rain plus snow) in winter, the extreme south-east and the extreme north have also very dry summers. Combining these two sets of facts we see that Russia may be divided into three climatic divisions, viz.:

(1) The northern region, where it is too cold for trees to grow or for crops to be cultivated.

(2) The central region, where the summer heat and summer rainfall are sufficient for the cultivation of crops. This region may, however, be further subdivided by the line marking off the parts which are frost-bound for five or more months in the year.

(3) The south-eastern district, where the summers are so hot and dry that trees will not grow, and crops cannot be cultivated by ordinary methods.

If we now turn to the map showing the natural vegetation of Russia (see Fig. 20), we shall see that Nature herself has marked out pretty much the same regions. This is, after all, what we might have expected, since temperature and rainfall determine what kind of vegetation will grow best in a given region. (The kind of soil is also an important factor in determining the kind of vegetation, but the nature of the soil is itself very largely determined by the temperature and the rainfall.)

Life in the various 'vegetation' regions of Russia differs so much that if we are to understand the life of the people of Russia we must consider each region separately.

(1) The **Tundra** region of the extreme north is frost-bound for nine months in the year, while in the brief summer it is a

mosquito-infested swamp. The region is inhabited by tribes who, like the Lapps, depend chiefly on herds of reindeer which provide milk, meat, clothing, and means of transport. In

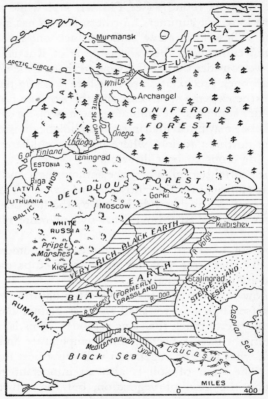

FIG. 20. RUSSIA: NATURAL VEGETATION

recent years the Soviet Government has done much to raise the standard of living of the peoples of the Tundra by the introduction of communal reindeer farms and improved methods of fishing and hunting. In some districts crops of potatoes, vegetables, and even wheat are grown during the short summer when the almost continuous sunshine causes plants to grow with great rapidity.

(2) **The Coniferous Forest** zone of European Russia is part of the great Northern Forest belt which extends from Norway to the Pacific coast. Timber is the chief resource of the region, the trees being cut in winter and floated down the streams to the ports and sawmills in spring and summer. Many factories, run by hydro-electricity derived from the rapid streams, manufacture pulp, paper, plywood, window-frames, doors, and sectional pre-fabricated houses.

The development of farming in the forest clearings has been hindered by the short growing season and the poor soils; nevertheless, it has been found possible by the use of specially selected types of seed to grow almost all the ordinary English crops as far north as the Arctic Circle.

The most highly developed part of this coniferous forest region is the lake-studded trough which stretches from the Gulf of Finland via lakes Lagoda and Onega to the White Sea. (See Fig. 22.) This lake belt is a remnant of a strait which formerly stretched from the Skagerrak across southern Sweden to the Arctic. As in the corresponding lake region of Sweden the soil is fertile, being composed of sediment deposited in the former strait; the White Sea ship canal and a main railway, both of which follow the trough, provide ample means of transport; rich deposits of iron and copper are worked near by; and rapid streams supply abundant electricity to the numerous sawmills and woodworking factories.

The ports for the region are Archangel, Murmansk, and Leningrad. *Archangel*, situated on the White Sea at the mouth of the Northern Dvina, is icebound for six months in the year, but is nevertheless Russia's chief timber port, and is also an important centre for the manufacture of wood-pulp, paper, and linen. *Murmansk*, though situated 300 miles farther north than Archangel, is ice-free throughout the year, since the coast is exposed to the mild westerly winds from the Atlantic, and is washed by warm surface water from them. It is therefore,

Russia's chief winter outlet by the northern routes, being specially important for the export of pit props, and as the centre of the northern fishing fleet.

The Kola Peninsula, between the Arctic coast and the White Sea, has rich deposits of nickel and apatite. *Petsamo*, an ice-free port near the rich nickel-mining area, was ceded by Finland to the U.S.S.R. after the Second World War.

Leningrad, originally named St. Petersburg, owes its origin and growth to the will of an individual, rather than to natural development due to obvious geographical advantages. The delta of the River Neva, on which Peter the Great built the nucleus of the city, was an unhealthy, almost unpeopled swamp. But Peter, with the eye of a geographer, saw the possibilities of the site. Though Nature had not quite completed her leisurely process of creating firm land, Peter could not wait. He drove great piles deep into the swamp, and upon them built the great fortress of St. Peter and St. Paul, which formed the nucleus of the new capital. The city, as seemed fitting for Russia's 'window to Europe,' was modelled upon the modern cities of western Europe. The architects were mainly Germans, and the style of building that common in all the great European cities at the time.

The Russian people did not like the new city, and Peter 'had not merely to conscript an army of workmen to build the city, he had to drive in a population to inhabit it. The Russian people writhed under his coercion, but his creative hand was heavier upon them than the rod of Ivan the Terrible. Ivan made them slaves, and they worshipped him as a national hero. Peter civilized them—and after some ineffectual struggles, they submitted sullenly, as to the hand of fate.'— A. MacCullam Scott.

Renamed Leningrad in honour of the leader of the revolution, the city has in modern times become the first port of Russia, the second largest city, and the third most important manufacturing area.

Natural handicaps to its development as a port were the

ICE-BREAKER AT WORK IN THE GULF OF FINLAND

A SUMMER SCENE IN ESTONIA

shallowness of the approaches from the Gulf of Finland, and the freezing of the harbour for four or five months in winter; it has, however, been connected to its outport, Kronstadt, by an artificially deepened channel, and by the use of ice-breakers it is kept open for navigation during the greater part of the winter.   As an industrial centre it is lacking in coal, iron, and all local raw materials except flax and timber.   In tsarist days industrial development was based on cotton and wool brought from the south of Russia and on coal and iron imported from England.   Even to-day it draws most of its fuel and raw materials from other parts of the U.S.S.R.—coal from the Donetz basin, oil from the Caucasus, metals from the Urals, and so on; increasing supplies of electricity are, however, now being obtained from local hydro-electric stations and from thermal electric stations using local peat.

The principal industries of Leningrad are engineering, machine building, shipbuilding, and the making of textiles and paper.

THE DECIDUOUS FOREST REGION

This central region of Russia, between the coniferous forests of the north and the grasslands of the south, is in the form of a triangle whose base runs from the Baltic to the Carpathians and whose apex is on the Urals.   Four subdivisions of this region may be recognized, viz.: (1) The Baltic Lands. (2) White Russia.   (3) The Moscow Region.   (4) The Eastern District. (See Fig. 21.)

(1) **The Baltic Lands.** Between the two World Wars the Russian lands bordering the Baltic formed the separate Republics of Estonia, Latvia, and Lithuania, but in 1940 these were re-incorporated in the U.S.S.R.   Nearness to the Atlantic gives them relatively mild winters and moist summers; consequently, though there are large areas which are marshy or sandy, this is the most important dairying region of Russia, and a considerable surplus of butter is produced.   Other important crops are rye, oats, flax, and potatoes.

D E

Estonia, situated to the south of the Gulf of Finland, is similar in some respects to Finland. Their peoples are of the same race, and their languages are so closely related that they can understand much of each other's speech; both are lands of forests and lakes; and in both forestry and dairying are the chief occupations.

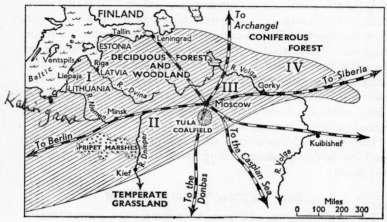

FIG. 21. RUSSIA: DECIDUOUS FOREST REGION
(The shaded area)

Estonia differs from the other Baltic lands of Russia in having some mineral wealth; oil-shale, quarried near the north coast, is used for fuel on the railways and in the cement factories.

Narva, situated near waterfalls north of Lake Peipus, may be compared with Tammerfors in Finland, since it has many textile factories which are run by hydro-electricity generated at the falls. *Tallinn* (Reval), situated near the entrance to the Gulf of Finland, can be kept open for navigation almost throughout the average winter.

Latvia consists mainly of the lower part of the basin of the Western Dvina. *Riga*, the largest city of the region, is situated at the mouth of the Western Dvina. The surrounding lowland is a rich dairying and mixed farming area, timber is floated

down the Dvina, flax and other raw materials are assembled
from the surrounding districts, and hydro-electricity is transmitted from the interior; consequently Riga has become the
most important manufacturing centre of Latvia. As a port it
is noteworthy for the export of timber and dairy produce.
In winter, when the landlocked Gulf of Riga freezes over,
trade is diverted to the ice-free ports of Ventspils (Windau)
and Liepaja (Libau) on the open Baltic coast.

   Lithuania, like the other Baltic lands, is predominantly a
farming region; practically half the total surface is under
plough, and though the methods are primitive and there are
large areas of barren, sandy woodland, a considerable surplus
of butter, eggs, flax, and grain is normally produced. Before
the re-incorporation into the Soviet Union in 1940 only about
one-sixth of the agricultural land was in small peasant farms,
but the Soviet Government has divided the large estates and
redistributed the land to the peasants.

   The coast of Lithuania is noteworthy as the world's chief
source of amber. This is fossilized gum from a pine forest
which has been submerged by the sea. Winter storms throw
up on the shore fragments of amber which are collected by
fishermen by means of nets. The amber deposits are of great
historic interest because of the spread of early civilization and
the development of trade routes. It was much prized by the
princes and rich merchants of Crete, Egypt, Greece, and
Phoenicia, and when it became known that the finest amber
was to be found on the shores of the Baltic, trade soon sprang
up between northern and southern Europe. In exchange for
the amber of the north the merchants from the south gave
bronze ornaments, tools, and weapons, and so the northern
barbarians were able to advance from the Stone Age to the
Bronze Age.

   After the Second World War, Russia extended her boundary
to include the northern part of the former German territory of
East Prussia, and *Königsberg*, the chief port of the region, is now
a Russian city, and has been renamed Kaliningrad.

(2) **Byelo-Russia.** This is a thinly populated region with large areas of bog and marsh. The Pripet Marshes are the remnant of a former lake which has been partly filled up by the growth of peat. Eastward of these marshes the land rises somewhat, and although the soils are poor, large areas have been cleared for the cultivation of flax, rye, potatoes, and meadow-grass. The introduction of agricultural machinery and the scientific use of fertilizers have greatly increased the productivity of the region in modern times.

The houses in the forest region are of wood, some being built of planks, others of roughly squared logs, with the interstices filled with moss. The most conspicuous feature of the interior is the great closed stove, which is necessary because of the intense winter cold. Around the sides of the living-room runs a broad bench, on which the family sleep; in very cold weather the top of the stove may be used for this purpose.

'The peasant of the forest region is extraordinarily skilful with his axe, fashioning with it his humble wooden home, and all the wooden furniture within, even to bowls and spoons. The forest has provided houses, sledges, carts, utensils, fuel for the home and for transport, and yet vast resources remain.'

Minsk, the chief city of the region, commands the historic route from western Europe to Moscow along the watershed between the rivers flowing to the Baltic and those flowing to the Black Sea. Its industries are based on locally produced raw materials—paper from the timber, linen from the flax, and starch and alcohol from the potatoes.

(3) **The Moscow Region.** *Moscow*, the present and historical capital of Russia, was, as we have seen, the centre round which the modern country developed. Founded in the eleventh century, it was for long merely a little wooden village surrounding the fortress which was built on a marsh-girt hill overlooking the little River Moskva; but as the power of the Muscovite princes spread it acquired ever-increasing importance as the capital of the realm. Though its early growth was due to the fact that its princes happened to be men of great

ability and initiative, rather than to its central position, the latter factor has been of great importance in determining its later development. In spite of the fact that St. Petersburg (Leningrad) was the capital from 1703 to 1918, Moscow almost inevitably became the chief centre of the transport system of the country. Its reinstatement as the capital by the Bolsheviks was due partly to the greater facilities it afforded for the control of the country, and partly to its remoteness from possible enemies in the west.

In spite of the cool climate and the rather poor soil, the region of which Moscow is the centre is one of the chief agricultural regions of Russia, producing foodstuffs and raw materials for the capital and the surrounding towns. The cooler northern areas specialize in the cultivation of flax, the centre in potatoes, vegetables, and milk, and the south in rye, oats, and wheat.

Manufacturing in the Moscow region first developed out of the domestic industries based on the local flax, timber, and iron; then, as the capital of the country and the centre of communications, it was able to draw other raw materials from various parts of Russia, and in tsarist days became the chief textile manufacturing centre of the country. In modern times, its rapid industrial development has been aided by: (a) Improved systems of communications by rail and canal. (b) The utilization of local sources of power, electricity being now generated by the use of local peat and the low-grade coal of the Tula basin. (c) The increasing needs of the people for machinery, clothing, and other manufactured goods. The principal manufactures of Moscow and the surrounding district are cotton goods, machinery, and ball bearings.

(4) **The Eastern District.** East of Moscow, the Deciduous Forest belt narrows to its apex near the Urals, and becomes a mere transition zone between the coniferous forests of the north and the grasslands of the south.

The principal town of the region is Gorki, formerly known as Nijni Novgorod, but renamed after the Communist

Revolution in honour of the Russian author and revolutionary, Maxim Gorki. The city is situated at the point where the great highway from Moscow to Siberia crossed the Volga, and at the point where goods coming up the Volga had to be trans-shipped to smaller vessels. In former times, Nijni Novgorod was famous for its annual fair at which goods from Europe and Asia were assembled for sale; in modern times Gorki has become one of the chief centres for the building of motor lorries, thus maintaining its function of providing facilities for the exchange of goods.

The Grasslands and Steppes

Between the forest belt of the north and the Black and Caspian Seas in the south, is a region where the rainfall is too small to support the growth of forest, and the area was, in its natural condition, one of the great temperate grasslands of the world. In former times, as we have seen, it was the chief highway by which nomadic hordes from central Asia pressed forward into Europe. When the Russians finally extended their power to the shores of the Black Sea they effectively stopped any further immigrations of this kind, and most of the land has long been under cultivation. There are, however, considerable differences in the temperature, rainfall, and soil, and consequently in the occupations of the people; hence it is necessary to subdivide the region.

(a) *The North-western Region.* This is the plateau region to the north-east of the Carpathians around Lvov (Lemberg). It is a junction zone between the Carpathian highland and the Russian plain, and between the forests of the north and the grasslands of the south. For many centuries it was debatable land between the Poles and the Russians, and after the Second World War it became part of the U.S.S.R.

Lvov (Lemberg) is one of the most ancient cities in Europe. Unlike most other large towns it is not situated on a river, for the valleys in this region are deep trenches which were

Above: RUSSIAN SEED-SOWING MACHINES

Left: MODERN TRANSPORT ON A RUSSIAN FARM

avoided by the early traders. Consequently Lvov grew up in a sheltered hollow on the watershed between the rivers Bug and Dniester, where the routes from the Black Sea and southern Russia meet others from the Baltic Sea and western Europe.

Some fifty miles to the south of Lvov is an oilfield which is capable of producing about one per cent of the world's supply.

(b) *The Black Earth District*. This region is characterized by a rich, deep, black soil, which is never less than three feet thick, and in places is fifty feet thick. It was formerly thought that this soil was composed of wind-blown dust, like the loess of China, but it is now considered to be the result of the alternation of winter frosts with hot and rather humid summers.

In spite of the long, cold winter and the occasional failure of the summer rains, the Black Earth region is potentially one of the richest farming areas in the world. About 80 per cent of the land is devoted to cereals, wheat being the chief crop. In the northern areas sugar beet is rotated with wheat, and in the southern districts, near the Black Sea, barley and cotton are dominant. Before the Communist Revolution methods of cultivation were very primitive, much land was wasted by boundary ridges, and the lots were too small to allow the use of agricultural machinery—many indeed were so small that the peasant could not even afford a horse with which to plough.

The peasants lived in untidy, straggling villages of wooden houses, similar to those of the forest region, except that the roofs were made of thatch instead of shingles. A writer, describing his native village of fifty years ago, says: 'At first sight it appeared unchanged; everything seemed to be as it was five, or twenty-five, or perhaps a hundred years ago: there were the bumpy barns with umbrella-like roofs of straw; stumpy log huts with their arrow-shaped straw-roofs overgrown in places with thick moss; brush fences crackling from dryness; towering sweeps over open wells, the butt ends of the cross-poles weighted down with stones and resting on the ground like dogs on their haunches; unpaved streets, with ditches in front of their houses to drain the waters after heavy rains and spring thaws; swells and hollows in the ground, with holes in which the mud never dried out . . . and the same seedy dogs, only more of them, as ever leaping, barking furiously, as if ready to devour passing strangers.'—Maurice Hindus, *Red Bread*.

Between the Revolution and the German invasion of 1941 a great increase in the productivity of the region and in the standard of living of the people was achieved by the introduction of scientific methods of farming on a basis of collective ownership. In many areas villages were rebuilt, electricity was installed, schools, nurseries, and hospitals were provided, and the formerly ignorant peasantry became skilled farmworkers, proud of their contribution to the strength and prosperity of the country.

East of the Volga the Black Earth lands suffer from low rainfall and frequent drought, which formerly resulted in periodic crop failure and famine. In such semi-arid areas the periods during which ploughing, sowing, and harvesting can be done are usually very short, and only the large-scale use of agricultural machinery, which enables the work to be done quickly, can ensure a profitable return; consequently, the Soviet Government has organized in this district many large-scale, highly mechanized farms which are run directly by the State. A large area has also been irrigated from reservoirs on the Volga. (See Fig. 22, page 80.)

The chief towns of this eastern Black Earth region are situated where the main routes cross the Volga. *Kuibishev* is situated on the Volga where the main Trans-Siberian railway crosses the river and near one of the great hydro-electric stations on the canalized river. It specializes in the manufacture of tractors and other transport equipment, and is a great centre for the distribution of timber, grain, oil, and cotton.

Stalingrad (now called Volgograd) is famous for the battle which was a turning point in the last war. Situated at the great bend of the Volga and at the terminus of the Volga–Don ship canal, it is a place of transhipment between road and rail.

(c) *The Arid Steppes.* Around the northern end of the Caspian Sea the scanty rainfall and the salt-encrusted soil prevent the growth of crops except in a few specially favourable areas. On these steppes a scanty population of pastoral nomads gain a meagre livelihood by rearing cattle, sheep, horses, and camels.

This region is in some ways comparable with the Tundra of the extreme north. Although 1,500 miles nearer the Equator, the Caspian Steppes are as cold as the Tundra in winter, since they are far from the moderating influence of the ocean, and are exposed to cold winds from the interior of Asia; in summer, however, the Caspian region is the hottest part of Europe, while the Tundra is the coolest. Both regions have very low rainfall, and both are deserts, yet in both people manage to earn a livelihood by herding animals.

In both areas, too, the Soviet Government has done much to raise the standard of living of the people by education, by the introduction of better methods of stock rearing, and by the successful cultivation of crops, even under adverse climatic conditions.

Astrakhan is situated on the delta of the Volga at the highest point reached by sea-going vessels. The lower Volga and the shallow sea around the delta are very rich in fish, and Astrakhan is the chief fishing and fish canning centre in the U.S.S.R., being specially noted for sturgeon and caviare (the salted roe of the sturgeon).

New Methods of Farming

One of the most startling innovations of the Soviet Government was the application of the principles of communism to farming. Two methods have been adopted, both of which abolished individual peasant ownership, and substituted communal cultivation of the land. The first method is that of the

kolkhoz or collective farm, to form which the peasants in a
particular district pool their land, stock, and implements. The
large farm thus formed is worked as one unit by the members
of the group, who are divided into brigades, each of which is
responsible for certain operations or for certain sections of the
farm. When the crops are harvested a certain amount has to
be sold to the Government at a fixed price, the remainder being
divided amongst the workers in proportion to their working
time and the quality of their work. Each member of the
kolkhoz may sell on the open market any portion of his share
of the crops.

In addition to the joint ownership of the 'collective' each
member has a plot of land which he may work in his spare
time, the produce therefrom being his own property. Many
of the smaller 'collectives' are now being amalgamated, and
the farm workers concentrated in large villages or 'agro-
towns.' In such cases the individual plots are reduced to
'gardens.'

The second new method which has been adopted is that of
setting up huge State-owned farms. This has been adopted
particularly in the drier regions, which were formerly uncultivated. These State farms, of which there are about 4,000 in
the U.S.S.R., are run on the same lines as factories. Ploughing,
sowing, harrowing, and reaping are done by the aid of huge
oil-driven tractors; the workmen are organized in brigades
as in the army; and, in case of need, the shift system is adopted,
work being continued through the night. In winter, when
little work can be done on the frozen land, most of the workmen are drafted into factories.

Most of the State farms specialize in the production of
wheat or cotton, but there are also large sheep and cattle
ranches which are run on the same lines.

THE INDUSTRIAL REGIONS

Although nearly two-thirds of the people of the U.S.S.R.
obtain their livelihood from the land, the country has great

The House of Industry: Kharkov, Russia

resources of coal, water-power, timber, metals, and raw materials of all kinds. In tsarist times these resources remained largely undeveloped, but after the Communist Revolution industrial development proceeded at an amazing rate, and the U.S.S.R. is now second only to the U.S.A. as a manufacturing country.

The following are the chief mining and manufacturing areas of European Russia. (See Fig. 22, page 80.)

(1) **The Donbas and Southern Ukraine.** The Donbas, so called because it lies mainly in the basin of the River Don, is part of Russia's greatest industrial region which occupies the southern part of the Ukrainian Socialist Soviet Republic. The industrial development of the region is based on supplies of coal, iron, manganese, salt, oil, and hydro-electricity. The Donetz coalfield produces 100 million tons of coal a year—50 per cent of the total production of the U.S.S.R., and nearly half as much as in the whole of Great Britain; iron ore is obtained from the Crimea and from Krivoirog, near the lower Dnieper; manganese, of which the U.S.S.R. is the world's largest producer, is also mined near Krivoirog; oil is brought by tankers and pipe-line from the Caucasus; and hydro-electricity is generated at a great dam on the Dnieper. An excellent network of railways facilitates free exchange of these resources, and the whole industrial region has been organized as one unit producing chiefly metal goods, machinery, and chemicals. Kharkov, the chief industrial centre, is engaged principally in engineering. The chief ports of the region are Rostov at the mouth of the Don, and Odessa on the Black Sea coast.

Kiev, the capital of the Ukraine, and the third largest city of the U.S.S.R., is well outside the main industrial area, but owes its origin and importance to its advantages of situation at the junction of the grassland and the forest, on the navigable River Dnieper, which has always been one of the chief highways of trade between the Black Sea and the Baltic, and at the confluence of that river with the Desna, which was followed

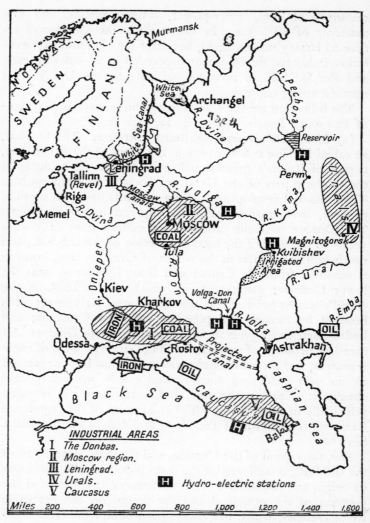

INDUSTRIAL AREAS
I   The Donbas.
II   Moscow region.
III Leningrad.
IV   Urals.
V   Caucasus

H Hydro-electric stations

Miles 200   400   600   800   1,000   1,200   1,400   1,600

FIG. 22. EUROPEAN RUSSIA: INDUSTRIAL

by the early trade routes from the central forest region. It declined in importance after the Tartar invasions, and for a long period was reduced to a mere village; but in modern times it has again become a great industrial and commercial centre, and the growth of its population has been remarkably rapid.

(2) **The Moscow Region.** This central forest region has long been the home of many 'domestic' industries carried on by the peasants in their own homes during the long, cold winters.

In Moscow itself, and in several towns around, large factories have been established for the manufacture of textiles, machinery, leather goods, etc. The coal-field of Tula, some distance to the south of Mos-

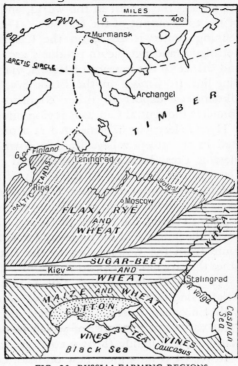

FIG. 23. RUSSIA: FARMING REGIONS

cow, supplies only poor quality fuel, but in recent years electric-power stations have been set up, using either coal or the peat which is found in great quantities in many parts of the region.

(3) **Leningrad** has shipbuilding, textile, chemical, and other industries. One great drawback to the development of the region is the lack of coal and other sources of power. (See page 69.)

(4) **The Caucasus Region.** Industrial development in this region is based on petroleum, water-power, mineral ores, and agricultural products.

The oil-fields which lie on the northern side of the Caucasus are among the richest in the world, and produce 40 per cent of the total output of the U.S.S.R. The chief producing and refining centre is *Baku*, on the Caspian Sea. From there petroleum and petroleum products are shipped to Astrakhan and thence to the interior of Russia, via the Volga, or sent by pipe-line to *Batum*, on the Black Sea, for transport to the Ukraine or export to other countries. Another pipe-line connects the central Caucasus region directly with the Donbas.

Hydro-electricity is generated at scores of generators situated in the steep valleys leading down from the Caucasus; metallic ores, such as manganese and copper, are mined in Georgia and Armenia, to the south of the Caucasus Range; and locally produced timber, fruit, cotton, tobacco, and oil-seeds have given rise to miscellaneous industries.

Tiflis (Tbilisi), the capital of Georgia, is an ancient fortress city at the junction of the highway across the Caucasus with the route from the Caspian Sea to the Black Sea. In modern times the city has developed an important textile industry.

(5) **The Urals.** Though this region lies mainly on the Asiatic side of the Urals, it is most conveniently considered with European Russia. The Urals are amazingly rich in a great variety of minerals, of which iron, manganese, copper, platinum, and lignite (brown coal) are the chief.

In recent years a great new oil-field, called by the Russians the 'Second Baku,' has been developed between the Urals and the Volga, and further supplies of oil are brought by pipe-line from Emba on the Caspian coast. Coal is brought from Kuznetsk and Karaganda in Soviet Asia, and hydro-electricity is generated in the central Caucasus. On the basis of these resources the Soviet Government has in recent years built up one of the world's most productive and highly organized industrial areas.

Magnitogorsk, the chief iron and steel centre, grew in a few years from a tiny village to a town of 200,000 people. Iron ore for its blast furnaces is obtained from the neighbouring Magnet Mountain, a solid mass of some 500 million tons of magnetic iron ore.

Sverdlovsk, situated in the broad gap in the central Urals which carries the main Trans-Siberian railway, is the great machine-building town of the region. *Perm* is situated on the European side of the same gap, and at the head of navigation of the Kama tributary of the Volga. It is a great boat-building centre, and local deposits of salt, phosphate, and coal provide the basis for the manufacture of chemicals and fertilizers.

TRANSPORT

An efficient system of transport is a vital necessity for the development of a large country like Russia. She has great supplies of coal, timber, metals, and other raw materials, but if these cannot be brought together they are of little use. In spite of the fact that Russia has many long navigable rivers (see Fig. 22) and is a vast plain on which it should be easy to build roads, railways, and canals, her transport facilities are quite inadequate for her needs.

The rivers have from time immemorial been the chief highways of the country; but their courses are tortuous, and they are closed by ice for three to seven months in the year. Roads are poor and relatively few. The greater part of the country is served only by rough tracks which become 'rivers of mud' after thaw or heavy rain. Realizing the necessity of adequate means of transport, the Soviet Government has built thousands of miles of new roads and railways, and has made ambitious plans for the further development of the transport services. By 1938 the total length of railway had been increased by 50 per cent as compared with the 1913 figures, but even so the railways are unable to carry all the traffic resulting from the rapid industrial development of the country, and great efforts have been made to develop the system of water transport. In 1933 Leningrad was linked to the White Sea by a ship canal running through lakes Ladoga and Onega. The Dnieper dam, which has already been referred to as the largest hydro-electric dam in the world, has greatly improved navigation on the upper Dnieper by deepening the river so that it is now navigable to Kiev. Locks situated at the dam itself enable vessels to pass from the lower to the upper course, and vice versa, and the Russians look forward to the time when the river will be 'the Rhine of Russia.'

The Moscow-Volga Canal, which was completed in 1937, has made the city one of the most important inland ports in the world, with access to the White Sea, the Baltic Sea, and the Caspian Sea. It enables millions of tons of coal and grain from the south, timber and ores from the north, and fish and oil from the Caspian to be brought direct by water to the capital. It also supplies the city with an unfailing source of drinking water, while hydro-electric schemes at locks on the canal generate electricity for domestic and industrial purposes. In size the Moscow-Volga Canal, with a length of 80 miles, can only be compared with the Panama Canal (50 miles) and with the Suez Canal (102 miles).

The Volga project is the most ambitious of all the schemes of river regulation. Though the Volga has always been a great highway—it is calculated that it carries as much traffic as five main lines of railway—it suffers from freezing in winter, floods in spring, and low water in summer. Several great dams are being built to store the spring flood water, improve navigation, and provide hydro-electricity for pumping water from the lower Volga to irrigate a large area on the eastern bank. (See Fig. 22.) At the same time the total water supply of the Volga is to be increased by diverting surplus water from the Arctic rivers Dvina and Pechora. When the scheme is completed it will be possible for river steamers to sail from Archangel to Astrakhan. The Volga-Don Canal, connecting the two rivers at the great bend of the Volga near Stalingrad, was completed in 1952, thus providing an outlet for the grain region of the middle Volga, and facilitating the transport of coal from the Donetz basin to all parts of Russia.

EXERCISES

1. In the U.S.S.R. 18 per cent of the people were classed as 'urban' in 1926, and 43 per cent in 1956. Give reasons for this change.

2. In Britain 85 per cent of the people are 'urban.' Why is the proportion so much higher than in Russia?

3. The chief exports from Russia are: metals, petroleum, cotton, timber, furs.

Draw a sketch-map showing the parts of European Russia from which these products are drawn.

4. The chief imports of Russia are: engineering products, rubber, tin, and wool.

Say why Russia needs these products.

5. Draw diagrams to show the following increases of production in the U.S.S.R.:

	Coal	Iron and Steel	Electricity
	(million tons)	(million tons)	(million kilowatt hours)
1913	29	12	2,000
1938	133	46	40,000
1960	500	200	320,000

POLAND

POLAND is both one of the newest and one of the oldest countries in Europe. In the middle of the eighteenth century, after its union with Lithuania, it comprised nearly all the land between the Dneiper and the Oder, and between the Carpathians and the Baltic Sea. See Fig. 19. At the end of that century, however, the country was torn asunder, and partitioned between her powerful neighbours Russia, Austria, and Prussia. For more than a century the Polish peoples were subject to these foreign governments, each of which did its best to stamp out all ideas of a separate Polish nationality. Yet the Poles clung tenaciously to the hope that they would again become an independent nation. Their chance came with the defeat of Germany and Austria in the First World War, and a new Poland was created by the Peace Treaties. The boundary was drawn to include not only the territory inhabited solely by Poles, but also considerable areas in the east and south-east, where the people are of mixed nationalities, as well as the so-called 'Polish corridor' between East Prussia and the rest of Germany. After the Second World War Poland lost some of her eastern lands to Russia, but was compensated by the extension of her western borders to include Silesia and all the land up to the Oder.

Physically, Poland may be divided into the following regions (see fig. 24, p. 87):

(1) The low, lagoon-fringed Baltic coastlands.

(2) The sandy, lake-studded Baltic heights.

(3) The central zone of low valleys, such as those of the Vistula and its tributary the Bug.

(4) The southern plateau, mostly between 600 and 1,200 feet in height, but rising in the ancient block of the Lyso Gory to over 2,500 feet.

(5) The Carpathians, which are fold mountains consisting of many parallel, east to west ranges.

Climatically Poland shows a transition from the equable west European type to the extreme type of Russia; thus, while the Oder is blocked by ice for eighty days in the year, the Vistula is ice-bound for one hundred days, while the Niemen is closed for one hundred and twenty days, and the rivers of central Russia for one hundred and sixty days.

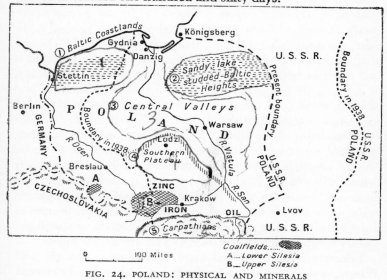

FIG. 24. POLAND: PHYSICAL AND MINERALS

Agriculture. Poland is essentially a farming country, and nearly two-thirds of her people are engaged in agriculture. Though the word 'pole' means 'plain' or 'field,' Poland has no fields in our sense of the word; there are no hedges, and 'the country is one great field from the Oder to the Dnieper.' Until recently the land was cultivated on the 'strip system,' each peasant possessing several scattered strips of land. This system not only caused the peasant to waste much time in going from one plot to another, but also made it impossible for him to use modern agricultural machinery. Between the two World Wars much of the land was redistributed, so as to give each peasant his holding all in one piece. As elsewhere in eastern Europe the Soviet Government is trying to impose collective farming in Poland, but only about a fifth of the farm land is in collective or state farms.

The most productive part of present-day Poland is the western region which was taken from Germany after the Second World War. Here the land has for long been intensively farmed and has produced rich crops of wheat, sugar beet, potatoes, hops, tobacco, fruit, and vegetables. Though the region was devastated in the later stages of the war, and is still short of fertilizers, live-stock, and agricultural machinery, it is gradually being restored to its former productivity, and will far more than counterbalance the loss of a much larger area of poor and primitively farmed land in the east.

In the basin of the Vistula the chief crops are rye, potatoes, flax, and sugar beet. Rye, which is made into the so-called 'black' bread, is the chief food cereal, even in the areas where wheat will grow. Potatoes are grown in such quantity that in normal years the yield is sufficient to provide each person with more than a ton a year. Much of the crop is used as food for pigs and cattle, and for the manufacture of starch and potato syrup, which can be used as a substitute for sugar.

Forestry. In its natural state Poland was covered with forests, and although the lowlands have been largely cleared, nearly a quarter of the total area is still forested. The largest areas of coniferous forest are to be found in the western half of the country, and on the lower slopes of the Carpathians. Much of the timber is floated down the Vistula in the form of huge rafts, and as it takes several weeks for these rafts to reach the port of Danzig, huts are erected on them for the accommodation of the crews.

Mining and Manufacture. Though Poland is mainly an agricultural country she possesses resources which should enable her to become one of the chief manufacturing countries of Europe. The chief industrial areas are Lower Silesia and Upper Silesia.

Lower Silesia is the district in the upper basin of the Oder which centres on Wroclaw. Here small coal-fields, hydro-electric power, timber, and local agricultural products provide the basis for miscellaneous manufactures such as textiles, paper, chemicals, musical instruments, and foodstuffs.

Wroclaw, formerly called Breslau, is the great city of the region. It grew up where the River Oder breaks up into a

FIG. 25. POLAND: AGRICULTURE

number of channels, thus determining the natural head of navigation and the easiest crossing place for the east-to-west routes across the plain. During the Middle Ages the city was the outpost of the civilization of western Europe, and so became the great centre of trade between Germany and eastern and south-eastern Europe. As the focus of roads and railways it has become the most important industrial centre of the region, being specially noteworthy for the manufacture of machinery, linen goods, paper, and furniture.

The Upper Silesian Coal-field lies in the angle between the Bohemian Block and the Carpathians. The coal is of excellent quality and occurs in thick seams at moderate depths, and the

region now rivals the Ruhr as the chief coal-producing area
in Europe. The output is now nearly half the total produced
in Britain, and there is a surplus for export to Sweden.

Some iron ore is also produced, but the great iron and steel
industry which has grown up in Silesia is largely dependent
on ore from the Ukraine and Sweden. Zinc is mined to the
north-east of the coal-field and has led to specialization in
the manufacture of galvanized iron. The chief mining and
manufacturing centres are Katowice and Gleiwitz.

Krakow, though not actually on the coal-field, is the chief
manufacturing town of the south. It is an ancient town
which owes its origin and early importance to its situation at
the intersection of two of the great cross-routes of Europe,
viz. the route from the North Sea to the Black Sea, along the
northern edge of the German highlands and the Carpathians;
and the route from the Mediterranean to the Baltic, through
the Moravian Gate.

Rock salt and potash are also mined in the foothills of the
Carpathians, and have given rise to an important chemical
industry. *Nova Huta*, near Kracow, is an important steel-
making centre.

Lodz is the greatest industrial centre of the whole country,
although it is situated far to the north of the coal-field. It
owes its existence and its characteristic textile industries to the
fact that a Polish government, which was set up by Napoleon,
gave special facilities to German firms to induce them to
set up factories here. In 1809 it was a squalid village of
800 inhabitants; in 1860, although it had not a single railway, its population was 28,000; in 1900 it had grown to
325,000, and at the present day it contains nearly half a million
people.

Warsaw, the capital and the largest city of Poland, is situated
on the west bank of the Vistula, where a ridge of higher ground
restricts the channel somewhat, thus providing both a natural
bridge-place and the means of defence. Its central position
caused it to be chosen as the capital when Poland united with

Lithuania, and in modern times it has become the centre of the road and railway system of the country, as well as one of its greatest industrial centres. Its situation at the intersection of the highways across Europe has given it great economic and commercial advantages, but the same factor has also caused it to suffer at the hands of invaders. In the course of its tumultuous history it has been occupied by the armies of all the neighbouring nations—Swedes, Austrians, Germans, and Russians. At the partition of Poland in 1795 it was ceded to Prussia, but from 1813 onwards it was under the rule of Russia. The public buildings reflect this chequered history, some being of the German and some of the Russian type.

Danzig, at the mouth of the Vistula, is the natural outlet for Poland. Founded by German colonists in the thirteenth century, it became an important Hanseatic port and the principal focus of the trade of the eastern Baltic. Its character was predominantly German, and when the modern country of Poland was established after the First World War, Danzig was not included in that country but made into a Free City under the protection of the League of Nations. The German seizure of the city in 1939 signalized the outbreak of the Second World War.

Though Danzig was almost completely destroyed in that war, its natural advantages are such that as the chief port of Poland it has regained much of its former importance as the outlet for the Vistula region.

Gdynia is situated on the coast of the former 'Polish corridor,' the strip of territory which, between the two World Wars, separated East Prussia from the rest of Germany. The Poles, wishing to have a port of their own as an alternative to Danzig, transformed Gdynia from a tiny fishing village into a well-equipped modern port which, before the Second World War, was able to handle more than half the overseas trade of Poland.

Stettin, formerly the chief port for Berlin, is now a Polish port, and as such competes with Danzig and Gdynia for the export of coal from Upper Silesia and the import of iron ore from Sweden.

THE DANUBE LANDS

THE Danube basin is a region of great physical variety, but the essential features will readily be grasped by a comparison of the physical sketch-map with the small inset diagram. (Fig. 26.)

Note particularly:

(1) The way in which the 'old blocks' of Bohemia and the Rhodope have turned aside the folds of the Alps, the Carpathians, the Transylvanian Alps, and the Balkans.

(2) The 'vice-jaws' of high land at Bratislava, Pressburg, Budapest, and the Iron Gates.

(3) The Plain of Austria, the Upper Hungarian Plain (the Little Alfold), the Lower Hungarian Plain (the Great Alfold). and the Plain of Walachia.

(4) The gateways into the basin, viz.:

(a) The Gate of the Upper Danube,
(b) The Moravian Gate,
(c) The Semmering Pass,   } converging on Vienna
(d) The Bratislava Gate,
(e) The Iron Gates.
(f) The Morava valley.

During the course of history the Danube has been sometimes a barrier between peoples, sometimes a highway for invaders, and sometimes the link between similar peoples on opposite banks. In Roman times it was the boundary between the Roman Empire and the barbarian tribes to the east. (See Fig. 11.) Later it was the highway along which the Magyars and the Turks entered central Europe, and along which the Germans pushed into the Austrian plain. (Note on the sketch-map, Fig. 27, how the Slav peoples have thus been divided into two sections.)

Though the Danube is of some importance as a highway,

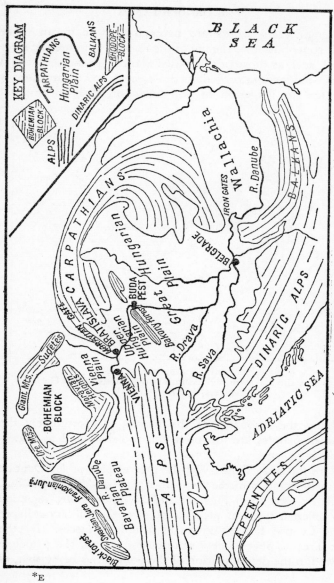

FIG. 26. THE DANUBE BASIN: SIMPLIFIED PHYSICAL MAP

(The lines within the mountain belts indicate only the general trend of the ranges)

*E

great engineering works are necessary before it can make
its full contribution to the life of the region. A system of river
control, such as those of the Volga and the Tennessee, would
improve navigation, provide hydro-electric power, and supply
water for the irrigation of arid lowlands, thus enormously

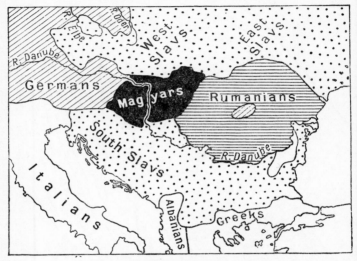

FIG. 27. THE DANUBE BASIN: RACES
(Note how the Slavs are divided into two sections by the Germans,
Magyars, and Rumanians)

increasing the resources of the region. Unfortunately the
Danubian peoples are too poor and too disunited to undertake such projects.

Before the First World War the greater part of the Danube
basin was included in the Empire of Austria-Hungary. But,
as will be seen from Figs. 27 and 28, this empire included
many different types of people, and after the military collapse
of the Central Powers in 1918, it fell to pieces. By the
Peace Treaties several new states were set up, the principle
followed in the determination of the boundaries being that, as

FIG. 28. THE DANUBE COUNTRIES IN 1914

FIG. 29. THE DANUBE STATES TO-DAY
(Compare with Figs. 27 and 28)

far as possible, people of the same race and language should be included within one country. (See Fig. 29.)

CZECHOSLOVAKIA

CZECHOSLOVAKIA, like Poland, is one of the new countries set up by the Peace Treaties following the First World War. It was formed by the union of the former Austro-Hungarian provinces of Bohemia, Moravia, and Slovakia, with the addition of part of Silesia (Fig. 30.) The Czechs, who

FIG. 30. THE BOOT-SHAPED COUNTRY OF CZECHOSLOVAKIA
(Showing former political divisions)

inhabit the western part of the republic, and the Slovaks, who occupy the eastern part, are two closely related branches of the Slav race. Between the sixth and tenth centuries the present republic was part of an empire which extended far beyond the Danube. In the tenth century the Magyars conquered Hungary, and brought the Slovaks within their rule. Bohemia, however, remained for several centuries a powerful independent kingdom. 'Every schoolboy' knows that the blind king of Bohemia was killed at Crécy fighting on the side of the French, and that his arms, with the motto 'Ich dien,' were adopted by the Black Prince. But the most influential Bohemian of that period was John Hus, who was the forerunner of the Reformation. His teaching won over the majority of the Czechs of Bohemia, but caused neighbouring Roman Catholic countries to make war on them. Weakened by the war, Bohemia entered into a confederation with Austria and Hungary, and from that time her power waned, and she finally became absorbed by Austria.

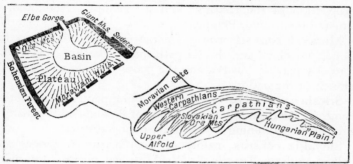

FIG. 31. DIAGRAM MAP OF CZECHOSLOVAKIA
(Showing physical divisions)

Slovakia, though inhabited by people of the same race and language as the Czechs, was under the domination of Hungary from the tenth century until 1918. In spite of all difficulties, however, the Czechs and the Slovaks kept alive their sense of common nationality. The defeat of Austria-Hungary in the First World War was the opportunity for the realization of their hopes, and in 1918 the provinces of Bohemia, Moravia, Silesia, and Slovakia united to form the republic of Czechoslovakia. After the Second World War Soviet power was firmly established and Czechoslovakia became a Communist country.

The four provinces have now been replaced by smaller administrative units, but as they corresponded so closely to the physical and economic divisions their names may be conveniently retained for descriptive purposes. (See Fig. 31.)

Bohemia is one of the hard old blocks of Europe; but while the outer edges are raised so as to form mountain ranges (the Ore Mountains, the Bohemian Forest, etc.), the inner part of the block has subsided, forming a fertile basin which is drained by the Elbe and its tributaries.

Bohemia is by far the most highly developed part of Czechoslovakia. Though it comprises only about one-third of the total area, it contains nearly half the people, and a large proportion of the factories and workshops. Here, too, is situated the capital, Prague.

Moravia consists mainly of the low land between the Bohemian block and the Carpathians. Like Bohemia it was formerly part of Austria, and the people belong to the Czech branch of the nation.

Silesia is a small part of the former German province of that name. Like the adjoining portions of Poland and Germany it is a busy coal-mining and manufacturing district.

Slovakia consists mainly of the Carpathian ranges and valleys, with small portions of the Danubian plains. It is much less highly developed than the foregoing provinces. As might be expected from its mountainous character it is much less densely peopled, and the inhabitants lead a more primitive life, aiming primarily at producing as many of the necessaries of life as possible, and therefore having little trade with other districts.

FARMING IN CZECHOSLOVAKIA

In spite of the large proportion of her surface which is occupied by mountains and forests, Czechoslovakia is one of the most productive countries of Europe. In Bohemia and Moravia the farm land is intensively cultivated, and even in Slovakia the proportion of totally unproductive land is very small. A journey through the lowlands of Czechoslovakia would bring home to us the fact that there are far more ploughed fields and fewer pasture fields than in our country. Indeed, whereas in Britain only one-third of the land is arable, and nearly half is under grass, the proportions in Czechoslovakia are nearly one-half and one-sixth respectively. Another striking feature is the great subdivision of the land. 'The fields are divided into long narrow strips, and as every strip carries a different crop from the one next to it, the whole effect is that of a many-coloured striped carpet, spread out over the whole land, not only in the level parts, but folded over the lower hills as well, and tucked down well into the hollows.' [1] Formerly many of the strips were only a few feet wide, though possibly half a mile long, and each farm would consist of many widely separated strips. This state of affairs was due to the inheritance laws, which give all children an equal share of the father's property, so that each field might have to be cut up into several strips when the owner died, and each inheritance might entail a further subdivision. Even though holdings have been redistributed and much of it 'collectivized,' as in Poland, the peasants like to grow a variety of crops on their farms, so that the land still looks somewhat like a 'striped carpet.'

The farmers of Czechoslovakia are able to grow not only the greater part of the staple foodstuffs required by the country, but also many crops which form the basis of manufacturing industries. The chief of these industrial crops are sugar beet, hops, and potatoes, all of which are grown mainly on the Bohemian lowlands. In an average year the republic produces over a hundred pounds of sugar per head, so there is normally a surplus available for export. Indeed, Czechoslovakia is one of the few sugar-exporting countries in Europe. The hops are used for the brewing of 'Pilsener' beer, which is made chiefly at Pilsen and sold all over Europe. Potatoes are, next to sugar beet, the most valuable agricultural product of the country, and are used not only for animal food, but also for the manufacture of alcohol, starch, and motor

[1] J. Mothersole, *Czechoslovakia*.

spirit. The cultivation of these industrial crops is so profitable that 'in some districts the growing of grain has been
abandoned altogether in favour of the production of crops
necessary for the agricultural industries.'

The pastoral farming is also of considerable importance,
especially in Slovakia, where there are large areas of common
pastures on which all the cattle of one village are grazed
together under the charge of a single herdsman. On the
average there is one cow or ox for every three people, so even
though there are many oxen (used as draught animals) the
country is able to supply all the dairy produce it requires.

The ordinary cool temperate fruits, such as apples, pears,
cherries, and plums, are widely grown throughout the lowlands, both in orchards and along the roadsides. In the
latter case the trees are the property of the community.

LUMBERING

Nearly one-third of the country is covered with forests
which supply all the timber needed for building and for the
paper and furniture industries. The rivers are largely used
for transport of the timber, and long rafts, jointed so as to
enable the crew to steer them round the bends in the rivers, are
often to be seen floating down the Elbe and its tributaries.
Timber is the most usual building material, except in the large
towns. The houses are often built of logs laid horizontally,
usually upon a stone foundation. In the Carpathian region
the most common type is a single-storied house, consisting
only of a living-room and a bedroom, and many of them still
have only a hole in the roof in place of a chimney. In the
more prosperous western half of the country, however, hous-
ing standards are similar to those of western Europe.

MANUFACTURING IN CZECHOSLOVAKIA

As an industrial country Czechoslovakia is well equipped.
Her portion of the Upper Silesian coal-field produces excellent

Cedok Ltd.

CZECHOSLOVAKIA: THE HAY MARKET AT SEVLUŠ IN
SOUTH CARPATHIAN RUSSIA

Ö. V. B.

VINE HARVEST IN AUSTRIA

coking coal, while she has also small but productive fields near Pilsen and Brünn. (Fig. 32.) In addition to these fields, which produce ordinary hard coal, she has large deposits of lignite, a soft brown coal which is used for the making of briquettes, the generation of electricity, and the preparation of by-products, such as ammonia and fertilizers. Iron is mined

FIG. 32. CZECHOSLOVAKIA: RIVERS, TOWNS, AND MINERALS

in the Slovakian Ore Mountains and near Pilsen. Uranium, the chief source of atomic energy, is mined near Karlsbad; silver, gold, copper, antimony, tin, graphite, and lead are also mined in small quantities. This mineral wealth, together with the supplies of raw material produced by her farmers, and the energenic character of her people, has made Czechoslovakia one of the chief manufacturing countries of Europe. Her central position is both an advantage and a disadvantage; on the one hand it gives her opportunities of trading with many neighbouring countries, but it also handicaps her by lack of cheap sea transport. The disadvantage of lack of sea-coast is to some extent counterbalanced by an excellent system of transport on the rivers Elbe, Oder, and Danube, which gives

*E 2   E

her access to the ports of the North Sea, the Baltic, and the Black Sea. Canals are planned to link the Danube with the Elbe and the Oder.

Glass is one of the most important manufactured products exported from Czechoslovakia. The industry is centred chiefly in the north-western part of Bohemia, where there are deposits of pure glass sand. Formerly wood was used as fuel, but this has now been replaced by locally mined coal. Window-glass, mirrors, electric globes, bottles, and fire-proof glass are manufactured in great quantity in many well-equipped factories; while beads, imitation jewellery, bangles, buttons, etc., are made chiefly in the homes of the people, or in adjoining sheds. Nearly 90 per cent of the total glass manufactured was exported prior to the Second World War.

Metal goods. Although considerable quantities of iron ore are produced in the Slovakian Ore Mountains and near Pilsen, these supply only about one-fifth of the ore used in the country, the remainder being imported, chiefly from Sweden, via the River Elbe. Pilsen is the chief centre of the industry. Agricultural machinery, motors, railway engines, and rolling stock form the greater part of the output.

Textiles (cotton, woollen, flax, jute, silk, and hosiery) are manufactured chiefly in Prague, Pilsen, Brünn, and Reichenburg.

Porcelain is manufactured near Karlsbad, where there are deposits of excellent china clay. *Boots and shoes* are manufactured at Zlin and Prague. As the factories are capable of producing about 30,000,000 pairs a year, it will be obvious that the industry depends mainly on export trade.

Towns

Prague (Praha) is the capital and largest city of the republic. It is situated on the Moldau, a navigable tributary of the Elbe, and almost in the centre of the Bohemian lowlands. Like so many other ancient cities of Europe, Prague grew up round a fortress built on a rocky eminence which dominates the river

CZECHOSLOVAKIA

crossing. The name Praha means doorway, and an old legend says that it was so called because a certain queen directed her followers to go to a place in the forest where they would find a man making a doorway, and there build a city. Whatever the truth of this story, the name is certainly appropriate, for all roads in Bohemia lead to Prague, and the city is the objective of many great lines of railway.

Brünn (Brno) is the second city of the republic. It is the chief centre of the woollen industry, and also manufactures cotton goods, machinery, and leather goods.

Plzen (Pilsen) is an important manufacturing city, though its small coal-field is nearly worked out. It is specially notable for the great Skoda armament factories, and for the brewing of Pilsener beer.

Bratislava (formerly called Pressburg) is situated on the Danube, near the junction of the boundaries of Czechoslovakia, Austria, and Hungary. It is an important manufacturing centre, and is Czechoslovakia's chief outlet via the Danube.

EXERCISES

1. The following table gives the population of the various divisions of Czechoslovakia:

Bohemia	7,106,000
Moravia and Silesia	3,563,000
Slovakia	3,331,000

Make a map showing the distribution of population by drawing an outline of the political divisions, and inserting one dot for every 100,000 people. While doing this, keep your eye on the physical map, and place most of the dots on the lowlands.

Say why certain parts are densely peopled, while others are scantily peopled.

2.

OCCUPATIONS OF THE PEOPLE

Province	Agriculture per cent	Industries per cent
Bohemia	32	41
Moravia	41	35
Silesia	29	46
Slovakia	61	20

On an outline map draw half-inch squares in each province, and

divide each square so as to show the percentages employed in
agriculture and in industries.

3. What relationship do you notice between the maps drawn for
exercises 1 and 2?

4. Slovakia occupies about one-third of the area of the republic,
and has less than a quarter of the people; but it produces 40 per
cent of all the wheat, and has 85 per cent of the sheep in the
country. Show on a sketch-map the parts specially suitable for
wheat growing and sheep rearing.

5. Draw a sketch-map of Czechoslovakia to show its relationship to the rivers Elbe, Oder, and Danube. Why are rivers of
special importance to Czechoslovakia?

6. Several of the principal railways of Europe cross Czechoslovakia.

Illustrate this statement by a sketch-map.

AUSTRIA

THE Republic of Austria consists of three physical divisions, namely, the Alps, the Danube Valley, and the Vienna
Plain.

The Alps, which occupy about 80 per cent of the total area,
consist of high ranges which run from west to east, alternating
with deep longitudinal valleys, such as those of the Enns and
the Drava. Communication has, therefore, always been easy
from east to west, but difficult from north to south; this,
no doubt, helps to account for the country being so long in
proportion to its breadth.

The life of the peasants in these Alpine valleys is naturally
very similar to that of their Swiss neighbours. Agriculture
is restricted to the lower slopes, and, in west-to-east valleys,
to the sunny northern sides. Dairy farming and stock raising
are the chief means of livelihood, and, as in Norway, the
cattle are driven to the mountain pastures in summer.

Farming is not the only economic resource of the region.
Timber from the mountain sides forms an important item of
export, and the region is rich in minerals. Considerable quan-

tities of iron ore are mined in the province of Styria, where a prosperous iron and steel industry has arisen; magnesite, a mineral used in the preparation of magnesium, is of considerable importance, while lignite, lead, zinc, and mercury are also mined. Tourists, attracted by the beautiful scenery and the facilities for winter sports, also bring much money into the country.

The chief reserve of wealth is, however, the water power. Already much more hydro-electricity is generated than is required, and a good deal is 'exported' to Germany. Some very ambitious schemes for further development are now in progress, the most noteworthy being one to harness the energy that now runs to waste on the highest mountains of Austria, near Salzburg. The complete scheme will use a fall of 4,500 feet in three stages, where would be a system of 'hanging canals' of hundreds of kilometres in length to collect the water and nearly 50 kilometres of tunnels. It is calculated that electricity equivalent to an annual consumption of 4,000,000 tons of coal will thus be generated, some of which will be 'exported' to central and northern Germany.

In spite of its great natural resources, the region as a whole is thinly peopled, since a large proportion of the land is quite unproductive.

The towns, many of which are of great historical interest, have grown up where the valleys open out to the plains (e.g. Graz and Salzburg), or at the meeting of north-to-south and east-to-west routes.

Innsbruck, the largest town of the region, is situated in the deep trench occupied by the upper portions of the Inn and the Enns. This longitudinal trough carries the main railway line from Basle to Vienna, and at Innsbruck it is crossed by the north-to-south line from Berlin via Munich and the Brenner Pass to northern Italy.

The Danube Valley. The Danube enters Austria a little way below the German town of Passau, where the river first becomes navigable by large boats. From this point one may sail right down to the Black Sea, though few steamers do the whole voyage. The river flows through a succession of rocky gorges, alternating with broad fertile basins on one of which stands *Linz*, the chief town of Upper Austria.

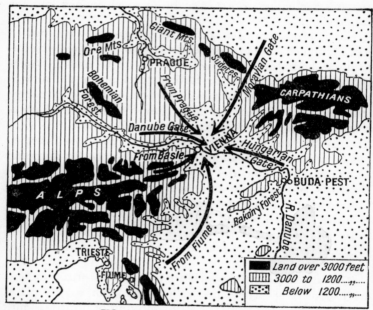

FIG. 33. THE POSITION OF VIENNA

The rapid current of the river through the gorges is a hindrance to navigation, but is a potential source of hydro-electricity, and it is hoped that here, as in the Alps, hydro-electric stations will be established in the near future.

The Vienna Plain. Although this plain occupies only one-tenth of the area of Austria, it contains about two-thirds of the people. *Vienna* itself contains 35 per cent of the total population of the country. The city, which has been described as the 'Key to Europe,' owes its importance to its situation on the largest river of our continent, in the midst of a fertile plain, and at the meeting-point of routes from the Baltic Sea to the Mediterranean, and from the North Sea to the Black Sea. (See Fig. 33.)

Before the war of 1914–18 Vienna was the centre of a great empire, whose rulers did everything in their power to make it the chief industrial city of the country. Special facilities were offered to producers of raw materials who sent their goods to Vienna, and to manufacturers who set up their factories there.

After the First World War, as we have seen, Austria lost the greater part of her territory, and so Vienna lost both her sources of raw materials and her market for manufactured goods and a period of great privation followed. Between the two world wars, however, great industrial development took place in both the Alpine valleys and the Vienna region. In Vienna and the surrounding region industry has developed on the basis of hydro-electricity from the Alps, coal from Silesia and Germany, iron and aluminium and timber from the Alpine provinces. In recent years a small oil-field has been developed some twenty miles north of the city. The central position of Vienna, at the focus of roads and railways, ensure its continuing importance as an industrial and commercial metropolis.

EXERCISES

1. Austria has to import nearly one-half of the cereals required for making bread. Give reasons why she cannot be self-sufficing in this respect.

2. (*a*) State in words the difference between Austria and Poland shown by the following figures, which show comparable amounts per acre of agricultural land.

	Fertilizer used	Yield of Wheat	Agricultural Population
Austria	3	$1\frac{1}{2}$	1
Poland	1	1	$1\frac{1}{3}$

(*b*) In 1937 the death rate of children under one year was 50 per cent higher in Poland than in Austria; what connection can you see between this fact and the figures in the above table?

3. In a typical recent year Austria bought goods worth £230,000,000, but only got £180,000,000 for those she sold. Can you suggest any ways by which Austria made up the difference?

4. Draw sketch-maps to show why Graz and Saltzburg became important route centres.

5. Draw a diagram to show the acreage of the chief crops of Austria, as given in the following table:

Rye	940,000 acres	Potatoes	470,000 acres
Oats	740,000 acres	Barley	380,000 acres
Wheat	510,000 acres	Turnips	150,000 acres

HUNGARY

THE great plain known as the *Alfold*, which comprises nearly the whole of Hungary, consists of sediment which has filled up a former inland sea. Much of the surface soil resembles the loess of China, and is of great fertility. Under natural conditions the plain was a succession of grasslands, known as *puztas*. The Magyars, whose descendants still form the greater part of the population, were nomadic herdsmen who came from the steppes of central Asia, and settled here in the

E. N. A.

WATERING CATTLE ON THE PUZTAS OF HUNGARY

E. N. A.

PEASANT'S HOUSE, RUMANIA

ninth century.   Even yet parts of the Alfold are used only as
pastures for cattle, horses, and sheep, which are tended by
semi-nomadic 'cowboys' and shepherds who live in temporary
huts made of reeds.   Both soil and climate are, however,
favourable to agriculture, and in summertime the greater part
of the plain is one vast expanse of golden grain, diversified by
occasional patches of potatoes, sunflowers, or sugar beet, and
by the fruit trees which cluster round every village.

The chief crops of the plain are wheat and maize, though
oats, barley, rye, tobacco, sugar beet, and sunflowers are also
grown.   Vines are grown on the lower slopes of the Bakony
Forest and the Carpathians.   Tokay, on the Theiss, gives its
name to a well-known wine.   Wheat is the chief source of
national wealth, and together with flour represents, in normal
times, a quarter of the total value of exports.   A large proportion
of the maize is fed to the farm stock, thus indirectly helping
to provide the second largest item of export—draught oxen,
and cattle and pigs for meat.

As these plains were formerly much subject to raids by
robbers and nomads, the farmers were compelled to dwell
together for protection.   Even to-day the majority of the
farming population live in the villages, and most of the isolated
buildings which are scattered about the plain are simply cattle
sheds or barns, though in recent years many isolated home-
steads have been built in newly developed parts of the country.
A characteristic feature of the landscape is the well poles
which stand beside each low whitewashed farmstead.   One
long pole is placed upright, and at the top of this is pivoted
a horizontal pole, to one end of which a bucket is attached
by a rope, after the manner of the Egyptian shaduf.

The typical Hungarian village consists of low, whitewashed
houses, each standing in its own plot of garden or orchard,
while in the centre of the village is a large space reserved as
a market.   The towns, too, conform to this plan, most of
them being merely overgrown villages.   In addition to their
work on the arable land the villagers grow much fruit, and

keep large flocks of turkeys and geese. In winter, when the land is snowbound, many simple industries, such as hand spinning and weaving, are carried on in the home.

Even before the defeat of the Axis powers in the Second World War the productivity of the farm land of Hungary was very low—the average farmer produced enough for one and a half families only, while in western Europe one farmer produces enough for four or five families.

After the Second World War all estates over 250 acres were divided up and given to landless peasants. Under Russian influences collective farming has been introduced, and 90 per cent of the arable land is now in collective and co-operative farms. Wheat production is now much less than in pre-war years, when Hungary was the chief wheat-exporting country of Europe. Maize, which was formerly the chief food of the peasants, is now used largely for the raising of pigs for export to the Soviet Union.

Manufacturing is but slightly developed in Hungary, for though there is a small coal-field near *Pecs* (Fünfkirchen), a small oil-field south-west of Balaton Lake, and large deposits of bauxite, other minerals are scarce, and the country does not specialize in the production of raw materials which could form the basis of large manufacturing industries. Nevertheless, recently established engineering works produce locomotives and machine tools, largely for export to the Soviet Union.

The Danube and the Theiss are both important highways of commerce; but the fact that the present boundary is drawn north of their confluence hinders the circulation of traffic. Other drawbacks to navigation on the Danube are that it suffers from frost in winter and from drought in summer; it does not serve any great industrial district; and its mouth is in the Black Sea, which is remote from the great centres of commerce.

Budapest (1,800,000) is the only city of Hungary worthy of detailed study. It is situated where the Danube valley narrows between the Bakony Forest and a spur of the Carpathians, and guards the passage from the Great Alfold to the Little Alfold, which, though now divided between Hungary and Czecho-slovakia, was formerly all Hungarian territory.

The old town, Buda, is situated on the east bank, and grew up around a citadel set on a hill which commanded the cross-ing of the river. Pest, situated on the lower west bank, formerly suffered greatly from floods caused by the blocking of the channel by ice during the spring thaws. Less than one hundred years ago it was almost destroyed by a disastrous flood; but the river was then carefully embanked, and the town rebuilt on modern lines. Buda and Pest are now one city, Budapest, which compares favourably with other European capitals. Industrially the city is noteworthy as the largest flour-milling centre in the Danube basin.

Debrecen (130,000) is the chief centre of the pastoral industry, and has four great fairs yearly. The surrounding country is the only part of central Europe where the primitive methods of large-scale ranching still prevail.

Szeged (140,000) is the only other town of Hungary whose population exceeds 100,000. Situated on the navigable Theiss, it is the chief wheat market and commercial centre of the plain.

EXERCISES

1. Make out a tabular comparison of Austria and Hungary with regard to relief, occupations of the people, exports, imports, industrial development, area, population, and density of population.

2. From the following table compare the output of agricultural produce per head of the population in the three countries.

Country	Population (millions)	Grain (m. tons)	Sugar beet (m. tons)	Potatoes (m. tons)	Milk cattle (millions)
Poland	28·0	11·0	7·7	28·0	7·4
C. Slov.	13·0	2·8	6·0	9·0	4·3
Hungary	10·0	2·3	1·2	1·0	2·1

YUGOSLAVIA

THIS Republic is another of the new countries which were established after the First World War. The nucleus of the new state was formed by the independent countries of Serbia and Montenegro; to these were added parts of the former Austro-Hungarian Empire, such as Bosnia, Herzegovina, and Dalmatia. The people all belong to the South Slav group, but the former official name of the country—the Kingdom of the Serbs, Croats, and Slovenes—is a reminder that it is composed of different types of people.

Serbia was conquered by the Turks about the middle of the fifteenth century, and for four hundred years her people were subject to Turkish rule. Montenegro, on the other hand, although acknowledging the overlordship of the Turks, always remained virtually independent. The Croats and the Slovenes, who live in the northern half of the country, had been under Austrian or Hungarian rule for two hundred years. These historical differences help to account for the differences of outlook among the constituent groups in the nation. As the Austrians were always a more civilized people than the Turks, the Croats and the Slovenes were better educated and more commercially minded than the Serbs and the Montenegrins. In the First World War, however, Serbia and Montenegro fought on the side of the Allies, while the Croats and Slovenes, being under the rule of Austria-Hungary, were compelled to fight with the Central Powers. Thus, when the new kingdom of Yugoslavia was formed after the war, the Serbian king was chosen as sovereign, and Belgrade, which had been the capital of Serbia, became the capital of the whole country.

Yugoslavia is now a Communist republic, but, unlike the countries of eastern Europe, she is not dominated by the U.S.S.R., and has entered into friendly relations with the western powers.

Great efforts are being made not only to increase agricultural production, but also to develop the country's resources of

minerals and water-power for the establishment of manufacturing industries.

The physical map shows that Yugoslavia consists of two
clearly marked regions, viz. a belt of mountains in the south
and west, and a plain in the north drained by the River
Danube and its tributaries, the Sava and the Drava. The
Dalmatian coast shows characters which distinguish it from
the neighbouring mountain belt, so, considering this as a
separate unit, we have the following physical and economic
division of Yugoslavia:

1. *The Dalmatian Coast*. A physical map shows this to
consist of numerous islands, peninsulas, straits, and gulfs, with
a general trend parallel to the coast. These features were
formed by the 'drowning' of a mountain range which ran
parallel to the coast; partial submergence caused the sea to
flow into the river valleys, and left the ridges standing out as
islands and peninsulas, separated by long and deep arms of the
sea. As the original rivers had zigzag courses, these straits
have many right-angle bends, and often open out some
distance from the sea to form fine land-locked harbours, such
as the Gulf of Cattaro.

The Dalmatian coast land and the Dinaric Alps, which rise
steeply behind it, are composed of limestone. This is easily
dissolved by rain-water, and in the course of ages the tiny
joints and cracks which exist in all rocks have become widened
and deepened, so that they form swallow holes down which
the surface water disappears. Thus, though the Dinaric Alps
receive a good deal of rain, they are one of the most waterless
regions in the world, and one may walk many miles without
seeing a drop of water. Much of the water which disappears
down the swallow holes never reappears on the surface of the
land; but off the Dalmatian coast are many springs of fresh
water, bubbling up through the sea, and these no doubt represent the outlets of some of the subterranean streams of the
mainland. As the limestone of this region is almost pure
calcium carbonate, it leaves little soil behind when it dissolves,

and so agriculture is impossible, except in a few scattered hollows where a few inches of soil, representing the residue of many hundreds of feet of limestone, have collected. Such regions, formed of pure limestone rock, with thin soil and few surface streams, are known as *karst* lands. The Causses of southern France, many parts of the Pindus Mountains of Greece, and parts of the northern Pennines are other examples of the karst type of scenery.

Near the coast there are patches of sandstone and shale which weather to form a deeper soil. Agriculture is rendered difficult by the drought of summer, but the careful farmer can grow most of the typical Mediterranean crops. The soil is ridged so as to form a succession of mounds and hollows. Vines are planted in the hollows, so that their roots can more easily penetrate to the moist subsoil during the rainless summer. Peas, beans, vegetables, etc., are grown on the intervening ridges during the winter, when there is a sufficiency of moisture.

The peninsula of *Istria*, situated in the north-eastern angle of the Adriatic, has long been debatable ground. Before the First World War it was part of the Austro-Hungarian Empire. By the Peace Treaties following that war it was given to Italy. After the Second World War the boundary was redrawn so as to give the whole peninsula to Yugoslavia, with the exception of Trieste and a small area around it, which is now Italian territory. Important deposits of mercury occur in the north of the peninsula, and there is a small coal-field in the south, near *Fiume* (Rijeka), which is the chief port of Yugoslavia.

2. The mountainous region between the Dinaric Alps and the interior plains is not formed of limestone, but of various types of rock, whose weathering has produced a fairly fertile soil. The mountain sides are forested, and the valleys support a fairly dense agricultural population. Each small community is almost self-supporting, producing such food crops as maize, wheat, oats, barley, and rye, and rearing the usual farm animals. Lumbering is an important industry, and fruit is grown in considerable quantity. Prunes (dried plums) are

the chief 'money' crop, especially in Serbia. This mountainous region is also rich in copper, lead, zinc, and bauxite.

3. The lowland drained by the Danube and its tributaries is, naturally, the most productive part of Yugoslavia. The climate is of the continental interior type, with cold winters and rather moist summers. Hence maize is a more important crop than wheat, though both are widely grown. Tobacco and prunes are the chief 'money' crops, and considerable quantities of both are exported. Pigs are reared in great numbers, and many thousands are exported to neighbouring countries.

Belgrade, the capital of Yugoslavia, holds a strong strategic position at the confluence of the Sava and the Danube, and at the northern end of the trans-Balkan routes via the Morava to Salonika and Constantinople.

Nish is situated where the route to Constantinople, via the Maritza valley, meets the route to Salonika via the Vardar valley.

In spite of the great length of her coast, one of the chief difficulties of Yugoslavia is the lack of easy access to the sea. The Danube is useful for local traffic, but is of little value for foreign trade, and the land routes southward to the Mediterranean lead to foreign ports. Consequently Yugoslavia looks to the Adriatic coast for her chief outlets. Two railways have been constructed across the parallel ranges of the Dinaric Alps to *Spalato* (Split) and *Dubrovnik*, but these ports are completely overshadowed by Fiume, which has easy access by rail to the interior

EXERCISES

1. Among Yugoslavia's chief exports are: timber, live pigs, wheat, and prunes. Draw a sketch-map to show the parts of the country producing these commodities.

2. Austria produces nearly twice as much milk per head of cattle as either Hungary or Yugoslavia; what reasons can you give for these differences?

3. Yugoslavia has considerable mineral resources. Draw a sketch-map to show the following facts: iron is mined chiefly in Bosnia; copper and bauxite in Serbia; lead in Slovenia; mercury in Carniolia.

4.   UTILIZATION OF THE LAND IN YUGOSLAVIA

Crop land	30 per cent
Grasslands	24 ,,
Gardens and vineyards . . .	2 ,,
Forests	31 ,,

What indication do the figures give of the work of the people in Yugoslavia?

5. The trade per head in Yugoslavia is only one-eighth that of Austria. Give reasons why this is so.

RUMANIA

THE name Rumania really means 'Roman-ia,' and the people are partially descended from Roman colonists who inhabited the region in the early part of the Christian era. The Rumanian tongue, too, is derived from Latin, and is, therefore, very different from that of the surrounding peoples, who speak Slavonic languages.

When the barbarian Goths began to attack the Roman Empire, the territory which is now Rumania was one of the first to be abandoned, and the Romans withdrew to the easily defended line of the Danube. From the third to the fifth century A.D. various tribes and races poured into the region, first Goths and other barbarian tribes, then Slavs, and in the ninth century the Magyars (Hungarians). At the end of the fifteenth century the region was conquered by the Turks, who were masters of the land for more than 300 years. It was not until 1877 that Rumania, after a war in which she had helped Russia to defeat the Turks, gained full independence.

Even then the district of Transylvania, though inhabited mainly by Rumanians, was compelled to remain a part of Hungary. In the First World War Rumania fought on the side of the Allies, and though she suffered complete defeat, she was able to claim her reward with the final victory of the Allies in 1918, and the districts of Transylvania, Bessarabia, and Bukovina were ceded to her by the Peace Treaties. After the Second World War Bessarabia was returned to Russia.

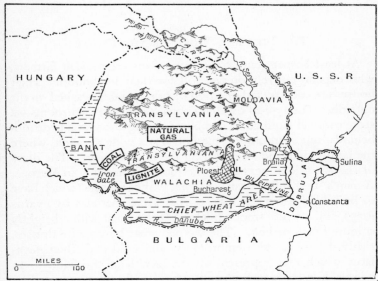

FIG. 34. RUMANIA: PHYSICAL, PRODUCTS, TOWNS

THE LAND SURFACE AND PHYSICAL DIVISIONS

The 'backbone' of Rumania is formed by the Carpathians and the Transylvanian Alps. Although these mountains rise to heights of over 8,000 feet, they are crossed by many low passes, and do not constitute a serious obstacle to communication as is shown by the fact that Rumanians occupy the plains on both sides of the mountains.

To the north of the Transylvanian Alps are the provinces of *Transylvania* and *Banat*. The lowlands are mixed farming districts, and the mountains yield timber and metals.

Between the Carpathians and the Danube is the broad plain

of *Walachia*, one of the 'granaries' of Europe.   The *Dobruja*
is the rather infertile region lying between the lower Danube
and the Black Sea.   *Moldavia*, between the Carpathians and the
Russian border, produces wheat and timber.

THE LIFE AND WORK OF THE PEOPLE

At least 80 per cent of the Rumanians are peasant farmers,
who depend entirely on the soil for their livelihood.   Their
houses are constructed of wood or of clay, whitewashed on the
outside.   The typical dwelling consists of only two rooms—a
store room in front and a combined dining-room and bedroom
behind—but surrounding the house is a wide veranda, where
the family dine and sleep during the hot summer.   The dress
of the Rumanian peasant is the most picturesque in Europe.
A man's 'best suit' consists of long white trousers (which have
to be folded about the legs, as they are sometimes two yards
long), and a white smock fastened at the waist with a brightly
coloured sash or belt.   The women wear long white dresses,
richly decorated with embroidery, and gold and silver neck-
laces which may represent all the wealth of the family.   In
winter, however, such costumes have to be supplemented by
thick coats of lambskin, for though the summers are very
hot and sunny, the winters are much colder than ours.

(How much more interesting do isotherms become if, instead
of being simply lines on a map, they help us to see people
dressed to suit the weather!   Look at the 80° F. isotherm for
July, and think of the thinly clad Rumanian peasant; let the
32° F. isotherm for January show you the same peasant with
his lambskin coat wrapped tightly around him; put both pictures together and label them 'effect of an extreme climate.')

One of the chief foods of the people is maize meal, which is
made into pudding so solid that it is cut into slices like bread.
Until recently the peasant seldom ate bread made from wheat,
but nowadays almost every village possesses a bakery.

Butcher's meat is seldom eaten, its place being taken by duck and fowl. Vegetable soups and haricot beans are other staple articles of diet.

Farming. Before the reorganization which followed the First World War a large part of the land, particularly in Walachia, was in the hands of large landowners. Nearly all these large estates have been broken up, and the land distributed as small peasant holdings, many of which have now been 'collectivized' on a Communist basis.

The two chief crops of Rumania are *maize* and *wheat*. The former, in spite of the above-mentioned change in the diet of the people, is still the chief food crop, while wheat is the chief 'money' crop. Before the redistribution of the land, maize was grown in preference to wheat by those peasants who owned their own land, since it provided them with their chief food, and was at the same time a more dependable crop. Wheat was grown chiefly by the large landowners, who preferred a 'money' crop which could be exported. Moreover, these large landowners were rich enough not to be ruined by a bad harvest, but could afford to wait for the good years which would bring them fortunes. When the land was redistributed in small holdings, wheat production greatly declined as the peasant preferred to grow maize to ensure his basic food supply. Even now, when nearly all the arable land is in collective farms, the output is low, and the peasants, like those of other Danubian countries, remain poor.

Other important crops of Rumania, in addition to wheat and maize, are: barley (used for fodder or exported for the brewing of beer), grapes, tobacco, which are grown chiefly in the lower valleys on both sides of the Carpathians and the Transylvanian Alps; hemp, flax, sugar beet, and sunflower-seed, which are grown on the Walachian Plain.

Sheep rearing is practised on an extensive scale, and Rumania has more sheep than any other European country except Russia, Britain, and Spain. Transhumance is still widely practised, though the redistribution of the land in small holdings has considerably restricted the movements of sheep. From the beginning of October to the middle of April the migratory shepherds live in villages on the plains of Walachia or the Banat. In summer they drive their flocks up to the mountain pastures, taking with them the necessary household goods and a supply of maize. The shepherds and their families live throughout the summer in primitive huts built of logs placed one upon the other between larger tree trunks which are driven into the ground at the four corners. Surrounding the settlement is a palisade, formed of tree trunks laid level and supported by poles. This forms a sheepfold into which the animals are driven at night to protect them from wild beasts.

Cattle rearing is most important in the valleys and on the lower slopes of the Carpathians and the Transylvanian Alps, and on the rich alluvial lands on the northern edge of the Danube delta. On the agricultural plains oxen are in general use for ploughing and for transport.

Lumbering. About one-quarter of the surface of Rumania is forested, and timber forms one of the chief exports. The lower mountain slopes yield beech and oak, the former being used mainly for railway sleepers, and the latter for constructional purposes. Above this zone of deciduous trees is a coniferous belt, yielding spruce and other firs, large quantities of which are floated down the Prut and its tributaries.

Mining. The most important mineral of Rumania is petroleum, which is obtained chiefly from oil-fields situated to the north of Ploesti. Though the oil produced in Rumania forms only one per cent of the world's total, it is one of the chief sources of national wealth, and normally provides about one-quarter of the exports. A pipe line has been constructed from the oil-field to the port of Constanta.

The country is also rich in metallic ores. Gold and silver are found in the Bihar Mountains, while chromium, copper, iron, lead, zinc, and bauxite are mined in the Transylvanian Alps. The total production is, however, comparatively small.

THE TOWNS

As Rumania is a land of peasants it is also a land of villages; even most of the towns shown on the atlas map are simply overgrown villages, composed of isolated houses and winding, unpaved streets. *Bucharest*, the capital, has a modern European portion, with fine streets and handsome buildings, but the greater part of the city is simply an agglomeration of villages. One might have expected the capital to have been situated on the Danube, which is the main waterway of the country. The Rumanian bank of the river is, however, marshy and unhealthy, and in any case a capital situated near the Danube would have been too close to the frontier. Bucharest has, moreover, the advantage of being situated midway between the mountains and the river, in the midst of the fertile plain, and at the focus of the railway system of the country.

All the other towns worthy of note are ports on the Danube or the Black Sea coast.

Braila is the chief centre for the exportation of grain. It is situated at the head of ocean navigation, and can be reached by large ships drawing twenty-four feet of water.

Galatz, situated near the confluences of the Danube with the Sereth and the Prut, has some share in the grain trade, but is notable chiefly for the exportation of timber.

Sulina is situated on the only distributary of the Danube which is navigable by large vessels.

Above Braila and Galatz shifting sandbanks reduce the river in places to a depth of two to six feet; consequently the ports at the mouth of the river are very important for the trans-shipment of goods.

Constanta, whose importance is rapidly increasing, has several advantages as a port. It is ice-free, in contrast to the above-mentioned ports of the Danube, which are closed by ice for an average of forty days in the year; its position opposite the point where the Danube turns northward enables it to 'short-circuit' much of the traffic on the Danube; and it is at the point where the Black Sea coast approaches nearest to Bucharest. It is also the only port which has direct railway communication with the capital. Between Constanta and the Danube this railway follows a depression which marks the channel by which the Danube formerly entered the sea. Along this trough ran the Roman wall, built by the Emperor Trajan to defend the Roman Empire against the attacks of barbarian tribes.

EXERCISES

1. 'Rumanian exports are about the same *value* as her imports, but seven times as large by *weight*.'
Make lists of Rumania's exports and imports to show why the former are so much heavier than the latter.

2. (*a*) Draw a diagram on squared paper to show the utilization of the land in Rumania: arable land, 41 per cent; natural grazing, 14 per cent; woodland, 14 per cent.
(*b*) Draw a sketch-map showing where these different types of land are chiefly to be found.

3. Compare and contrast Rumania and Hungary.

4. Draw a diagram on squared paper to show the fact that 40 per cent of Rumania's exports are cereals, 25 per cent oil and oil products, and 15 per cent timber. Draw a sketch-map to show the parts of the country from which these products are derived.

5. Compare Constanta and Braila as ports. (Consider their accessibility at different times of the year, and the ease of communication with the interior.)

THE BALKAN LANDS

BULGARIA (See Figs. 35 and 36)

THIS small Communist republic lies across two of the historic landways of the Old World: the one from Asia Minor via Constantinople and the Maritza-Morava valleys to central Europe; and the other from the Russian and Rumanian steppe southward to the Aegian Sea. It has, therefore, often been the battleground of warring peoples.

The Bulgars themselves are descended from tribes akin to the Huns, who came from the steppes of Asia by way of south-eastern Russia. It is said, indeed, that their name is derived from the River Volga. During the seventh century A.D. these tribes conquered the region now known as Bulgaria, and settled among the Slavonic peoples who already occupied that area. The Bulgars soon adopted the language and habits of the people they had conquered, but the mixture of races produced a people whose outlook is different from that of the neighbouring nations. Like the rest of the Balkan peninsula, Bulgaria was conquered by the Turks towards the end of the fifteenth century, and for nearly 500 years the land was under Turkish rule, the modern state being little more than 50 years old.

As in Rumania, practically the whole population outside the large towns is dependent on farming; indeed the term 'bulgar' is used in the Balkan Peninsula to designate a cultivator of the soil. Most of the cultivated land was formerly divided into small farms of five to fifteen acres. These individual farms, together with large areas of common pasture, have now been 'collectivized' on the Communist pattern. Here, as in the rest of the Balkan Peninsula, the former unsettled state of the country is reflected in the grouping of the peasants' houses in small villages, through the need for defence against raiders having been in the past more important than proximity to the farm land. The houses themselves, and the general mode of life of the people, are similar to those of the Rumanians. The chief food of the people is wholemeal wheat bread eaten with cheese or vegetable stews, though in a few districts maize replaces wheat.

The country may be divided into four roughly parallel belts, which run from west to east, viz.:

(1) The **plateau** country on the right bank of the Danube

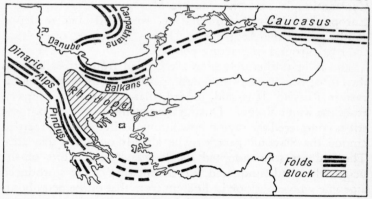

FIG. 35. SOUTH-EASTERN EUROPE: STRUCTURE

is covered with a fertile soil similar to the loess of China. More than half the wheat and maize grown in the country are produced here. Most of the people, however, live in the sheltered valleys, where maize and a variety of other crops are grown. The wind-swept plateaus are almost devoid of houses, although they form the best wheat-lands in the country. The yield of wheat on the collective farms is, however, very low in comparison with that of western Europe.

(2) **The Balkans** form a marked barrier between the Danube lowlands and the rest of the country. At the western end of the range, however, the valley of the Isker forms an important cross-route which is followed by the railway from Sofia to the Danube, via Trajan's Gate. In the western part of the mountains are valuable tracts of forest, while the regions above the timber line are used as summer pastures

for sheep, and the valleys produce the hardier cereals such as barley and rye, as well as cool-temperature fruits.

(3) **The valley of the Maritza** is a fertile, sheltered lowland,

FIG. 36. THE BALKAN COUNTRIES

producing wheat, maize, rice, sugar beet, tobacco, mulberry, and vines. The cultivation of roses, from which attar of roses is distilled, is an important industry.

(4) **The Rhodope Block,** in the south-west of Bulgaria, is the most backward portion of the country, but some agriculture is carried on in the more fertile valleys, and the

F   E

hill slopes provide pasturage for sheep and goats. In the west, where the rainfall is fairly heavy, the mountains are well wooded, and logs are floated down to the coast or cut up into planks for transport to the lowlands by mules.

Sofia, the capital, is the only large city of Bulgaria and the only important manufacturing centre. The Bulgarian name for the town means 'the central town,' and it owes its origin and importance to its situation at the focus of the chief routes of the country. From it railways diverge eastward to Instanbul, north-westward to Belgrade via the valleys of the Nishava and the Morava, north-eastward to Bucharest via the valley of the Isker, and southward to the Aegean via the valley of the Struma.

The surrounding region produces much oats, barley, and rye, though wheat is not of great importance. The chief 'money' crops of the district are tobacco, attar of roses, and sugar beet. To the south-east of the city lies a small coal-field which produces brown coal, or lignite, of sufficiently good quality to be the basis of local industries.

Plovdiv (Philippopolis) is situated in the centre of the fertile Maritza lowland, and has much trade in rice, silk, and attar of roses. *Burgas* and *Varna* are Bulgaria's chief ports on the Black Sea.

EXERCISES

1. 'Bulgaria has, in proportion to her population, more sheep than any other European country.' Give reasons why she has such large numbers of sheep.

2. Compare Rumania and Bulgaria from the point of view of the life and work of the people.

3. Draw a diagram-section across Bulgaria from north to south, and add brief notes of the geography of each of the divisions mentioned on pages 124–6.

4. 'The climate of the Maritza valley is less extreme than that of Walachia.' Explain the meaning of this statement, and give the causes of this difference of climate.

TURKEY IN EUROPE

THE Turks are an Asiatic people, whose ancestors lived in north-western China. Indeed, they are said to have received their name from a hill in that district which, because of its shape, was called Turku (helmet). During the fourteenth century the Turks swept westwards, and one branch of them, the Osmanli Turks, settled in Asia Minor. They then crossed into Europe, and eventually reached the gates of Vienna, where, in 1683, they were defeated by the king of Poland in one of the most decisive battles in the world's history. Though driven out of Austria and Hungary, they remained masters of the Balkan Peninsula for more than four hundred years. During the nineteenth century the Balkan States one by one freed themselves from the Turkish yoke, until at the outbreak of war in 1914 Turkey in Europe had shrunk to its present dimensions.

With the exception of Istanbul (Constantinople) and Adrianople there are no large towns in European Turkey, and most of the people depend on the products of the soil. Though modern methods are gradually being introduced, farming is generally conducted in a primitive and inefficient manner. The ploughs are simply pointed pieces of wood drawn by oxen; the corn is threshed by oxen, which drag over the threshing floor a heavy piece of wood through which nails are driven; there is little systematic rotation of crops, and much land is allowed to lie fallow for one or two years. The chief food-crops cultivated are wheat, maize, oats, barley, and oil-seeds, while sheep and cattle are raised in all districts. The culture of the silkworm is also widespread, but the output of silk is low in both quality and quantity. Except in the principal streets of the cities the houses are built of wood or of sun-baked mud. 'The house once built is rarely painted or repaired; shutters hanging loose, weather boards that have gone, and a general tumbledown appearance are common features. . . . Sometimes a group of houses leans in one direction, and the whole mass may be propped up by a single beam.' (Admiralty Handbook.)

Formerly Turkish women were kept in strict seclusion, and were not allowed to be seen by men, or to walk in the streets unless wearing muslin veils to conceal their faces. Though these restrictions are now a thing of the past, their effect is seen in the architecture of the larger houses, especially in the cities. These are often built round a courtyard or garden, with the living quarters of men and women on opposite sides; all the windows face the central courtyard, and on the women's side there are closed verandas, with latticed windows, which allowed the ladies to see out while they remained unseen.

Furniture is generally scanty, even in the better-class houses; rugs and cushions take the place of chairs, trays serve as tables, and curtains replace doors.

Like most other peoples in southern and eastern Europe, the Turks are not great meat eaters, and a favourite dish consists of 'tomatoes, marrows, cucumbers, and pumpkins stuffed with rice, chopped meat and cabbage, and served in the vine leaf in which it has been cooked.' Practically the only meat eaten is mutton and fowl; the former is prepared in little squares, alternately fat and lean, seasoned with salt and pepper, and strung on a wooden spit and grilled over a hot fire; chicken is usually mixed with rice and mutton fat, and seasoned with pepper, tomatoes, and honey.

THE LAND SURFACE

Turkey in Europe forms a triangle, each side of which is a strong natural barrier. The base of the triangle is formed partly by the Maritza River, which for fifty miles marks the boundary with Greece. The river is liable to floods, and the western bank is marshy, thus presenting difficulties to any approaching army, while the eastern bank is firmer and easily defended. Both the Black Sea coast and the Marmora coast are fringed by rugged, almost roadless mountains, which are practically impassable by hostile troops.

The physical map shows three well-marked divisions of the land, viz.:

(a) Near the Black Sea coast are the Istranja Mountains, which are barren and scrub-covered, and support only scanty flocks of sheep.

(b) In the middle of Turkey is a belt of land below 600 feet in height. This is a low plateau, through which innumerable streams have cut deep gorges. A tributary of the Maritza, flowing in a deep valley through the middle of the plateau, provides the only practicable approach from the west to Istanbul (Constantinople).

The region is naturally very fertile and, even under the primitive methods of the Turkish peasants, produces good crops of cereals. In good years there is a surplus of wheat available for export.

(c) In the south a range of hills terminates in the Gallipoli Peninsula, which, during the First World War, was the scene of the gallant but unsuccessful attempt of British and Australasian troops to outflank the Turkish defences of the Dardanelles.

Istanbul, formerly called Constantinople, is situated at one of the chief cross-roads of the Old World, where the waterway from the Black Sea to the Mediterranean crosses the landway from Europe to Asia. Its position (see Fig. 37) is equally good for defence and for trade. The Golden Horn, which provides a deep and sheltered anchorage, is only a quarter of a mile wide at the entrance, and can be closed by booms in case of attack.

The city itself was founded on seven hills, which dominate both the Bosporus and the Golden Horn, and terminate landward in an easily defended ridge, while some fifty miles to the west is another line of heights which form the outer defences of the city. No wonder the ancient Greeks, who founded there the city of Byzantium some six hundred years B.C., said

that only the blind would pass by a site with so many natural
advantages.

Though often attacked, and more than once destroyed,
Byzantium remained for a thousand years the chief centre of
trade between the Black Sea and the Mediterranean.   Then in
A.D. 330 it was chosen by Emperor Constantine as the eastern

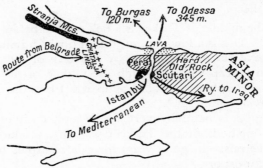

FIG. 37. POSITION OF ISTANBUL (CONSTANTINOPLE)

capital of the Roman Empire, and its name was changed to
Constantinople.   When the Western Empire was submerged
by the barbarian invasions, Constantinople, withstanding all
attacks, remained the capital of the Eastern or Byzantine
Empire, and kept alive the traditions of culture and scholar-
ship throughout the Dark Ages.   In 1453, however, it was
taken by the Turks, and soon became the capital of the
Turkish Empire.   So it remained until 1920, when the Turks
made Ankara, on the plateau of Asia Minor, their capital.
Istanbul has not only lost the prestige which accrues to a
capital city, but has also ceased to be a great centre of trade.
Relatively few of the ships passing through the Bosporus
enter its harbour, and in spite of the construction of a railway
through Asia Minor to Scutari on the Asiatic shore, it has only
a small share of the trade between Europe and the East.

The city itself consists of four sections.   Istanbul proper,
situated on the peninsula between the Golden Horn and the

Sea of Marmora, is almost entirely Turkish, with narrow winding streets, red-roofed wooden houses, and numerous Mohammedan mosques.

Pera, on the opposite shore of the Golden Horn, is the European quarter, and Galata is the chief shipping and trading centre. Scutari, on the opposite shore of the Bosporus, is also reckoned as part of Istanbul.

Edirna (Adrianople) guards the western entrance to European Turkey as Istanbul guards the eastern entrance. It is situated at the head of navigation of the Maritza River, and on the Simplon-Orient Express route from western Europe to Istanbul.

GREECE

THE backbone of Greece is formed by the Pindus Mountains, whose many branches enclose isolated plains or run out to sea as rocky peninsulas and islands. (See Fig. 36.) It was largely to the existence of these mountain-girt plains that ancient Greece owed the character of its civilization. Instead of being a single united country it was a collection of city-states, like Athens, Sparta, and Corinth, each of which occupied a small fertile plain ringed round by mountains or open only to the sea. As the population and the standard of living increased, each city-state was compelled to find some means of increasing its food supply. There were frequent wars between neighbouring states for possession of good farming lands, but as each fertile area was already producing to the limits of its capacity the Greeks soon began to spread overseas. Nature, too, seems to have invited the Greeks to become seamen and colonists, for not only does the sea penetrate far into the land, but the land itself is continued seawards by chains of islands which link Greece to Asia Minor.

We cannot, of course, say that because the Greeks were faced with difficulties if they stayed at home, while Nature provided opportunities for them to find a livelihood abroad, they were therefore *compelled* to take to the sea. Had they belonged to a different race (say, the Slavs) they might have refused to become seamen, and found some other way out of their difficulties. Be that as it may, the Greeks accepted the invitation of Nature, and, as we saw in the introductory chapter, Greece was at one time the greatest maritime power of the ancient world.

The modern Greeks are, in part, the descendants of the ancient Greeks. But although their predecessors were the leaders of civilization, the Greeks of to-day are a rather backward people. This difference is partially, but not entirely, due to historical and geographical factors. For nearly four hundred years the country was under the tyrannical and inefficient rule of the Turks; irrigation works and drainage schemes were neglected; malaria and other diseases undermined the health and vitality of the people; and Greece suffered like all other Mediterranean countries by the discovery of the New World, which made the Atlantic rather than the Mediterranean the highway of world trade. Yet the spirit of the people was never entirely broken, and in the early part of the nineteenth century Greece was the leader in the struggle of the Balkan peoples to throw off the Turkish yoke. Established as an independent country in 1829, Greece gradually extended her borders, until by 1914 she embraced nearly all her present territory. In 1917 she entered the First World War on the side of Britain, and at the Peace Conference claimed considerable territory on the northern and eastern sides of the Aegean on the ground that the coastal fringes are peopled largely by Greeks. Though not allowed her full claim, she was given the southern portion of Bulgaria and the region around Smyrna in Asia Minor, where lived half a million Greeks. The Turks, however, regained this latter region in 1922, and drove out the Greek population. In the Second World War the Greeks fought heroically against the Axis powers, but suffered four years of occupation by German and Italian troops.

Photo: Enrico Mariani

ATHENS: GENERAL VIEW OF THE ACROPOLIS

Photo: Enrico Mariani

MEGARA, A HILL TOWN IN GREECE, THE BIRTHPLACE OF EUCLID

The Life and Work of the Modern Greeks

In spite of the general infertility of the land, nearly two-thirds of the people are engaged in agriculture. The methods of farming are very primitive; much of the land is allowed to lie fallow every other year, and ploughing is still done by oxen that draw ploughs little different from those in use two thousand years ago. One of the chief difficulties is the lack of water. Except on the mountains the rainfall is rather low and the hot summers are practically rainless. Moreover, the predominant type of rock is limestone, which allows the water to soak rapidly through, leaving the surface dry and barren. In many places the water which disappears down swallow holes reappears in streams issuing from the cliffs on the edge of the plains. Such springs were the very waters of life to the ancient Greeks, and many of them were regarded as holy places. In many cases the only outlets for the streams which ran through fertile basins were subterranean channels; if these became blocked the valleys were converted into swamps or lakes, and the ancient Greeks took great pains to ensure the regular supply of water and keep the drainage channels clear. Indeed, some of the labours of Hercules are really concerned with problems of irrigation, drainage, and river control. One of the chief requisites for the revival of Greek agriculture is the reclamation of many formerly fertile plains which have become useless malarial swamps.

As in other parts of south-eastern Europe which have been subject to raids by Turks and other invaders, the houses of the peasants are grouped together in villages whose sites were chosen for ease of defence. Usually, too, the houses are built round a square, and all the windows and doors face inwards, so that only blank walls are presented to the outside. In all but the more fertile parts of the country the houses generally consist of only one room, which the family share with the domestic animals. In the more prosperous parts, such as the extreme south-east, 'the houses are mostly two-storied, with

*F   E

glazed windows and balconies, and have vine-trellised pergolas below, presenting an appearance of order, neatness, and comfort which contrasts with the villages of northern and central Greece.' (Admiralty Handbook.)

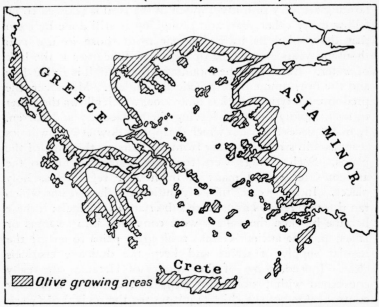

FIG. 38. THE BALKAN PENINSULA: OLIVE-GROWING REGIONS

The chief food crops of the people are wheat, barley, vegetables, vines, olives, and other fruits. It is interesting to note how the food of the people of south-eastern Europe varies with the distribution of rain through the year. Maize requires rain in summer, while wheat ripens best with little rain in that season. Hence, in Rumania, where most of the rain falls in summer, maize is the chief food; in Bulgaria, where there is less summer rain, more wheat than maize is eaten; while in Greece, where the summers are almost rainless, wheaten bread is the chief food. Similarly, in the moister countries of

Rumania and Bulgaria many milk cattle are kept, so that butter and cheese are common articles of diet.   The dry summers of Greece do not suit milk cattle, but provide exactly the conditions necessary for the ripening of olives; consequently olive oil replaces butter in the national dietary.   (See Fig. 38.)

In addition to their subsistence crops, most of the peasants cultivate some 'money' crops for export, the chief being currants and tobacco.

Currants are obtained by sun-drying a particular variety of stoneless grape.   The currant vine is grown only on the western and northern coasts of the peninsula of Morea, in Euboea, and in the Ionian Isles.   Conditions are so suited to the crop that these regions provide a large part of the world's supply.   The name currant is derived from Corinth, which was formerly the chief place of export.   Nowadays, however, the trade is centred chiefly in Patras.

Tobacco is widely grown on the eastern plains, especially in Thessaly and Macedonia.   A large part of the crop is exported to Egypt, there to be manufactured into 'Egyptian' cigarettes.

Cotton is grown on the eastern lowlands around Salonika. This is the only noteworthy cotton-growing area in Europe outside the U.S.S.R.

The chief domestic animals of Greece are sheep and goats, which can thrive on the poor grass of the limestone hills. Transhumance is widely practised, the flocks and herds being taken to the highlands in summer and to the plains in winter.

One of the most interesting groups of people in Greece are the Vlachs, who live in the mountainous backbone of the Pindus.   They differ in many ways from the Greeks, and speak a language similar to Rumanian.   They are probably descendants of the Romanized inhabitants of the peninsula, who fled before the invading barbarians, and took refuge in the mountains, just as the Celts did in Wales.   Indeed, the name 'Vlach' is similar to 'Welsh,' and may mean the same, i.e. foreigner. Most of the Vlachs are semi-nomadic shepherds who live in their mountain villages in summer, and encamp on the plains of Thessaly and Macedonia in winter.

TOWNS

Athens is the capital of modern Greece, as it was the most powerful city-state of ancient Greece. It grew up originally around the fortress of the Acropolis, which is situated in the middle of a small but fertile plain, and gradually extended its power over all the coastal lands around the Aegean. The chief reason for its modern importance is the fact that it is situated at the only great cross-roads of Greece, where the west-to-east route, via the Gulf of Corinth, crosses the only good route from south to north.

Piraeus, the port for Athens, is the chief trading centre for the whole country, and is also the most important manufacturing town, having many distilleries, flour mills, engineering works, and cotton factories.

Corinth, once the rival of Athens, is now a mere village. The Corinth Canal, which cuts across the narrow isthmus separating the Gulf of Corinth from the Aegean Sea, was cut during the last decade of the nineteenth century. It runs for four miles in a perfectly straight line between high banks of rock. Though the canal has no locks, and can accommodate vessels drawing twenty-three feet of water, it is not of much commercial importance, since the heavy canal dues make it more economical for cargo vessels to go round the peninsula of Morea. The only steamers making regular use of the canal are Greek passenger steamers.

Salonika, the second largest city of Greece, is situated near the mouth of the River Vardar, and at the terminus of the great cross-route of the Balkans, via the valleys of the Morava and the Vardar. As a seaport its hinterland includes not only all eastern Greece, but also large portions of Bulgaria, Serbia, and Albania. It is one of the most cosmopolitan of cities. 'The street vendors talk Turkish, Spanish, French, Greek, and

Italian with equal fluency. Spanish is the prevalent language of the slums. French is used for business and administrative purposes; ordinary shopping is carried on in Bulgarian, Turkish, or Greek. The boatmen swear in English and Italian, the cab drivers in Turkish and Spanish.' (Admiralty Handbook.)

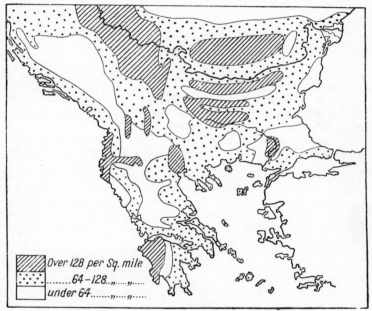

Over 128 per Sq. mile
........64 - 128...,,....,,....
under 64........,,....,,.....

FIG. 39. THE BALKANS: DENSITY OF POPULATION

When the Greeks were driven from Smyrna in 1922, most of them came to the district around Salonika. Without money, food, shelter, or means of livelihood, their plight was pitiable in the extreme. The Greek Government was quite unable to deal with the situation, so the League of Nations asked Dr. Nansen, the famous Arctic explorer, to undertake the care of the refugees. Doctors and nurses were sent out, and food and clothing distributed to meet immediate needs. Then, by arrangement with the Government of Greece, land was allocated to each family, and the League granted loans to enable them to build houses and buy implements and seeds. So successful were these and other efforts to re-colonize the homelands that, it is claimed, they have resulted in a threefold increase in the amount of arable land.

EXERCISES

1. Greece almost equals Sweden and Denmark in respect of the tonnage of ships in proportion to her population. (*a*) Are there any geographical reasons why this is so? (*b*) What connection is there between this and the fact that Greece imports nearly twice as much as she exports?

2. There are about as many sheep as people in Greece, but only one-eighth as many cattle. Give geographical reasons for these facts.

3. Horticultural products form three-quarters of the exports of Greece. What commodities are likely to be included in this list?

4. Agricultural products form a quarter of the imports of Greece. What are these likely to be? Why does not Greece grow her own foodstuffs? What steps could she take to increase her production of these?

5. The chief industries of Greece are the making of cotton goods, olive oil, wine, leather, and soap. Give reasons why these industries have developed in Greece.

6. Comment upon the distribution of the population in the Balkan Region. (See Fig. 39.)

CYPRUS

FROM the structural point of view Cyprus is a link between Europe and Asia, since its backbone of mountains is part of the Alpine system of folds running from Greece to Turkey. (See page 6.) This physical link between Europe and Asia is reflected in the composition of the Cypriot people, three-quarters of whom are of Greek origin and one-quarter Turkish.

The majority of the people are peasant farmers who produce the typical Mediterranean food crops, with citrus fruits, carobs (locust beans), and tobacco as money crops for export.

From Roman times the island has been an important source of copper, and it is indeed from the Latin name for the island that our word copper is derived. At the present time copper ore, either raw or concentrated, provides about half the total value of the exports.

Cyprus was until recently a British Crown Colony, but became an independent republic in 1960. *Nicosia*, situated near the centre of the island, is the capital, and *Famagusta* on the east coast is the chief port.

ALBANIA

THIS little republic seems out of place among the highly developed countries of Europe, for it is the most primitive political unit of the continent. It is so mountainous that invaders have never been able to occupy more than the narrow plains and the main valleys. The typical Albanians, who call themselves 'sons of the eagle,' live in little villages, which are often perched like eagles' nests on almost inaccessible ledges on the mountain sides. Cattle rearing is the chief means of livelihood, but each family also possesses sufficient arable land to provide them with maize and other essential foods.

Albania is strategically important in that it controls the entrance to the Adriatic as well as the land routes from that sea to the Balkan countries.

The chief towns, Tirana and Scutari, are situated near the inland margin of the malarial coastal plain. Durazzo and Valona are the chief ports, the latter being connected by pipe line to a small oil-field in the interior.

ITALY

THOUGH Italy as a modern country is less than a hundred years old, there are three periods in history when it was of paramount importance. Between the second century B.C. and the fifth century A.D. it was the centre of civilization, and from it the languages, laws, and systems of government of the countries of western Europe have been largely derived. After the fall of the Roman Empire the power of the Popes was for several centuries the only force making for unity in Europe.

In the Middle Ages Italy's ports conducted a large share of the trade of the world, and were the chief links between West and East. In the fifteenth century the Revival of Learning, which marks the passage from the Middle Ages to modern times, had its origin in certain Italian cities. At the present day Italy is again one of the most populous and productive countries in the world.

Like all other great countries of the modern world Italy comprises several physical units which have been welded together by Nature's age-long processes of land building. The first stage in the geological history of Italy was the formation of the Apennine folds, which link the Alps with northern Africa. (See Fig. 2.) Within the northern loop of the S thus formed was a shallow sea, which has since been filled up to form the plain of the Po. Within the southern loop was a block of land which subsequently subsided, forming the Tyrrhenian Sea; the tail of the S was broken at the Straits of Messina, making Sicily an island; odd bits of older land-masses were joined to the folded area (e.g. some hard old rock in Tuscany, and a block of limestone in the 'heel' of Apulia); and so Italy came to have something like her present form.

The various natural divisions of which Italy is composed differ considerably in their physical features, climate, and human activities, and each makes its own special contribution to the well-being of the state.

THE ALPINE REGION

In spite of their great height and breadth the Alps have never formed an absolute barrier between Italy and the rest of Europe. Numerous river valleys and passes provide ways

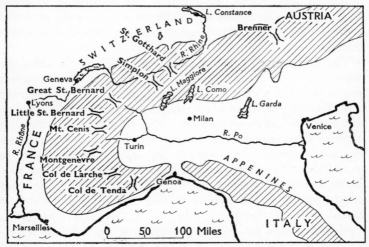

FIG. 40. DIAGRAM MAP OF THE CHIEF ALPINE PASSES

across the mountains into France, Germany, and Switzerland. (See Fig. 40.) Besides providing lines of communication these valleys are useful to Italy in many ways. Their rapid streams provide water-power, now transformed into hydro-electricity; the melting of the snow in summer gives a surplus of water which is used for the irrigation of the plains of the Po; the picturesque lakes which lie at the foot of the mountains attract thousands of tourists, who bring much money into the country; and the protection afforded by the mountains from cold northerly winds makes it possible to grow olives, oranges, and lemons in these valleys, whereas these crops can hardly be grown on the exposed lowlands of the Po basin.

As the Alpine slopes are steeper on the southern than on

the northern side, it has always been easier for northern peoples
to advance into Italy than for Italians to penetrate northward.
One result of this is that Switzerland stretches right over the
Alps, so as to include even part of Lake Maggiore.   Farther
east, in the region of the Brenner Pass, Austrians overflowed to
the south of the watershed, and in the district of Southern
Tyrol, which was finally ceded by Austria to Italy after the
Second World War, the majority of the people still speak
German.

The *Brenner Pass* is only 4,500 feet high, and provides the
easiest route across the Alps.   It has, therefore, been of great
importance from earliest times, and even before the Roman
period it was a highway of commerce between the half-civilized
tribes to the north and south.   The Romans built through
it a fine road, which was of great service to their trade and
military operations, but towards the end of the fifth century it
served to facilitate the invasions of the barbarian tribes who
finally destroyed Rome.   In the fifteenth century the road
again became one of Europe's chief highways, and along it
passed most of the spices, precious metals, and silks which
Venice imported from the East and sent overland to north-
western Europe.   To-day it is the main route by road and
rail from Germany and northern Europe to Venice and
southern Italy.

THE NORTHERN PLAIN

The whole of the plain between the Alps and the Apennines
has been built up of sediment which has filled up a former sea.
It has been calculated that the volume of alluvium needed to
build up this plain is equal to that of the Alps, and that the Po
still carries down to the sea every year enough solid matter to
form a million square yards of land.

The coast of the Gulf of Venice is gradually moving eastward, and Adria, which was the chief port in Roman times, is
now thirteen miles inland.   The first stage in the conquest of
the sea by the land is the formation of sandbanks known as

lidi (singular, *lido*), like the famous bathing beaches of Venice. Behind these the water is held up in lagoons which gradually fill up with mud, first forming noisome swamps and eventually dry land. (See Fig. 41.)

The Alpine tributaries of the Po are larger and more numerous than those from the Apennines; consequently the alluvium they have deposited has pushed the Po southwards, so that instead of being in the middle of the plain it flows along the foot of the Apennines. Another effect of the large quantities of alluvium carried by the river is that the bed of the Po tends to be choked with mud, so that the river raises itself above the level of the surrounding country, which thus becomes liable

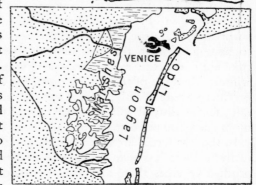

FIG. 41. POSITION OF VENICE

to floods. To prevent this, many hundreds of miles of dykes have been built in the lower part of the basin. The level nature of the ground, however, facilitates irrigation, which is made necessary by the great heat of summer. The western half of the plain, particularly north of the Po, is intersected by a network of canals which distribute water from the Alpine streams to every part of Lombardy and Piedmont. The most famous of these irrigation canals is the Cavour Canal, which runs from the upper Po and its tributary the Dora Baltea to the Ticino. 'The upper Po waters are relatively warm, those of the Dora Baltea fed by melting snow, cold. By proper regulation of the amount admitted into the canal from each, considerable temperature control over the irrigated fields is possible.'—W. O. Blanchard. Another important source of irrigation water, especially on the northern side of the plain, is the line of springs known as *fontanili*, which provide a regular flow of water at unvarying temperature.

The northern plain of Italy differs in many ways from the southern or peninsular part, for it is not a typical Mediterranean region. Its climate is of the continental type, with hot moist summers and cold winters. Milan, for example, is nearly as cold as Iceland in winter, having an average January temperature of 32° F.; but its July average is 75° F. It is not surprising, therefore, that while the peasants find it necessary to have a siesta in the hot summer afternoons they not infrequently use the cattle sheds as living-rooms during the winter. In spite of the cold winters, the Po basin is the most productive part of Italy, since it has the advantages of summer rain, fertile alluvial soil, abundant water for irrigation, and a more energetic population than southern Italy.

In the less fertile areas the land is divided into small farms, many of them less than three acres in extent, but in the most productive areas there are large farms, on which the smallholders often work as day-labourers in the harvest season. The life of the Lombardy peasant is one of great toil. In summer the whole family is up at dawn, and after a frugal meal of coffee and bread, or of vegetable soup, they work in the fields until noon. Then follows another meal, generally consisting of sausage, bread and cheese, and onions. After a short siesta, necessitated by the great heat of summer, they return to the fields, where they work for another five or six hours. At about half-past eight, after a supper of soup, or maize 'polenta,' salad, bread, and wine, they retire to rest. In spite of the long hours of work, the peasant finds it difficult to make a satisfactory living, especially where his holding is small.

The chief crop, particularly in the irrigated districts of Lombardy, is hay. Three crops a year are regularly obtained, and some specially favoured fields produce as many as seven crops a year. Cattle rearing is therefore of great importance, the dairy farms specializing in the production of cheese (e.g. Gorgonzola and Parmesan). Wheat, maize, and vegetables are widely grown food crops, and rice is widely cultivated on irrigated lands in Piedmont and the lower valley of the Po. Sugar beet is specially important in the Venetian plain, which also specializes in the production of wheat and maize.

Sericulture—the production of raw silk—is characteristic of such districts as Veneto, north-west of Venice, where the family farms are so small that there is a permanent surplus of labour.

The culture of the silkworm is almost invariably done by the women in their homes. The eggs are hatched in spring in boxes kept at an even temperature; the silkworms are then placed on shelves built one above the other to a height of several feet; for some time they are fed on mulberry leaves, then twigs are placed on the shelves, and on them the worms spin their silk cocoons. Though the raw silk produced in Italy forms only 4 per cent of the world's production, it is of the highest quality, and has helped to make northern Italy one of the chief silk-manufacturing districts in the world.

Industrially, too, the northern plain is the most productive part of Italy. Although it has no coal, and produces practically no raw materials, except silk and a small quantity of iron ore, the region has three great assets as a manufacturing district: a dense population of energetic and skilful work-people; large supplies of hydro-electricity generated in the Alpine valleys; and natural gas from wells in the Po valley and east of the Apennines. The chief industries are the manufacture of textiles (cotton, wool, and silk), iron and steel goods, machinery, and motor cars.

ROUTES AND TOWNS OF NORTHERN ITALY

There must always have been two great west-to-east routes across the plain: one at the foot of the Alps, and the other at the foot of the Apennines. Where these routes were crossed by others leading from the mountain passes, forts and trading stations were established, and many of these have become

important cities. (Fig. 42.) Thus on the northern side of the
plain there is a line of cities, the chief of which are Milan,
Bergamo, Brescia, Vicenza, and Treviso; at the foot of the
Apennines, Alessandria, Pavia, Parma, Modena, and Bologna
form a similar series, each controlling a pass in the Apennines.

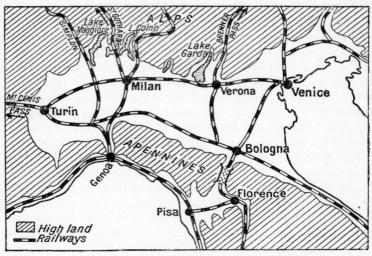

FIG. 42. NORTHERN ITALY: RELIEF, RAILWAYS, AND TOWNS

All are ancient cities, noted for their magnificent buildings and
priceless works of art. Some have lost much of their former
greatness, but others, situated at the junctions of main lines
of railway, have developed modern industries, and become
great cities of the modern world. Of these the most important
are Milan and Turin.

Milan, the capital of Lombardy, and the second largest city
of Italy, owes its modern importance to the fact that it is the
great road and railway centre of northern Italy and has thus
become one of the most important industrial cities of Europe.
The chief manufactures of the city and of the surrounding
towns and villages are textiles, machinery, motor cycles,
electrical goods, and chemicals. The necessary power is

supplied by hydro-electricity generated in Alpine valleys, by natural gas from wells at Cortemaggiore and other places in the Po Valley, and by imported oil brought by pipe line from Genoa. Canals, which serve the double purpose of navigation and irrigation, link it with the River Po, and with lakes Como and Maggiore, and a new canal to the sea at Venice is in course of construction.

Turin is situated where the routes on the northern and southern sides of the Po basin converge to meet routes across the Alps by the Mont Cenis and other passes. Both its historic and present importance are due to its command of these routes across the Alps. In former times it was the capital of the small state of Savoy, which by its position astride the Alps often held the balance between France and Italy. In modern times the convergence of railways, and supplies of hydro-electricity, oil, and natural gas, have led to the development of great industries, the most noteworthy of which is the manufacture of motor cars (e.g. the Fiat cars). Other industries include aeroplanes, locomotives, textiles, and chemicals.

Venice was established in the ninth century by a group of merchants who sought safety from the barbarian invaders of Italy. They settled on a number of small islands set in a lagoon, which was cut off from the mainland by *lidi*, or sandbanks. At first their only means of livelihood was fishing and selling salted fish to the people of the rich farming lands behind the coast. Soon, however, the advantages of the site gave opportunities for trade, and Venice became the chief port of exchange between the western world and the East. Protected seaward by the *lidi* and landward by marshes; situated almost in the centre of the Mediterranean world and at the head of the most northerly branch of the Mediterranean Sea; and connected by road to the easiest pass (the Brenner) across the Alps, Venice became the chief port of exchange between western Europe and south-eastern Asia, and was for centuries the most powerful city in the world.

But two factors which had contributed to her success helped

to cause her decline. As ships grew in size her lagoon harbours, formerly so valuable because of the shelter and protection which they afforded to ships, became incapable of accommodating the larger vessels; and when America and the route to India via the Cape were discovered, her central position in the Mediterranean proved as great a handicap as had formerly been an advantage.

Though Venice quickly lost her eastern trade, her wealth and power were so great that she remained an independent state until the beginning of the nineteenth century. The city is still world famous for the beauty of its architecture, and its priceless historic treasures. The Grand Canal, which winds like an S through the heart of Venice, is only one of a hundred waterways which form the streets. Among its most famous buildings are the Palace of the Doges (Dukes) of Venice; the cathedral of St. Mark, filled with the spoils of battle and historic mosaics; the Bridge of Sighs, connecting the old criminal courts with the doges' palace; and the Rialto bridge, whose beautiful marble arch spans the Grand Canal at its second great bend.

But Venice is not content to be a museum of ancient glories. It now ranks as the third port of Italy in respect of tonnage of goods. Until recently the port suffered greatly from the fact that its harbour was too small to accommodate large vessels; but a new deep-water harbour has been created in the vicinity of the ancient city. The new port is reached by a ship canal three miles long, and is connected by rail, road, river, and canal to the rich hinterland of the Po basin and north-eastern Italy. Genoa, although situated south of the Apennines, is essentially a port of northern Italy. The city is built round a deep bay, which is backed by steep and infertile hill slopes. Like the Venetians, therefore, the Genoese turned to the sea for a living; but fish are not plentiful in the immediate neighbourhood, and so the fishermen soon found their way to more distant waters. The Genoese thus became skilful navigators, but their city would not have become a great trading port if

LITTORIA, BUILT ON THE PONTINE MARSHES

E. N. I. T.

AN ITALIAN HYDRO-ELECTRIC STATION

it had not been that a pass in the Apennines immediately to the north gives it easy connection with the Po basin, and makes it the natural focus of routes through the passes of the western Alps. Though in the Middle Ages it was never the equal of Venice, it was a powerful city-state, and is noteworthy as the birthplace of both Christopher Columbus and Cabot, who discovered North America. Its modern commercial prosperity dates from the cutting of the Suez Canal, and the piercing of the western Alps by railway tunnels. It has thus become a port for France, Switzerland, Germany, and other parts of central Europe, as well as for the whole of northern Italy. The outstanding characteristic of its trade is that it normally imports six times as much by weight as it exports. This is because the imports are chiefly heavy goods like iron ore, petroleum, cotton, coal, and timber, while the exports are special foodstuffs, such as fruit and olive oil, or manufactured goods whose weight is small in proportion to their value.

Genoa, with its industrial suburbs on the Ligurian coast, is now the chief centre of the iron and steel, shipbuilding, and engineering industries of Italy.

Trieste. Originally built by Austria to serve as her chief port, Trieste still conducts more trade for Austria and Czecho-slovakia than for Italy. It is also important as a shipbuilding and engineering centre.

SOUTHERN ITALY (See Figs. 43 and 44)

The peninsula and the islands which constitute the southern half of Italy differ in many ways from the northern plain. Among these differences the following may be specially noted:

(1) A large part of southern Italy is occupied by mountains, and the plains, though numerous, are small and separated by spurs of the Apennines.

(2) The climate is of the Mediterranean type, with hot, dry summers and moist, warm winters, which contrast strongly with the moist summers and the cold winters of the north.

FIG. 43. THE PHYSICAL DIVISIONS OF ITALY

(3) The population is not only less dense in the south than in the north, but is also more unevenly distributed, almost uninhabited districts being found in close proximity to very densely peopled areas. This is especially noteworthy in central Italy, which combines many of the characteristics of both north and south.

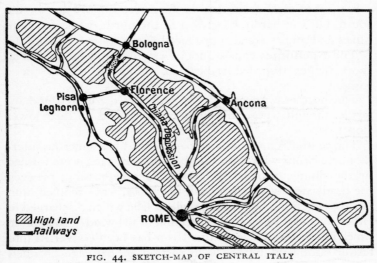

FIG. 44. SKETCH-MAP OF CENTRAL ITALY
(Showing how routes are controlled by the relief)

(4) A very large proportion of the people of the south are peasant farmers, and relatively few of them work in factories. The Government is, however, now making great efforts to increase the standard of living in the south by establishing industries in the towns and by providing facilities for irrigation in the rural districts.

(5) Though the more fertile lands are usually divided into small, intensively cultivated farms, much of the land in Italy south of Naples is in large estates or 'latifundi,' which are worked by labourers hired by the day. There agricultural methods are primitive and the peasant population very poor.

(6) Cattle rearing is much less important in the south than in the north, as the hot, dry summers do not favour the growth of good grass. Sheep, on the other hand, are more numerous in the south, since there are extensive areas of poor pasture on the Apennines.

(7) Among the cultivated products oranges, lemons, and other subtropical fruits are of foremost importance in the south, but can hardly be grown in the north, while far more olives and grapes are also produced in the south.

The Apennines consist, not of a single range but of several short ranges disposed rather like dominoes set up for a game.

The northern Apennines are generally deforested and infertile, though wheat and vines are cultivated on their lower slopes.

The central Apennines are characterized by numerous intermontane basins which, during the course of ages, were formed by the silting up of lakes. The Chiana depression, between the headwaters of the Arno and the Tiber, was occupied until fairly recent times by a broad, shallow lake which discharged to either river according to the direction of the wind. In modern times nearly the whole of this basin has been converted into fertile farm land by the construction of drainage channels which conduct the surplus water to the Arno. In other intermontane basins, however, Nature long ago completed her process of land building, forming fertile plains which centre on such historic cities as Perugia and Assisi. Above the intensively cultivated plains the hills rise steeply through terraced olive groves and patches of woodland to the scanty sheep pastures of the summit. In winter, when the upland pastures are often thickly covered with snow, the sheep are driven to the coastal lowlands, but this practice of *transhumance* is now severely restricted by the increased enclosure of the drove-ways and lowland pastures to form agricultural land.

The southern Apennines, in the 'toe' of Italy, are composed mainly of hard old granite rocks, forming large tracts of completely barren land and poorly cultivated latifundi, which contrast strongly with the intensively cultivated and over-populated coastal strip.

The Eastern Lowlands. In the Marches and Abruzzi the coastal plain is narrow and infertile, but the valleys and lower hillsides support a dense agricultural population, while the upper slopes form good pasture lands. **Apulia**, in the 'heel' of Italy, is composed largely of limestone like the Dalmatian coast. The uplands show the karst type of scenery characteristic of high limestone areas, but the lowlands are noted for the production of olives and wine, and of hard wheat, which is used for the making of macaroni. Recently discovered reserves of natural gas have fostered the development of manufacturing industries, notably at *Bari* and *Taranto*. *Brindisi* is a minor port and an air station on the route from north-western Europe to Africa and India.

The Western Lowlands. Four large areas of low land may be distinguished, viz. the Arno Basin, the Ombrone Basin, the Plain of Latium around the lower Tiber, and Campania around Naples. Of these the first and the last are among the most densely peopled and intensively cultivated areas in Europe, while the second and third are comparatively sparsely peopled.

(a) *The Arno Basin.* Here the undulating lowlands have been carefully drained, terraced, and irrigated, and agricultural activity reaches a level hardly surpassed elsewhere in Europe. Ruskin thus describes the plain-lands of Tuscany: 'Undivided by hedges, the fields are yet meshed across and across by an intricate network of posts and chains. The posts are maple trees, and the chains garlands of vine. The meshes of this net each enclose two or three acres of cornland, with a row of mulberry trees up the middle. . . . Here and there a mound of crag rises out of the fields, crested with stone pine, and studded all over with the large stars of the white rock cistus. . . . On each side of the great plain is a wilderness of hills, veiled at their feet with a grey cloud of olive woods.'

Every season brings its harvest—hay in spring, wheat in

summer, grapes in autumn, and olives in winter. Yet, in spite of their incessant labour the people remain poor, since the farms are small, and little land can be spared from the production of food crops to grow 'money' crops. Not only is the peasant too poor to be able to buy his own land, but he often finds it difficult to purchase seeds, manures, and agricultural implements, and in many cases these are provided by the landowner, who takes a half-share of the products.

Among the well-known agricultural products of the region are the olive oil of Lucca, Chianti wine, and the fine wheat straw which is used in the manufacture of Leghorn hats. *Florence* is situated where the route from the Po basin to Rome crosses the Arno. To the north of the city is the lowest pass through the Apennines, while the above-mentioned Chiana depression leads southward to Rome. In the Middle Ages Florence was one of the most powerful city-states of Italy, and the home of wealthy merchant princes, who were such generous patrons of the arts that the city became the home of many of the world's greatest poets, painters, sculptors, and architects. Even to-day, although it has become a great railway centre, and an important manufacturing city, its chief glories are its magnificent buildings and works of art which attract visitors from all over the world. *Pisa,* situated at the mouth of the Arno, was once the chief commercial outlet of Tuscany, and a great rival of Florence, and even of Venice. Though its harbour has completely silted up, it retains some importance as the market town for the rich agricultural region around. Its famous belfry, the Leaning Tower, was the scene of Galileo's dramatic and epoch-making demonstration that the velocity of falling bodies does not vary with their weight. *Leghorn* stands on an artificial harbour which was constructed to replace that of Pisa. It is the fifth port of Italy, and has large manufactures of straw plaiting, glass, and metal goods.

(*b*) *The Ombrone Basin*, though at one time a fertile region, has been depopulated by the deposition of silt which caused the formation of malarial marshes. In recent years, however,

drainage channels have been dug, and many dairy farms have
been established.

(c) *The Plain of Latium*, also known as the Roman Campagna
(see Figs. 43 and 45), was in ancient times a fertile, well-
cultivated region, but the channels which served for irrigation
or drainage were neglected, and the region became an almost

FIG. 45. POSITION OF ROME

unpopulated malarial waste. Formerly the only use made of
the land was for the winter pasturage of flocks of sheep which
spent the summers on the Apennines. In recent times, however, much of the land has been reclaimed; marshy areas have
been drained, wells bored, irrigation channels dug, roads
constructed, great estates broken up into small holdings, and
model villages built to house the peasants who have been
settled on the land. *Rome* so dominates the plain that it has
prevented the growth of any other large city near it. The
city grew up at the head of navigation of the River Tiber,
where the Seven Hills dominated an island in the river which
facilitated crossing. For several centuries after the founding
of their city the Romans had to fight against neighbouring
tribes; when these were subdued there followed the Punic
Wars against the Carthaginians, who held much territory on

the shores of the western Mediterranean. Having finally
destroyed Carthage in 146 B.C., Rome became mistress of the
Mediterranean, and turned her attention to lands beyond its
shores, until at the beginning of the Christian era all Europe
west and south of the Rhine and the Danube was under her
rule. For four hundred years the civilized world enjoyed
peace and prosperity within the Roman Empire. After the

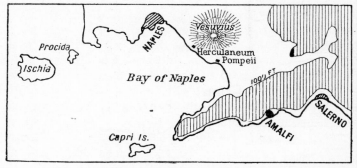

FIG. 46. POSITION OF NAPLES

conquest of Rome by barbarian tribes in the fifth century the
peninsula split up into small states, and was not again a united
country until 1870. But throughout the centuries Rome remained the centre of western Christianity, and when modern
Italy was established it was the inevitable choice for the
capital, and though in modern times many of the factors which
assisted its early growth have ceased to be of great importance,
its advantages as the central city of the peninsula and as the
religious and political capital have caused it to grow with
great rapidity.

(d) *Campania*. This region, which centres on Naples, should
be carefully distinguished from the Roman Campagna, to
which it affords the greatest contrast. The subtropical
climate, the fertile volcanic soil, and laborious cultivation
have combined to make this one of the most productive and
densely populated agricultural regions in the world. 'The

intensity of the garden cultivation and the huge harvests derived therefrom are well known. Under the grape vines which hang in garlands, like heavy draperies between the tall trees, grow corn and all vegetables. The verdure is an expression of fertility quite overwhelming to a northerner.' [1] Maize, wheat, hemp, olives, oranges, and lemons are the chief crops cultivated. *Naples*, beautifully situated on a deep harbour near the foot of Mount Vesuvius, ranks next to Rome and Milan in population and to Genoa as a port. Its miscellaneous industries are based on the productivity of the surrounding countryside, locally generated hydro-electricity, imported coal and oil, and the over-abundant supply of labour. In spite of the efforts of the Government to promote the expansion of manufacturing industries, a large proportion of the million inhabitants of the city live in dire poverty through lack of employment.

SICILY

The Straits of Messina, which separate Sicily from the mainland, were formed 'like a rift valley' by the sinking of the land along fault lines. The effects of this sinking of the land are still to be seen in the volcanic activity of the surrounding region. Mount Etna, a gigantic cone formed of lava and ashes, is an active volcano, whose regular contours and overhanging pall of smoke form a conspicuous landmark which was of the greatest service to the early navigators in the Mediterranean. The Lipari Islands are composed almost entirely of volcanic rocks. Vulcano, so called by the ancient Greeks because they imagined it to be the home of Vulcan, the god of fire, gave its name to all volcanoes. Stromboli, still famed for the frequency of its eruptions, was said by the ancient Greeks to be the home of the wind god Aeolus, who sent out all the winds that blow over the earth.

[1] H. W. Ahlmann, *Geographical Review*.

G E

From the point of view of agriculture, Sicily, like the rest of southern Italy, is a region of great contrasts. Where irrigation is practised, as on the slopes of Etna and on parts of the north and east coasts, intensive cultivation yields large crops of oranges, lemons, figs, and vegetables. Over most of the island, however, extensive 'dry' farming produces only scanty crops of wheat, barley, and olives. In these districts, as indeed in many other parts of southern Italy, the peasants live crowded together in small towns, and travel many miles each day to their few scattered fields, or to the estates on which they work as day labourers. Governmental efforts to increase the productivity of the land by irrigation are hindered by the opposition of the land-owners and the powerful secret society known as the *mafia*.

Palermo, on the fertile lowland called Conca d'Oro (Hollow of Gold), is the chief port and largest city of Sicily.

Messina, on the strait of the same name, is the chief link with the mainland.

SARDINIA

This island differs from the rest of Italy in being composed of hard old rock, and is, indeed, a remnant of the old land-mass which formerly stretched over the western Mediterranean. The infertility of the soil, the predominance of high land, and centuries of bad government, help to account for the low standard of productivity which characterizes the island.

Vines, olives, and corn are the chief crops, but the methods of cultivation are very primitive, and the yield is low. Considerable quantities of tomatoes are, however, tinned for export. Pastoral industries predominate, sheep being kept on the plateaus in summer and on the agricultural lands of the plains in winter. Large numbers of goats are kept on the drier hill slopes, which are covered with the dry bush known as 'maquis.'

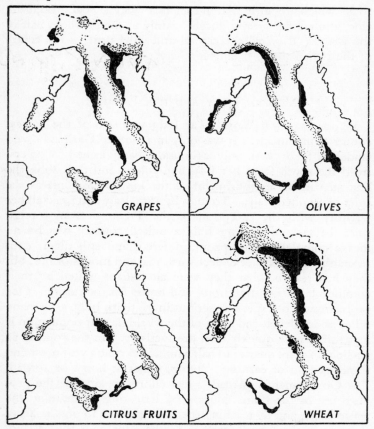

FIG. 47. ITALY: CHIEF PRODUCTS

In recent years several large schemes of water-control have been initiated, and in the south-east one of the world's largest reservoirs has been constructed to serve the threefold purpose

of irrigation, prevention of floods, and the generation of
hydro-electricity.

Minerals. Sardinia is composed mainly of ancient crystalline
rocks which are fairly rich in minerals. Some coal, iron, lead,
zinc, and copper are produced, mainly in the southern half of
the island. *Cagliari*, the capital and chief port, is the centre
of the Italian tunny fishing industry. TUNA FISHING

MODERN ITALY AND HER PROBLEMS

Before the First World War Italy was one of the newest
countries in Europe. It was only in 1860 that Garibaldi, who
landed in Sicily with only a thousand badly armed followers,
freed the south from her Bourbon rulers, and thus took the
first step in the establishment of the king of Sardinia as the
ruler of a united Italy. Though by 1870 Italy had freed all her
territory with the exception of the Trentino from foreign
rule, the task of making Italy a united country was by no
means complete. The people differed, and still differ, considerably in matters of dialect, customs, and modes of life; but
they had realized that they were all Italians united by their
common language, traditions, and hopes for the future. One
problem which is specially serious in southern Italy, as in many
other under-developed areas of the world, is that population is
increasing more quickly than productivity. In the country as
a whole an extra quarter to half a million people a year must find
some method of earning a living, either at home or abroad.
The Government has made great efforts to increase the productivity of the home country by irrigating or draining the
waste lands, and by teaching the peasants how to obtain larger
crops from their small farms. By these methods the production of wheat and maize, for example, has been doubled in the
last fifty years, and agriculture now supports ten million more
people than it did in 1914.

The Italian peasant works long and hard for a small return in

money or goods; but Italian farms employ less than half
the population, and there is little likelihood that the large
numbers who will be added to the population in the next few
years will all be able to find work on the land.   In former
times large numbers of Italians, unable to find work at home,
emigrated, chiefly to the United States.   In modern times,
however, the problem of surplus population has been partly
solved by increasing industrialization, and Italy now ranks
as one of the greatest manufacturing countries in the world.
Two important factors in the modern industrial development
have been the discovery of natural gas, and the increased
generation of hydro-electricity.

Natural gas, which provides not only light and power but
also raw materials for the chemical industry, is produced in
vast quantity from bores in the Po Valley and near the Adriatic
coast, and distributed by pipe-line to all the industrial centres.

Nearly three-quarters of the available water-power is situated
in northern Italy, where the rivers are swollen by melting snows
in summer, and large lakes provide natural reservoirs.   In
southern Italy, though the rainfall is smaller, most of it falls in
winter, when the northern stations suffer from lack of water.
As electricity is so easily transmitted by wires, steps are being
taken to link up the northern and southern water-power plants,
so that they may supplement each other.   Among the most
notable schemes is that of the Sila River, in the toe of Italy,
where dams have been constructed to serve three purposes:
the reclamation of marshy lands around Salerno, which were
formerly flooded by the river; the irrigation of dry plains on
the eastern side of the Apennines; and the generation of hydro-
electricity.   In winter, when there is excess of water, electricity
is sent across the Straits of Messina to Sicily, so that the rain
there may be stored in reservoirs to provide both irrigation
water and electricity in summer.

THE FOREIGN TRADE OF ITALY

Italy buys raw materials like cotton, wool, iron ore, coal, oil, skins, timber, and staple foodstuffs like grain and fish. She sells manufactured goods (textiles, chemicals, motors, etc.), and special foodstuffs such as fruit and cheese and olive oil. When the total value of her imports and exports are considered it seems that she spends every year more on imports than she receives for her exports. Of course this cannot really be so or the country would soon be bankrupt. One way in which Italy bridges the gap in her national balance sheet is by 'selling' her climate, her scenery, and her history to tourists and holiday makers. In a recent year some 17 million people visited Italy and spent some £400 million on fares, food, accommodation, etc. In this way the Italians received money for their *services* just as they do for *goods* they export. Such services are, therefore, called *invisible exports*.

EXERCISES

1. On an outline map of Europe show the following routes to Italy:
   (*a*) London—Dover—Calais—Paris—Dijon—Lausanne—Simplon Pass—Milan—Bologna—Florence—Rome—Naples.
   (*b*) Ostend—Brussels—Basle—Lucerne—St. Gothard Pass—Milan.
   (*c*) Paris—Dijon—Lyons—Mont Cenis Pass—Turin—Bologna—Ancona—Brindisi.

2. Italy with a population of 50 millions has a mercantile fleet aggregating 5 million tons; Greece with a population of 7 millions has 1·6 million tons. Give reasons why Greece has a larger tonnage in proportion to her population.

3. Italy's chief imports of raw materials are: oil, coal, wool, cotton, scrap iron, and timber. In the case of each commodity name countries from which supplies are obtainable.

4. Italy's chief exports are: vehicles, machinery, textiles, fresh fruit, and vegetables. Draw a sketch-map to show the parts of Italy in which these goods are produced.

5. Draw sketch-maps to show: (*a*) the degree in which the Adriatic is an Italian sea; (*b*) the relationship of Italy to Mediterranean trade routes.

6. Draw graphs of the following temperature and rainfall statistics:

		J.	F.	M.	A.	M.	J.	Jy.	A.	S.	O.	N.	D.
Milan	Temp. (° C.)	0	3	8	13	17	21	24	23	19	13	7	2
	Rainfall (inches	2·4	2·3	2·7	3·4	4·1	3·3	2·8	3·2	3·5	4·7	4·3	3·0
Palermo	Temp. (° C.)	10	11	13	14	18	22	24	25	23	20	15	12
	Rainfall (inches)	3·2	2·7	2·8	1·9	1·1	0·7	0·2	0·4	1·8	3·2	3·3	3·6

State briefly the differences they indicate between the climates of northern and southern Italy. Account for these differences, and say what differences they cause in the lives of the people.

7. The areas of land growing wheat in the different parts of Italy were as follows in a recent year (million hectares):

Northern 1·5; Central 1·1; Southern 1·5; Sicily 0·8; Sardinia 0·3.

On an outline map of Italy write the word WHEAT over the various regions, in letters proportional in height to these amounts.

8. Make notes of recent developments in agriculture and industry in southern Italy.

9. Draw diagrams to show the following sources of energy in Italy:

	Coal	*Oil*	*Water Power*	*Natural Gas*
% of total	26	40	28	12

10. Draw diagrams to show that during the last ten years Italian exports have increased by 100 per cent, industrial production by 75 per cent, and agricultural production by 30 per cent.

MALTA

THIS British Colony, which includes the islands of Malta and Gozo and several islets, is situated in the middle of the Mediterranean Sea between Sicily and Africa. Its situation has made it of strategic importance throughout the ages, and it was until recently the chief British naval and air base in the Mediterranean. During the Second World War the island was awarded the George Cross in recognition of the courage and fortitude of its people in face of enemy attacks.

Valletta, the capital, is situated on one of the most magnificent harbours in the world. Though no longer our naval base it still has large naval engineering workshops, and is a port of call for vessels passing to and from the East via the Suez Canal.

The islands are intensively cultivated, but the lack of perennial streams so restricts irrigation that the Maltese are unable to produce more than a quarter of the food they need. Nevertheless, one of their chief sources of income is the export of 'out of season' market-garden produce such as tomatoes, potatoes, and vegetables.

Such exports are, however, quite insufficient to pay for the necessary imports of food, clothing, and manufactured goods, the balance being made up by work in the factories, service and sales to tourists, and by grants from Great Britain.

THE IBERIAN PENINSULA (SPAIN AND PORTUGAL)

MUCH of the interest of geography lies in asking ourselves questions about various countries, and then trying to find out the answers. Study the map of Spain and Portugal, think of any interesting facts you have learnt about these countries, either in history lessons or from the newspapers, and make a list of questions you would like to be able to answer. Perhaps your list will include such questions as these:

Why is Iberia so nearly square?

Why do nearly all the rivers flow westward?

How did Portugal become an independent country?

Why have none of the other marginal lowlands become independent?

What is meant by the saying 'Africa begins at the Pyrenees'?

Why were Spain and Portugal the two most powerful countries in the world in the sixteenth and seventeenth centuries, and how did they lose their supremacy?

Why has Portugal so often been allied with Britain, while Spain has seldom been closely connected with our country?

Of course, geography alone cannot answer all these questions, but it does throw much light on them; so keep this list, and your own additions to it, in mind while studying the geography of Spain and Portugal.

How Nature built Iberia

The most ancient part of Iberia, round which the whole peninsula has been moulded, is the central plateau called the Meseta. (See Fig. 48.)

For untold millions of years this block of hard, old rock stood out as an island, while in the surrounding seas were laid down the sediments which now form the rocks of the marginal lands. Then came a period of folding, when the earth 'shrugged its shoulders,' tilted up the eastern and southern edges of the Meseta, and crumpled vast masses of rock against its unyielding sides, thus forming the fold ranges of the Cantabrians, the Pyrenees, and the Sierra Nevada.

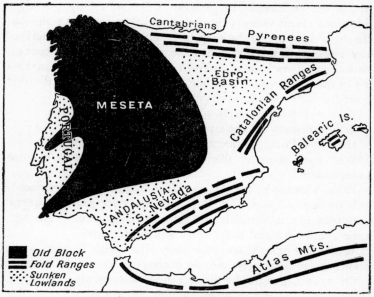

Cantabrians

Pyrenees

Ebro Basin

MESETA

Catalonian Ranges

Balearic Is.

PORTUGAL

ANDALUSIA S. Nevada

Atlas Mts.

■ Old Block
▬ Fold Ranges
∴ Sunken Lowlands

FIG. 48. IBERIA: STRUCTURAL DIVISION

Between the folds and the plateau the land sank to form the lowlands of Portugal, Andalusia, and the Ebro basin. During the many millions of years that have elapsed since Iberia assumed something like its present form, the weather has been constantly wearing away the rocks of the plateau and the fold mountains, inland seas have been filled up, valleys have been carved out, and rivers have carried away the rock waste and deposited it as fertile alluvium on the plains. Throughout these vast periods the Meseta was always the centre and nucleus of Iberia; its original form determined the present shape of the peninsula, for the fold mountains were compelled to run parallel to its sides; having shaped the land, it fertilized it by alluvium, which represents the wastage of its own body; and to-day its high mountain rims condense the moisture which flows in life-giving streams over the lowland, providing water for irrigation and power for industrial development. Is it not appropriate, then, that the unification of Spain was achieved by the people of the plateau, and that the capital of the country, from which roads and railways diverge to the outlying provinces, is situated in the centre of the Meseta?

How Spain became a Country

The first people to rule over the whole of Iberia were the Romans, who conquered the peninsula in the last two centuries before Christ. Under their rule the country became completely Romanized; an excellent system of roads was built; Christianity was introduced; commerce, art, and literature flourished; and Latin, from which both Spanish and Portuguese are derived, became the common language.

In the early part of the fifth century A.D. Iberia was conquered by the barbarian tribes who had swept over western Europe, and southward to the Mediterranean. The Vandals secured a foothold in southern Spain, and gave their name to Andalusia; but the strongest and most numerous barbarian tribe to settle in Iberia were the Visigoths, whose power rapidly extended over the whole peninsula. Though the Visigoth kings eventually accepted Christianity as their official religion, Roman civilization was destroyed, and the country was divided between warring nobles.

In A.D. 711 Moors from northern Africa were invited to help in rebellions against the Visigoth king. After defeating the king the Moors turned against their own allies and proceeded to conquer the country for themselves. The lack of unity among the Visigoth nobles made this task so easy that within seven years they had overrun practically the whole of the peninsula, and by 732 they were at the gates of Tours in central France. Here they were defeated by Charles Martel, leader of the Franks, in one of the most decisive battles of history. Though as a result of this battle they were turned out of France, they remained masters of Iberia for more than five hundred years. (See Fig. 49.)

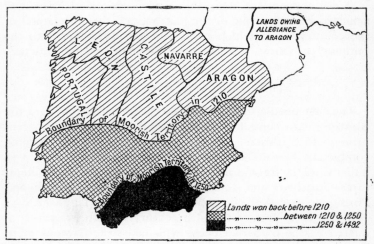

FIG. 49. STAGES IN THE EXPULSION OF THE MOORS FROM IBERIA

The Moorish occupation was in many ways a good thing for Spain. By the construction of ingenious systems of irrigation, and the introduction of new crops, such as sugar, cotton, and date-palms, the productivity of the land was enormously increased. In southern Spain the Moorish civilization reached a level hardly equalled in any other part of Europe. The north-west, however, on account of its inaccessibility and its humid climate, was never settled by the Moors, but was divided into small Christian kingdoms acknowledging the overlordship of the Moorish rulers. From the eleventh to the fifteenth century the history of Spain is that of the gradual reconquest of the country by these Christian kingdoms.

The great hero of the wars against the Moors is the Cid, a Spanish nobleman, who, after being exiled by his king, 'lived the life of a free-lance magnate, conquering Spain from the Moors by means of . . . a combination of raiding, settling, warring, and establishing protectorates over weak Moslem princes.'

By the end of the thirteenth century nearly all the Moors had been expelled from Spain, though it was not until 1492 that Granada, their last refuge, was finally conquered. But the expulsion of the Moors did not bring unity to Iberia. It will be seen from the physical map that the surface of the peninsula is divided into many small regions, cut off from each other by mountain ranges; and as each of these isolated districts freed itself from Moorish rule, it became an independent kingdom, suspicious and even disdainful of its neighbours. Just as the Meseta was the physical centre round which Nature built Iberia, so it became the political centre round which modern Spain grew; the kingdom of Castile gradually extended its power over first one and then another of the marginal lands, until its kings became rulers of the whole of Spain.

Portugal, however, became an independent country. It differs from the rest of Iberia in being a lowland facing the Atlantic, and communication with the Meseta is rendered difficult by waterfalls and rapids which mark the junction of the plateau and the plain. But these facts alone are not sufficient to explain why Portugal became an independent country, while other lowlands, like Andalusia and Valencia, were absorbed by Spain. One reason is that when the Moors were being driven from Iberia, the line of the Spanish advance was diagonally across the peninsula, from north-west to south-east, so that Portugal, once free from the Moors, was left on one side and allowed to manage her own affairs. Later, the discovery of America, and the opening up of trade routes to the East, enabled Portugal to become a great trading nation, who regarded Spain as a rival rather than as a friendly relative. Again, her position on the Atlantic coast made her a useful ally for Britain, who thus had an interest in helping her to maintain her independence.

During the Middle Ages Spain and Portugal were only on the edge of the main lines of traffic between Europe and the East, via Asia Minor and the Red Sea. In the fifteenth century, however, the Turks blocked these trade routes, and men's thoughts were turned to the possibilities of opening up ways to the Indies via the Atlantic. As both Spain and Portugal have Atlantic coasts it was only natural that they should play a leading part in this movement. Portugal pinned her faith on the southern route, and in 1497 Vasco da Gama sailed to India via the Cape, and enabled Portugal to capture the trade between south-eastern Asia and north-western Europe.

In 1492 Columbus, in the service of Spain, set out on what must have seemed to most people the mad project of finding India by sailing directly away from it. His discovery of the West Indies was rapidly followed by the establishment of Spanish rule over Mexico, Central America, and most of South America.

So vast were the claims of Spain and Portugal at this period that the Pope, in an attempt to remove causes of war, drew a north-to-south line through the mouth of the Amazon, and declared all new territories to the west of that line to belong to Spain, while all to the east were to be Portuguese.

For hundreds of years wealth poured into Spain from her overseas empire, and Portugal for a time held a practical monopoly of the trade with the East. But the final result of this sudden access of wealth and power was not advantageous to either country. The home lands were neglected, and the nations were weakened by the drainage of man-power to overseas possessions. Portugal did not long remain a great trading nation, and though Spain retained her South American colonies until the early part of the nineteenth century, she was never able to develop them in such a way as to bring real prosperity to the home country.

LIFE AND WORK OF THE PEOPLE

Iberia is a peninsula of great physical variety and its constituent parts show great differences in the mode of life of the people. A very important line of division is that marking twenty-five inches annual rainfall. (See Fig. 50.) North and

FIG. 50. IBERIA: RAINFALL

west of that line the climate is generally moist enough for the cultivation of such 'West European' crops as oats, wheat, barley, apples, and sugar beet, while it is also warm enough for the cultivation of vines, maize, and chestnuts. The methods of farming are, however, generally rather primitive, little up-to-date agricultural machinery is used, and oxen are the chief draught animals.

In central and south-eastern Spain, where the rainfall is less than twenty-five inches, other methods of farming must be adopted. Large areas, particularly on the plateau, in the Ebro basin, and in the extreme south-east, are arid steppes, supporting only scanty flocks of sheep which move from one poor pasture to another, frequently under the care of a communal shepherd. Even where the land is sufficiently fertile to grow cereals, either irrigation or dry farming is necessary. By this latter method the land is left fallow every second or third year in order to allow moisture to accumulate. During this time it is constantly harrowed or hoed in order to keep down weeds which would extract much water from the soil, and to close up the cracks through which the moisture would be drawn by the great heat of summer.

Though this method makes it possible to produce crops in regions where the annual rainfall is insufficient for ordinary farming, it means that one-third, and in some places a half, of the land is lying idle. In recent years a better method of dry farming, whereby the land can be kept constantly in use, has been introduced. By this method the crops are sown in lines two or three feet apart, the land between the rows being constantly hoed to keep in the moisture. Thus the land can be cropped every year, and the total yield of the farm increased by one-third or more, without expenditure of additional money or labour.

The most productive regions of Iberia are the irrigated lands of the south-east. The Moors, who came from the arid lands of northern Africa, established irrigation systems in all the valleys and coastal plains of the south-east. Some of these, such as those of Valencia, are still in operation very much on the lines established by the Moors; but many were destroyed in the wars which resulted in the expulsion of the Moors, and others were allowed to fall into disuse during succeeding centuries. It is in large measure due to the neglect of the ancient systems of irrigation that modern Spain owes much of her poverty. In recent years, however, the Government has done a little to restore fertility to the land by the building of storage reservoirs in the Pyrenees, the Sierra Morena, and the Sierra Nevada. These reservoirs serve the double purpose of irrigation and the generation of hydro-electricity.

Although less than half the total area of Spain and little more than half the surface of Portugal is cultivated, more than half the exports of both countries consist of such agricultural products as oranges, grapes, wines, olives, lemons, and nuts.

FIG. 51. IBERIA: ECONOMIC

On the other hand, such staple foods as grain, meat, and fish are imported in large quantities.

Oranges form the chief single item of export from Spain. In normal times more than 90 per cent of the oranges sold in Britain come from that country, and orange wrappers have made the names of the chief shipping ports well known to all. All these ports are situated in the irrigated land of the south-east, for it is only in the dry, sunny, 'Mediterranean' climate that the fruit grows to perfection. (See Fig. 51.)

Vines are particularly suited to the 'Mediterranean' climate, since they have long roots which penetrate far into the soil to find moisture, while the fruit will only ripen in hot, dry

H   E

weather, and the juice of the grapes is available for making wine just at the time when drinking-water is scarce and liable to be tainted with disease germs.

The vine can be grown in specially favoured regions throughout Iberia, but the chief areas of production, apart from the port-wine district of Oporto in Portugal, are the southern and eastern coastlands. *Tarragona* in the north-east, and *Jerez* in the extreme south are the largest wine-producing districts. The latter town gave its name to the wine known as 'sherry,' which is produced exclusively in that district. *Almeria* is specially noted for its export of grapes, while *Malaga* and *Alicante* send out large quantities of raisins.

Olives are even more typical of Mediterranean regions than grapes or oranges. The tree can be grown without irrigation, since it has long roots which penetrate far into the soil in search of water, and low, spreading branches and small hairy leaves which prevent loss of moisture. It grows best on the poor, limy or sandy soils of the hillsides, so the peasant of the Mediterranean countries is able to reserve his richer valley floors and lower hill slopes for other food crops. The hot, dry summers, which are necessary for the cultivation of olives, do not favour the growth of grass for cattle; and it is fortunate that the olive provides a thick oil which is used by the natives in place of butter and other animal fats. Purified olive oil is exported in large quantities from south-eastern Spain, Andalusia being the chief area of production.

Wheat is the chief food crop of Iberia, although the yield per acre is low on account of the lack of moisture. The most noteworthy wheat-growing regions are the basins of the Ebro and the Guadalquivir, and the plain around Valladolid, which is served by the Castile Irrigation Canal.

Barley is grown mainly on the drier lands of the south-east, while **rye** is confined to the cooler and wetter lands of the north-west.

Rice is grown only on the irrigated lowlands of Valencia, where its cultivation was introduced by the Moors.

Sugar is obtained from beet grown in the north-west and in the Ebro basin, and from sugar cane grown on the irrigated lowlands of Andalusia. **Esparto grass,** which is exported for the making of paper, grows wild on the arid plains and plateaus of the south-east.

Cork is the inner bark of the cork oak, large sheets of which are stripped from the tree at intervals of eight to ten years. Much of it is exported in boards and cubes, for manufacture into various articles, and large quantities are manufactured into corks for bottles, while the cork dust and shavings are used for packing grapes, etc., for export. Although most of the cork is produced in the south-eastern districts, the chief centre for the manufacture of cork articles is on the extreme north-east coast.

Pastoral Farming

Since a large part of the surface of Iberia is unsuitable for agriculture, pastoral farming predominates. **Sheep** are most numerous on the dry, barren land of the Meseta. This is the original home of the merino breed, which has been introduced with such success into Australia, New Zealand, and the Argentine. Transhumance is still widely practised, the sheep being wintered on the lowlands and summered on the plateau.

Goats are able to derive sustenance from coarse grass and even bushes, which other animals are unable to eat. They are, therefore, kept in even the most arid districts of Spain. In many towns the milkman is the goatherd, who drives his animals through the streets and milks them to supply the requirements of his customers.

Pigs rank second in number among the domestic animals of Iberia, but they are not so numerous as in the countries of north-western Europe, and there is no export of pork or bacon. Among the chief pig-rearing districts are the Cantabrian regions of the north, and the island of Majorca, where chestnuts form a valuable feeding stuff.

Cattle are relatively few in Iberia, since the hot, dry summers do not favour the growth of good grass. The chief cattle-rearing districts are, naturally, the mild, moist coastlands of the north-west. Andalusia, however, is still famous for the bulls which are reared for the national pastime of bull-fighting.

Throughout Iberia agricultural processes are generally very primitive. Each village has its threshing floor, where the grain is separated from the wheat by oxen or mules, which drag round and round a heavy sledge studded with nails. The wheat is winnowed by the equally primitive process of throwing it in the air, so that the chaff is blown away by the wind, while the wheat accumulates in a heap. Yet, strong as is the liking of the Spanish peasant for his old customs, modern machinery is gradually being adopted, and one sometimes sees petrol-driven threshing machines working on the village threshing floor, side by side with the primitive machines described above.

THE MINERAL WEALTH OF IBERIA

Spain has considerable mineral wealth, but the working of it is hindered by lack of capital and difficulties of transport.

Coal occurs in several districts, but the Asturias coal-field, around Oviedo, is the only one of any great extent. In other fields transport costs or the poor quality of the coal rendered working unprofitable so long as coal could be imported from Britain. The general European shortage of coal has, however, compelled Spain to work these minor deposits, and she now produces almost enough for her needs.

An interesting recent development is the co-operation between the coal-fields and the hydro-electric power stations, whereby the electricity is supplied from the latter in winter and from the former in summer, when the water supply is low. By this means she utilizes some of the poorer coal which does not pay for transport.

Iron is mined chiefly in the Cantabrian region, around Oviedo,

Santander, and Bilbao.   Some of it is smelted locally, but the greater part is exported, chiefly to South Wales.

Copper, as well as iron and manganese, is produced in the Rio Tinto district, on the edge of the Sierra Morena, and exported from the port of Huelva. **Mercury** is produced at Almaden, on the northern slopes of the Sierra Morena.

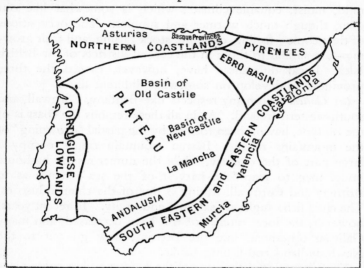

FIG. 52. IBERIA: NATURAL REGIONS

In addition to these, Iberia yields almost every mineral of commercial importance, though usually the deposits are not sufficiently rich to be worth working on a large scale.

THE NATURAL DIVISIONS OF IBERIA

It will be seen from the above accounts that the various parts of Iberia differ considerably in their physical features, climate, and occupations of the people.   The map (Fig. 52) shows how Iberia may be divided into Natural Regions, in each of which the conditions of life are similar throughout the region itself, but different from those in neighbouring regions.

(1) The Northern Coastlands

This region comprises Galicia, Asturias, and the Basque Provinces. Being situated in the path of the 'depressions,' and the moist westerly winds from the Atlantic, these mountainous provinces differ from the rest of Spain in having a mild, moist, equable climate, which is somewhat like our own, though much warmer and sunnier. The occupations of the people—fishing, dairying, stock raising, and fruit growing—are similar to those in the coastal districts of the British Isles. Local differences have, however, caused the three provinces to develop on somewhat different lines.

(a) *Galicia* is in many respects like Brittany, Cornwall, and south-western Ireland. As in all these regions the coast is of the *ria* type, having been formed by the partial 'drowning' of the mountains ranges. Barren mountain ridges occupy a large part of the country, while the numerous *ria* harbours invite men to reap 'the harvest of the sea'; hence as in Brittany and Cornwall, fishing is one of the chief industries. The chief fish caught are sardines and tunny. In recent years, however, the local catches of fish have decreased, and many Galician fishermen, like the Bretons, now go out to the Newfoundland cod-fishing banks.

The mountainous character of the country and its consequent isolation helped the people to retain their own language, which shows greater similarity to Portuguese than to Spanish. In this, too, Galicia resembles the above-mentioned parts of France and Britain, for in Brittany some of the people still speak the Breton language, which is very different from French, and in Cornwall a similar Celtic tongue was formerly spoken.

The infertility of the country makes it incapable of supporting all its people in comfort and so there is much emigration, chiefly to the former Spanish territories of South America. The chief port of the region *Vigo* is situated on a magnificent *ria* harbour. It is therefore, comparable with Plymouth and

Brest; but its development has been hindered by the difficulty of communication with the interior, and it ranks only as one of the minor ports of Spain, though it is an important fish-canning centre. *Corunna,* the ancient port which is remembered in connection with the retreat of Sir John Moore during the Peninsular War, has lost most of its trade to Vigo.

Ferrol, on the opposite side of the bay, is a naval station and shipbuilding yard, whose position may be compared to the British naval station of Devonport, and to the French naval port of Brest.

(*b*) *Asturias* is noteworthy for its mineral wealth. *Oviedo* uses the local coal and iron for the manufacture of steel, and *Gijon,* the port for Oviedo, exports iron ore.

(*c*) *The Basque Provinces.* This region has the economic advantages of having large supplies of iron ore, good harbours, and railway communication with both France and Spain. More important, perhaps, than these, is the fact that the Basques are more energetic and enterprising than most of the Spanish people, consequently there has been much industrial and commercial development. *Bilbao* is the second port of Spain; it exports iron ore to South Wales, and receives coal in return It has also developed iron and steel manufactures, of which it is the chief Spanish centre.

(2) The South-eastern and Eastern Coastlands

The coastal regions of the south-east are very different from those of the north The summers are hot and dry, and even the winter rainfall is scanty in many places. While the Cantabrian region is clothed with forests and meadows the coastlands of the south-east were, in their natural state, steppes and semi-desert. Irrigation, which is quite unnecessary in the northern coastlands, is absolutely essential for cultivation in the south-eastern regions of Valencia and Murcia. In *Valencia* the irrigation system was initiated by the Romans, and considerably extended and improved during the Moorish occupation of the country. An intricate system of channels and pipes convey the life-giving water from the mountain slopes to the terraced fields and gardens. Representatives elected by the cultivators decide the amount of water which shall be supplied to each plot, and though in times of exceptional drought the tribunal may decide that water can be given only to certain valuable crops, while others must be left to perish, their authority is never flouted. The areas which can be supplied with sufficient water to produce two crops per year are known as 'huertas,' while those areas which can produce only one crop per year are called 'vegas.'

The greater part of the land is devoted to the cultivation of food crops, such as wheat, maize, rice, and beans, for local consumption; but large areas are also planted with oranges olives, and vines, which provide the chief 'money' crops for export.

Valencia, the third city of Spain, is well known for oranges and raisins. Other towns, whose names are familiar on orange wrappers, are Denia and Gandia.

The province of Murcia has even less rain than Valencia, hence, while the need for irrigation is greater, supplies of water are more difficult to obtain. In contrast to the democratic system of control in Valencia, the Murcian irrigation schemes are usually in the hands of wealthy individuals, who sell the water—sometimes by public auction—to the peasant cultivators. The great heat and the scarcity of water give this region great similarity to parts of northern Africa, and the irrigated areas are very like the oases of the Sahara.

In some of the driest regions 'the distant blue hills assume the pointed, triangular aspect of far-reaching desert, the isolated groups of palms, and the great transparent bowl of burning sky, and the geometrical cone on the horizon, etched in deep turquoise, presents a faithful mirror of Egypt.' Around Elche are veritable forests of date palms, 'planted in long succession, with their heads in the sun, and their roots watered by little artificial streams.'

E. N. A.

A Palm Grove at Elche

Catalonia. This coastal region is very different from those already described. Though its climate is of the 'Mediterranean' type, the rainfall is heavier than in the more southerly coastlands, and sufficient water for agriculture can easily be obtained from wells and streams. But it is as a manufacturing region that Catalonia is specially noteworthy, though why industries should have developed here is rather difficult to explain. Usually we find that an industrial region has the advantage of local supplies of coal, or iron, or other raw materials, but Catalonia has none of these. Coal and iron are brought from Asturias, cotton from North America, wool from South America, and so on. Perhaps the only geographical reasons that can be given for the development of industry here is that it is a coastal region which has access to the water power of mountain streams; but there are many similar districts which have never developed any manufacturing industry, and we must look to human and historical factors for the real causes. Perhaps the most important reason is that the Catalans are hard-working, energetic, determined, and business-like people; another is that the historical connections of Barcelona with the Mediterranean gave her opportunities to gather raw materials; and a third reason is that the Spanish Government helps her own manufacturing industries by imposing heavy taxes on imports of manufactured goods. So in Catalonia, as indeed in all other civilized countries, man does not allow Nature to have the last word.

Barcelona is the chief manufacturing city, and the largest port of Spain, with a population of over 1,000,000 people. Hydro-electricity is derived chiefly from the rapid tributaries which flow from the Pyrenees to the Ebro. The chief industry is the manufacture of cotton goods; woollen, linen, and silk goods, paper, pottery, leather, and machinery are also manufactured.

(3) The Sunken Lowlands of Spain

The provinces of **Aragon** in the north-east, and **Andalusia** in the south, are in some ways very similar and in other ways very different. Each region has been formed by the sinking of the land between fold ranges and the ancient block—the former between the Pyrenees and the Meseta, and the latter between the Sierra Nevada and the Meseta; and each is drained by a great river, the soil being formed largely of sediment brought down by these rivers. But the basin of the Ebro is shut off from rain-bearing winds, while the basin of the Guadalquivir opens towards the Atlantic. So Aragon is an arid region, where farming is difficult and life is hard, whereas in Andalusia there is heavier rainfall, life is easy, and the people, though poor, are typically care-free. In both regions, however, irrigation is necessary in the hot, dry summer. In Aragon a considerable area around Zaragoza has been irrigated, but the greater part of the lowland is still unproductive steppe or semi-desert. In Andalusia dams are being constructed to supply water for both irrigation and hydro-electricity, thus restoring the prosperity which the region enjoyed during the Moorish occupations.

Seville is situated at the head of navigation of the Guadalquivir. It was an important centre of the Moorish civilization, but its modern importance dates from the discovery of America. The port was granted a monopoly of the American trade, and though this had soon to be shared with Cadiz, its sheltered position gave it much advantage over that city. In the last century it suffered much from the silting up of the river, but recent engineering and dredging operations have again enabled it to become an important shipping centre. The chief exports are olive oil, pickled olives, cork, and oranges.

Cordoba was one of the chief centres of the Mohammedan religion, and its partially ruined mosque, second only in size to the Kaaba of Mecca, is still one of the architectural wonders of the world. After the expulsion of the Moors the irrigation

system which they had established was allowed to fall into disuse, and the city became 'the dead centre of a dead province.'
Irrigation schemes now in progress aim not only at restoring
the former productivity of the surrounding country, but also
at the establishment of large industries based on the water
power generated at the outlets of the irrigation reservoirs.

Cadiz is situated at the end of a long sandbank which partially encloses a broad land-locked harbour. From the air it
looks as if Andalusia, 'whose towns are so white, wanted to
whitewash the sea—a long narrow handle—which in reality
is a sandbank—and then, at the top of it, the brush that has
been dipped in whitewash.'—H. Baerlein, *Spain: Yesterday,
To-day and To-morrow.*

Cadiz is one of the most ancient ports in Spain, for in Phoenician times it was the chief market for the tin brought from
Cornwall. It is well situated for trade with both the Mediterranean and the Atlantic, and when America was discovered its
merchants demanded a share in the transatlantic commerce,
and for a time Cadiz was the chief port of Spain. Its very
accessibility, however, proved to be its greatest danger, for it
was frequently attacked by the pirates who flourished off the
Barbary coast, and by English buccaneers like Drake, who, in
1587, burned many ships which were waiting in the harbour
to join the Great Armada. In modern times it has become
the third port of Spain, ranking after Barcelona and Bilbao.

Huelva, at the mouth of the Rio (River) Tinto, is the port for
the copper mines at Minas de Rio Tinto, on the edge of the
Sierra Morena. Jerez is the centre for the production of
sherry, a wine which derives its name from that town. As
the Spaniards are often accused of being poor farmers, it may
be well to learn something of the production of this wine.

The vines are first grown in nurseries, and after being carefully tended there for a year, they are planted singly in holes
three feet apart. For three years the vines are carefully tended
and pruned, then when the fruit is perfectly ripe, it is placed
in small baskets, and exposed to the sun for twenty-four hours.

The juice is then pressed out in the wine-press, allowed to ferment for several months, and stored for many years in order to mature.

Zaragoza is the only large town of the Ebro basin. Its position is somewhat similar to that of Seville, but it has no importance as a port since the River Ebro is unnavigable for large vessels. Its chief industries are those associated with the preparation of the food products of the surrounding irrigated lands—wheat, olive oil, and wine.

(4) The Meseta

This mountain-rimmed and mountain-ribbed plateau is divided into two parts by the high range of the Sierra de Guadarrama. To the north of the range lies the 'basin' of Old Castile and Leon, while to the south lies Estremadura and the 'basin' of New Castile.

Situated in the middle of the compact peninsula and shut off from oceanic winds by high marginal mountains, the plateau has an arid climate, with cold winters, hot summers, and a clear atmosphere which causes great difference between the temperatures of day and night, and between the sunny and shady sides of the street. Madrid, for example, is as cold as eastern England in winter, but almost as hot as the Equator in summer. (Jan., 40° F. (4° C.); July, 76° F. (25° C.).)

The predominant features of the landscape are the undulating, dusky yellow plains, broken only by bare rocky hills, or by watercourses which are dry in summer and raging torrents after a thunderstorm. Trees and cultivated fields are rare, and the scanty brown grass serves only to support flocks of sheep and goats. Isolated dwellings are almost non-existent, and the peasants live in little walled towns and widely scattered villages built on the sides or crests of hills.

In the extreme south-east of the plateau are the plains of La Mancha, the most desolate part of Spain, which recall northern Africa by their desert-like character. Scanty flocks of sheep

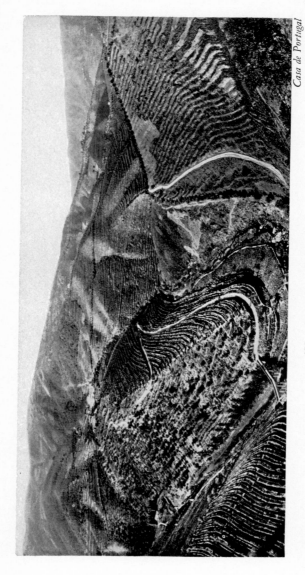

Casa de Portugal

'Un Aspecto do Douro'

move from place to place, and the only vegetable product of commercial importance is esparto grass, which gathered is exported for making paper. 'From time to time a mule cart travels through the solitude; its destination will be one of the rare villages that live—and God knows how—upon the plain, or one of the still rarer villages that you can see on the bare slope of a hill, the tawny ruins of a castle standing on the summit.

Madrid is situated on the Manzanares, a tributary of the Tagus, and almost exactly in the centre of the country. Roads and railways converge upon it from all parts of the peninsula, thus adding greatly to its one natural advantage of centrality. Like most other capitals, it has many miscellaneous industries, mainly connected with the preparation of clothing, foodstuffs, and furniture.

Toledo, situated on a high rocky peninsula, within a great horseshoe bend of the Tagus, is one of the most ancient cities in the peninsula. The surrounding country has suffered greatly from neglect, but recent installations of hydro-electric plant in the gorge of the Tagus are doing much to restore prosperity.

PORTUGAL

The boundary between Spain and Portugal follows fairly closely the line of gorges which mark the limit of navigation on the rivers Douro, Tagus, etc.; but, as we have seen, historical factors have played a large part in determining the separation of the two countries.

As in Spain the great majority of the people obtain their living from the land, but agricultural methods are primitive, the yield of crops is low, and there is a large proportion of waste and uncultivated land. As it has larger areas of mild, moist, coastal lowlands, dairy farming and cattle rearing are of greater importance than in Spain, while the wetter summers cause more maize and less wheat to be grown. A much smaller proportion of the area of Portugal is devoted to the cultivation of olives, oranges, and other fruits, but the production of cork is much greater than that of Spain.

Portugal is fairly rich in minerals, but production is hampered by lack of transport and fuel. The chief mineral produced is wolfram, from which the metal tungsten (used in hardening steel and for electric filaments) is obtained.

The Sierra da Estrella, and its continuation south-westwards to Cape da Roca, divide the country into two contrasting physical and economic divisions. To the north of this range the land is well-watered and fertile, while to the south of it are large areas of unproductive marsh and semi-arid pasture lands.

The most intensively cultivated district is that around the mouths of the Minho and Douro. The 'hub' of this region is *Oporto*, famous for its exports of port wine.

Lisbon, the capital of the country, is situated at the mouth of the chief navigable river (the Tagus), and at the focus of land routes from north and south and east. It is approached from the sea by a rather narrow channel, which opens out at Lisbon into an extensive land-locked basin. This narrow entrance has not only facilitated defence of the city, but also causes strong tidal races, which help to keep the channel clear of sediment. Lisbon is the nearest port to South America, and has considerable trade with Brazil, which was formerly a Portuguese colony.

EXERCISES

1. Draw a map of Spain and Portugal to emphasize the fact that Madrid is the centre of the railway system of Iberia.

2. On the above map mark in red the following through express routes:

(a) Bayonne—San Sebastian—Burgos—Medina— $\begin{cases} \text{Madrid.} \\ \text{Lisbon.} \end{cases}$

(b) Madrid—Alcazar—Cordoba—Algeciras (Pier)—Gibraltar (steamer).

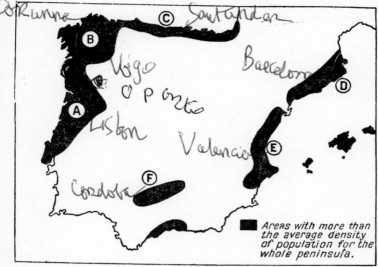

FIG. 53. IBERIA: POPULATION (See Exercise 5, p. 188)

3. Use the following table as the basis of a series of simple comparisons of Spain with Portugal:

	Portugal	Spain
Area	34,500 sq. miles	196,000 sq. miles
Population	8·8 millions	29 millions
Cattle	1·1 ,,	4·2 ,,
Sheep	3·7 ,,	20 ,,
Goats	1·5 ,,	4·7 ,,
Pigs	1·2 ,,	5·8 ,,

4. Spain grows six times as much wheat as maize but Portugal grows only twice as much wheat as maize. Draw sketch-maps to show the climatic factors which help to account for this difference between the countries.

5. (a) Fig. 53 shows the most densely peopled parts of Iberia. Say why each of the districts A, B, C, etc., has above the normal density of population.

(b) The average density of population in Iberia is 160 per square mile; in Italy it is 382. Give reasons for this difference.

6. In Britain farmers form only 2 per cent of the working people, but in both Spain and Portugal they form 50 per cent of the total. Give reasons for the difference.

SWITZERLAND

THE earliest inhabitants of Switzerland of whom we have certain knowledge were men of the New Stone Age and the Bronze Age. Excavations on the lake shores have shown that these primitive peoples lived in houses built of wicker-work and mud, on a foundation of piles which were driven deep into the mud near the edges of the lakes. They lived by hunting, fishing, rearing cattle and sheep, and cultivating the fertile lands around the lakes.

Later, Celtic tribes, known as Helvetians, settled in the valleys. It is from these Celts that the country received the name of Helvetia, which it bore in Roman times, and which is still to be found on Swiss stamps. Julius Caesar conquered the Helvetians in the last century B.C., and they became thoroughly Romanized. The barbarian invasions of the third and fourth centuries destroyed their civilization, and the country sank into a state of savagery and paganism, in which it remained for hundreds of years. It is interesting that certain Irish missionaries, notably St. Columba and St. Gall, were the means of reintroducing Christianity and civilization into the country. The town of St. Gallen, now famous for its cotton industry, owes its name to the latter saint, who rested there when taken ill while on a journey to Rome. When he recovered he was so touched by the misery of the people that he remained there to teach them Christianity and the arts of civilized life, including spinning and weaving.

In the Middle Ages the north-eastern part of the country was conquered by German tribes, and the south-west was invaded by the French. In the thirteenth century the land was under the rule of tyrannical Austrian dukes; but the spirit of independence was strong in the people, and in 1291 three cantons on the shores of Lake Lucerne (Uri, Schwyz, and Unter-walden) united in a confederation to free themselves of the

Austrian yoke.   The story of William Tell, though it may not
be strictly accurate, illustrates the determination and heroism
of the people in their fight for liberty.   Eventually the
Austrians were driven from the country, and other cantons
joined the confederation, forming the country of Switzerland,
which took its name from one of the original insurgent
cantons.

Though it is such a small country it still retains the federal
form of government, which has been copied by some of the
largest countries of the world. Each of the twenty-two cantons
manages its own local affairs, and even raises taxes for its own
needs; but members are also elected to serve on the National
Council and the Council of States, which conduct the affairs of
the country as a whole, and raise taxes for national expenditure.   No doubt this federal form of government is due in
large measure to the mountains which divide the country into
a number of rather isolated areas, whose inhabitants like to
manage their own affairs.   At the same time this very isolation
makes it all the more remarkable that the people should have
been able and willing to unite so effectively as to establish
themselves as an independent nation.   Still more remarkable
is the fact that the country has no language of its own.
Government notices have to be printed in three languages, for
71 per cent of the people speak German, 21 per cent speak
French, and 6 per cent speak Italian, while the remainder speak
a dialect descended directly from Latin.   No doubt the mountainous character of Switzerland helped the people to become
free, just as the sea helped the Dutch; but it must not be
assumed that Liberty is the gift of the sea or of the mountains;
all that we can say is that they may provide the opportunity
for men to be free; whether or not they make use of the
opportunity depends on the people themselves.

As Switzerland is a small country surrounded by powerful
neighbours, she has realized that her safety is best assured by
neutrality, and since the sixteenth century she has never taken
sides in the quarrels between European nations.   For this

reason, and because of her central situation, she has become
the home of international organizations, such as the Red Cross
Association.

THE SURFACE OF THE COUNTRY

Switzerland is so closely associated in the mind with the
Alps that we are apt to assume that mountains occupy nearly
the whole of the country. A glance at the map will show
that this is incorrect, and that there are three main physical
divisions of the country, viz., the Jura Mountains in the north-
west, the Swiss Plateau in the middle, and the Alps in the

FIG. 54. TYPES OF FOLDS IN THE JURA MOUNTAINS

south. Each of these divisions is of great interest from the
point of view of its physical formation.

The Jura consist of numerous parallel ridges and valleys,
formed by simple upfolds and downfolds. As shown in
Fig. 54, the tops of the folds have been worn away by the
weather, but in most cases the upfolds still form the ridges,
while the downfolds form the valleys. In a few cases the
arch, which is the weakest part of the fold since there the rocks
have been stretched and cracked, has been worn away to such
an extent as to form a valley. (In more complex mountains
the weathering has often gone so far that the valleys are carved
out of the upfolds, while the peaks are formed from the downfolds.) A characteristic feature of the Jura is that there are
numerous gorges or 'cluses' in the ranges forming ways from
one longitudinal valley to the next. The numerous right-
angle bends of the River Doubs show where it used these
'cluses' to break through one range after another.

The commonest type of rock in the Jura is limestone, which

allows the water to soak through easily. Consequently much of the land is suitable only for pasturing sheep and goats. In some parts, however, the mountain sides are forested; indeed, the name 'Jura' is thought to mean 'forest.' (Compare 'Lysa Gora' in Poland.)

The Swiss Plateau occupies an area which was once part of a great sea running from the Rhône valley, round the northern side of the Alps, to the present plains of Hungary. Gradually this sea was filled up with pebbles, sand, and mud brought down from the Alps. These deposits were then compressed to form the rocks which now constitute the Swiss Plateau.

FIG. 55. A MUCH SIMPLIFIED SECTION ACROSS AN ALPINE MOUNTAIN

The Alps are fold mountains of a very complex type. A section across the ranges, coloured to show the layers of rock, resembles a bunch of ribbons which have been twisted, knotted, and torn, and then thrown in a heap. The section shown in Fig. 55 is very much simplified, and gives only a general idea of the complexity of the folding. How stupendous must be the forces which have contorted the solid rocks in this manner!

So complex is the structure of the Alps that it is not possible to speak of them as a 'chain' of mountains. Indeed, an ordinary atlas map shows a score or more well-known sub-divisions; and while it is unnecessary to attempt to learn these by heart, it is interesting to work out, with the help of the atlas, imaginary journeys among the ranges and valleys, and to collect photographs illustrating their scenic beauty. The simplified map in Fig. 40, page 141, will serve as a guide to such map study, and details may be inserted as desired.

GLACIERS AND THEIR EFFECTS

Since the Alps extend well above the snow-line, snow is constantly accumulating in hollows high up on the mountain sides. The great pressure of the overlying layers of snow, and the alternate thawing and freezing of the surface layers, turn the masses of snow into ice, which is pushed down the valleys in the form of glaciers. Sometimes glaciers are spoken of as 'rivers of ice'; but while there are certain obvious similarities between glaciers and rivers, there are many important differences in their movements and effects on the land surface. Both wear away the surface of the land; but whereas rivers generally cut both sideways and downwards, glaciers cut chiefly downwards. Again, a river cannot gouge large hollows in its beds, but a glacier frequently does so, leaving basins in which lakes form when the glacier ceases to exist.

Though the glaciers move very slowly—often not more than a few inches a day—the pressure of the ice is so great that it quickly wears away the surface of the land. The high amphitheatres in which the ice collects are deepened and their sides are cut back until they form almost vertical walls of rock. Where two such amphitheatres or 'cirques' meet they make a straight, narrow ridge or 'arête.' If three cirques meet they will form between them a great triangular peak like the Matterhorn. The glaciers themselves wear away the sides and floors of the valleys, grind rocks into rock flour, and carry down large quantities of stones and mud. Such material when deposited by the glacier is known as *moraine*. *Terminal moraine* is that left at the end of a glacier when the ice melts; *ground moraine* is that deposited on the valley floor under the glacier; *lateral moraine* is the rock-waste which collects in lines at the edges of the glaciers; and *medial moraine* is formed where two glaciers join. (See Fig. 56.)

We have seen that glaciers, like rivers, carve out valleys; but whereas a valley formed by a river is usually V-shaped, that formed by a glacier usually has steep sides, so that a cross-section is U-shaped.

During the Ice Age glaciers extended farther down the Alpine valleys than at present, and their effects are to be seen

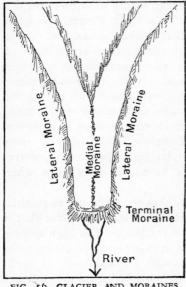

in the flat valley floors, in the lakes which are held up by moraine, and in the precipitous slopes of the valley sides. Many such valleys consequently have a cross-section like that represented by the block diagram, Fig. 57. Valleys of this kind have had far-reaching effects on the life of the Swiss. The waterfalls formed where the tributary streams enter the steep-walled main valley are utilized for the generation of hydro-electricity, and Switzerland has been able to make up for her lack of coal by using this 'white coal' for her railways and factories.

FIG. 56. GLACIER AND MORAINES

The shape of the valleys also profoundly affects the location of villages, and the work of the farmers. The villages are usually built on the edge of the flat floor of the valley, preferably with a southerly aspect, as the sides of the valleys are often so steep as to shut off the sun from the southern side. The sheltered alluvial lands of the valley produce such crops as hay, wheat, barley, potatoes, and rye, which are stored for winter use in one of the numerous wooden buildings which make up the farmstead. In some of the deepest valleys the lower slopes are terraced for the cultivation of vines. Above these the steep slopes are often clothed with coniferous trees, which provide timber for fuel, for building purposes, and for industries. But great care is taken lest the forests be depleted, since they help to protect the villages from destructive avalanches. In some districts, indeed, people are not allowed to keep goats, since these destroy young saplings.

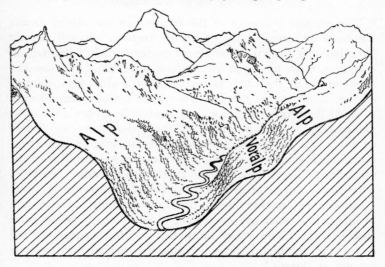

FIG. 57. BLOCK DIAGRAM OF A GLACIATED VALLEY

Between the steep edge of the over-deepened valley and the foot of the high peaks, are the gently sloping 'shoulders' which the Swiss call 'alps.' For a few months in summer these 'alps' are free from snow; bathed in bright sunshine, and fertilized by mud-laden streams which are fed by the melting snow and ice, they are quickly clothed with rich grass and nutritious flowering plants, which form excellent pasturage for cattle. To these summer pastures the Swiss peasants take their cattle in June. They stay with them for two or three months, living in roughly built wooden huts, where milk is made into butter and cheese, as in the Norwegian saeter.

In many valleys there is an intermediate shelf known as the 'mayen,' or 'voralp' between the real 'alp' and the valley floor; there the cattle make a short stay on their upward journey in May, and on their downward journey in September.

FARMING IN SWITZERLAND

The general character of the farming in the *Alpine portion* has been indicated in the preceding section. It will already have become clear that the chief 'money crop' of this region —as it is of the whole of Switzerland—is milk. The summer food-supply of the cattle is assured by the abundant pastures of the 'alps,' so the chief efforts of the farmers are directed towards the production of winter foodstuffs. Hay is the most valued crop, and the peasant often faces great danger to secure an extra bale. Tiny natural meadows, situated on almost inaccessible ledges on the mountain sides, are harvested with the scythe or sickle, and the hay slung down to the valley below by wire ropes, or transported by sledges after the first fall of snow.

Another interesting feature of Alpine farming is the system of irrigation practised in certain valleys which suffer from lack of rain. The water from the melting glaciers is led down the mountain sides in wooden tunnels or troughs known as 'bisses.'

An important factor in Alpine farming is the *Föhn*, a warm dry wind which blows down the Alpine valleys, most frequently in spring. The wind originates on the southern side of the Alps, and is drawn northward towards low-pressure areas in central Europe. As it rises up the mountain sides it is robbed of its moisture, and though it is temporarily cooled by expansion, it gains a considerable amount of 'latent heat' which is liberated when water vapour condenses. This latent heat, added to the heat the wind regains on its descent, makes the Föhn very warm when it blows down the Swiss valleys. Its beneficial effects are seen in the way in which it 'eats up' the snow, without any apparent melting, thus laying bare the mountain pastures and extending the grazing period by several weeks. On the other hand, the Föhn brings added dangers

Schneiter, Thun

THE VILLAGE OF MÜNSTER, CENTRAL SWITZERLAND

German Railways

A CLOVER-LEAF CROSSING ON A NEW GERMAN HIGHWAY

to many Swiss valleys, since it is responsible for the starting of many destructive avalanches. So numerous are these in certain districts that the peasants dare not build their houses in the main valleys which are specially subject to the Föhn, but live in villages situated in the side valleys.

The Swiss Plateau. This is, naturally, the most productive part of Switzerland. As the plateau has an elevation between 1,200 feet and 3,000 feet above sea-level, and as its general slope is towards the north, 'cool-weather' crops, such as hay, barley, rye, oats, and potatoes, predominate. Some wheat is also grown, but not in sufficient quantities to meet home requirements. Vines are grown on sheltered, sunny slopes around lakes Geneva and Neuchâtel.

The characteristic farm-house of the Swiss plateau is a four-square building, which has a steeply pitched roof of thatch descending nearly to the ground on all sides. 'The house is protected by its roof on all sides; there are nowhere any large clear spaces. If we walk around it we can catch only a glimpse of the bottom of the door, or here and there the beginning of a window between the bare line of the roof and the ground.' —Brunhes, *Human Geography.*

Such a house is obviously well designed for a region where the winters are cold and wet, with frequent falls of snow.

The Jura. As these mountains are composed mainly of limestone, the soil is generally too thin and the slopes too dry for agriculture. Consequently pastoral farming is the chief occupation, and condensed milk and cheese are the chief sources of income. Many of the mountain sides are covered with pine-trees, and lumbering is one of the chief sources of livelihood.

SWITZERLAND AS A MANUFACTURING COUNTRY

We so often see pictures of Swiss pastures and mountain chalets that we are apt to assume that nearly all the working people of Switzerland are farmers. Actually, little more than a quarter of the working people are engaged in farming, while

nearly twice as many are engaged in various manufacturing industries. Again, the foreign trade per head is larger in Switzerland than in any other continental country except Denmark, and
this obviously implies a high degree of industrial development.

At first sight it may seem that Switzerland lacks all the advantages possessed by other manufacturing nations: she has no
coal, practically no minerals, and produces very little raw
material of any kind; transport is costly on account of her
distance from the sea and her lack of navigable rivers; she has
no colonies, the population of the country (5,000,000) is too
small to form a large home market, and the populous countries
around her naturally prefer to use their own manufactured
goods. Yet, in spite of these difficulties, Switzerland has
become an important manufacturing country. In modern
times the utilization of hydro-electricity derived from her
numerous waterfalls has given her cheap and abundant power,
while her situation in the middle of Europe has made her the
centre of a network of railway routes which put her in touch
with markets in many countries.

But industries flourished in Switzerland before the use of
electricity, and even before the building of railways. The
early rise of her manufacturing industries was largely due to
her independence and her neutrality. In the sixteenth and
seventeenth centuries religious refugees from France and Italy
settled in the country, and established such characteristic industries as the manufacture of watches and silk. Her policy of
peace made it possible for these industries to develop and find
markets in countries which were frequently engaged in wars.

In spite of these historical advantages, however, Swiss industries could never have survived if they had been directed
towards the production of heavy, low-priced articles, which
would be costly to transport. Instead, she has specialized in
industries in which much time and labour are expended on a
small amount of raw material, so that transport adds very little
to the cost of the finished article. In fact, the Swiss export
labour rather than *material*.

Textiles. In these, as in all other Swiss manufactures, the chief characteristic is high quality based on the efficiency of both workpeople and machinery.

Cotton manufacturing is carried on chiefly in the north-east, silk in Zürich and Basle, and rayon (artificial silk) at Lucerne.

Engineering. The chief specializations are the manufacture of electrical apparatus, motors, Diesel engines, rack-and-pinion locomotives, and machinery for the textile industries.

Watch-making is one of the oldest of the Swiss industries, having been established at Geneva in the sixteenth century by French refugees. From there it has spread over the Jura district, and as far as Basle and Schaffhausen. Formerly most of the work was carried on in the homes of the people, but now it is done almost entirely in factories. In a normal year about twenty million watches, in addition to clocks and parts of watches, are exported, chiefly to the United States of America and Great Britain.

The Chemical Industry is a direct result of the abundance of electrical power, which is used for the manufacture of nitrates and many other chemical compounds. As in Scandinavia electrical furnaces are used for the smelting of aluminium, and for the manufacture of high-grade steel.

The Preparation of Foodstuffs. The pictures of Alpine pastures which we so often see in advertisements of chocolate, cheese, and condensed milk, leave us in no doubt that the preparation of these is one of the chief industries of Switzerland. More than a third of all the milk produced in the country is exported in a condensed form, while another third is used in the manufacture of cheese and butter.

THE ALPINE PASSES

Although the Alps are the highest and broadest range of mountains in Europe, they have never formed a complete barrier between peoples, and various passes have been used from the earliest times as lines of communication between the lands to north and south of the ranges. (See Fig. 40, p. 141.)

The *Great St. Bernard* (8,120 feet), the most westerly of the Swiss Alpine passes, is famous for its hospice from which St. Bernard dogs were sent out to rescue snowbound travellers. The pass provides a route from the Rhône valley to the Dora Baltea, and so to the plain of northern Italy. The route was in frequent use even before the days of the Romans, and remained until modern times one of the most important ways over the Alps, although the carriage road through the pass was only completed in 1905. The pass is not utilized by a railway tunnel, but a road tunnel carrying a motor highway was completed in 1962.

The *Simplon Pass* (6,600 feet), which leads from the Upper Rhône valley to Lake Maggiore, was little used in early times, probably because the path through it was difficult and dangerous. In 1801, however, Napoleon constructed a military road through the pass, which therefore acquired considerable importance.

In 1906 the railway tunnel under the pass was opened, and the Simplon thus became one **of the** great international routes of Europe. The Simplon tunnel itself is only one of a series of eighty, many of them in the form of a spiral, which had to be constructed in the Alpine portion of the railway.

The *St. Gothard Pass* (6,930 feet) leads from the Upper Reuss valley to the Ticino, and provides the most direct route between the Rhine valley and northern Italy. 'One great physical drawback the St. Gothard has, however, always suffered from, and that, no doubt, accounts for the relatively late appearance of the pass in history—the valleys of the Reuss and the Ticino are very rugged and very narrow, and so the tracks through them were exposed to great dangers, though to realize this nowadays one must not content oneself with merely sitting in a through train from Lucerne to Milan, but cross the pass on foot. These obstacles could only be overcome by the aid of time and patience, but when overcome, the prosperous future of the pass was secured. Its fortunes, too, have had an enormous influence on those of Lucerne, its starting point on the north, for the opening of the mule path (about 1293), of the carriage road (1820–30), and of the tunnel (1882) have marked successive great steps forward in the commercial importance of that town.'—W. A. B. Coolidge, *The Alps in Nature and History.*

THE CITIES OF SWITZERLAND

The three obvious natural gateways into Switzerland are those via the Lower Rhine valley, Lake Constance, and Lake Geneva. At each of these points a great town has grown up —Basle at the great bend of the Rhine, Geneva and Constance on their respective lakes. The last-named town is in Germany, but St. Gallen, a little to the south of the lake, may be taken as the third of the Swiss gateway towns.

Basle is situated at one of the great cross-roads of Europe, where the north to south route from the Rhine valley to Italy crosses the east to west route via the Upper Rhine and the Burgundian Gate. It was a strong military post in the Roman period, and throughout succeeding centuries has been an important trading and manufacturing centre. Though the Rhine below this point is obstructed by shallows and rapids, Basle has considerable river traffic, and is, indeed, the only notable 'port' of Switzerland. Its facilities for both trade and manufacture will be considerably increased by the construction of the Grand Canal of Alsace. This will not only make Basle the head of normal navigation of the Rhine valley, but will also supply ample hydro-electricity, which will be generated at the great weirs on the canal.

Berne was originally a fortress town, built on a rocky headland within a great bend of the River Aar. Its people often took the lead in the struggle for freedom, and as it is fairly centrally situated, and near the dividing line between the German- and French-speaking peoples, it was chosen as the capital of the country.

Geneva is an excellent example of towns which grew up because of the facilities for defence and for trade. It is situated on a hill between the lake shore, the River Rhône, and its tributary, the Arve; it controls the Rhône Gate between the Alps and the Jura; its situation at the end of the lake and at the natural bridge-place of the Rhône has added considerably to its importance as a route centre. As a frontier town it was a favourite refuge for political and religious exiles from surrounding countries. To such immigrants it owes two of its chief industries—printing and watch-making—and a good deal of its cosmopolitan character. Among the 'exiles' who made their home in Geneva, the most famous was Calvin, the Protestant reformer of the sixteenth century.

Zürich is by far the largest town in Switzerland. Situated where the route along the northern edge of the Alps crosses the River Limmat at its exit from Lake Zürich, it is a natural focal centre. In modern times transport facilities and abundant supplies of hydro-electricity have aided the development of industries, and it is now one of the world's largest silk-manufacturing cities, and has also numerous cotton mills and machine shops.

St. Gallen is noted as the chief centre of the cotton industry.

Lucerne is one of the most picturesque of the Swiss towns. The influence of the St. Gothard Pass on the development of the town has already been noted, but its chief fame is due to its convenience as a centre for tourists and Alpine climbers.

St. Moritz, the famous 'winter sports' centre, is situated at a height of nearly 6,000 feet at the head of the Engadine, or valley of the Inn. The Engadine electric railway, which connects it with Chur, in the valley of the Vorder Rhein, is one of the world's most remarkable feats of railway engineering. In the last twenty-four miles the average gradient is one in twenty-nine, and in the final ridge separating the Rhine basin from the Inn valley three spiral tunnels had to be constructed in order that this gradient should not be exceeded.

EXERCISES

1. In what ways does Switzerland resemble and differ from (*a*) Norway, (*b*) Holland?

2. 'Nature does not *compel* men to adopt certain ways of life; she merely provides the opportunities.' Discuss this statement in regard to Switzerland.

3. 'Much of Switzerland's trade is transit trade.' Say what is meant by this, and why Switzerland has so much of this trade.

4. The following commodities figure prominently in the lists of both imports and exports of Switzerland: cotton goods, silk goods, animal food substances. Can you explain this?

5. Of the total area of Switzerland 22 per cent is unproductive, 22 per cent is forest, 41 per cent is grassland and pasture, and 12 per cent is arable land. Draw a diagram, preferably on squared paper, to show these facts, and explain why these three classes of land make up so large a percentage of the surface.

6. 'If it were not for the avalanches, the Swiss Alps would be colder and the Swiss peasants would be poorer.' Explain this.

GERMANY

How the Country Grew

To understand Germany of to-day we must know something of the way in which it has grown up.

Shortly after the fall of the Roman Empire a confederacy of German tribes, known as Franks, made themselves masters of a large part of western Europe. Their greatest ruler, and one of the greatest men of all time, was Charlemagne, who became King of the Franks in 768. In the west he extended his dominions beyond the Pyrenees; in the east he conquered the Bavarian and Saxon tribes, and so severely defeated the Northmen as to divert their attacks to Britain and other less well-defended lands; in the south his sway extended over Switzerland and the greater part of Italy. Realizing the power of the Roman Church, and the assistance which the bishops could give him in controlling his vast dominions, he defended the Pope against the Roman citizens and in reward was proclaimed 'Roman Emperor.'

On the death of Charlemagne (814) his empire was divided into three parts: a western portion which eventually became France, an eastern portion which was the basis of modern Germany, and a 'middle kingdom,' embracing the 'corridor' of the Rhine and the Rhône, as well as northern Italy. (Fig. 58.) Though this 'middle kingdom' was too long and narrow to survive, it was difficult to divide it fairly between France and Germany; indeed much of the enmity that has existed between these two countries has been due to their rival claims to the 'corridor-land' of the Rhine.

The eastern half of Charlemagne's empire broke up into a number of feudal states, each practically independent, though acknowledging the overlordship of one king. In the middle of the tenth century one such overlord, fearing the power of his

vassals, sought the friendship of the Pope, who crowned him
'Emperor of Rome.' Thus was established the 'Holy Roman
Empire,' which lasted until 1806. There was, however, little
unity within the Empire, and as we turn over the pages of an

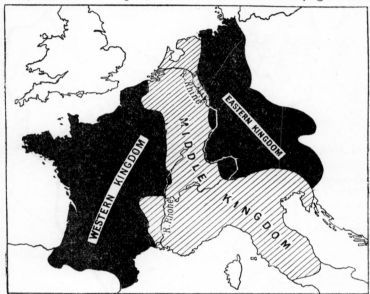

FIG. 58. HOW CHARLEMAGNE'S EMPIRE WAS DIVIDED AT HIS DEATH

historical atlas we see Germany represented by a maze of small
states which make the maps look like intricate jig-saw puzzles.
Perhaps the chief cause of the survival of these small states was
the lack of communication. In the north the land was largely
covered with forests, which formed a barrier between the
various states; and in the south were many semi-isolated basins,
separated from each other by forests and ridges of high land.

Among the strongest of the constituent states of the empire
were those on the eastern border, where the Germans were in
frequent conflict with the Slavs and other peoples. Instead of
building walls, as the Romans had done to keep out the

I   E

barbarians, the Germans set up border states or 'marks,' whose
special duty it was to guard the empire, and extend German
power eastward. (See Figs. 59, 60.) It was, therefore, necessary for the rulers of the 'marks' to maintain an efficient

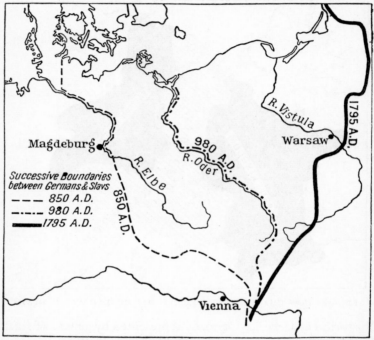

FIG. 59. HOW THE GERMANS EXPANDED AT THE EXPENSE OF THE SLAVS

army, and as each new conquest increased their territory and
military strength, certain of them eventually became very
powerful. Thus the Mark of Brandenburg was the nucleus
from which the modern State of Prussia developed, while the
Austrian dukes, who had to fight against the Turks and
Magyars, became so powerful that they held the crown of
the Holy Roman Empire for several centuries.

During the latter part of the nineteenth century Germany

developed her industries, agriculture, and commerce at a very
rapid rate. Her three great coal-fields of the Ruhr basin,
Silesia, and the Saar basin, not only provided for her own

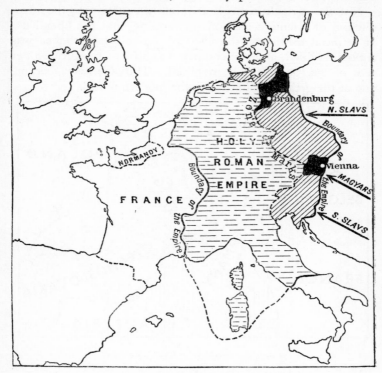

FIG. 60. WESTERN EUROPE, A.D. 1100
(Note the 'marks' which eventually grew into Prussia and Austria)

needs, but also produced a large surplus for export. Thus
her ships could go out laden with coal, coke, and manufactured
goods, and bring home the raw materials required for her
industries. In addition to her supplies of coal, she had large
deposits of iron ore, potash, and other minerals, while abroad
she gained tropical colonies which provided her with many
raw materials. Railways and canals were constructed to link

up her mining and manufacturing districts with each other
and with the sea, and her business men built up industrial
organizations which were a model of efficiency.

Nor was agriculture neglected; on the contrary, by the introduction of scientific methods of farming, and the liberal use
of artificial fertilizers, the yield of agricultural produce was
almost doubled, and the country was able to produce 80 per
cent of the foodstuffs she required. Thus Germany became
one of the greatest countries of the modern world.

FIG. 61. WEST AND EAST GERMANY

Unfortunately, there is another side to the story. German
unity had been largely achieved through her military might
and, in attempts to extend her territory and power, she engaged
in the two world wars of 1914–18 and 1939–45. After her
total defeat in the Second World War she lost all the territory
east of the Oder to Poland, while the remainder of the country
was divided into two separate states—the totalitarian Communist state of East Germany and the democratic republic of
West Germany. *Berlin* lies in the eastern division of the

country, but is itself divided into an eastern zone under Communist rule, and a western zone under the supervision of the Western Powers. (See Fig. 61.)

By the post-war division of the country West Germany retained most of the fertile farm land, the mineral deposits, and the industrial resources of the formerly united country, and is, therefore, far more highly developed than East Germany. Nevertheless, as there is no natural line of division between them the two states may most conveniently be studied together as one geographical area.

THE NATURAL DIVISIONS OF GERMANY

The physical map shows that Germany consists of two well-marked physical divisions, namely, the great plain of the north, and the highlands of the south.

In each of these divisions, however, there is considerable diversity of life and work; so if we wish to make an adequate survey of Germany it will be necessary to subdivide each of these large regions.

Before considering these regions in detail, however, it will be well to note certain aspects of the country as a whole. In the first place it will be seen from the climatic maps that Germany is divided into two almost equal portions by the $32°$ F. January isotherm, the western half being generally ice-free in winter, while the eastern half is generally ice-bound during January. Thus Germany is a passage-land between the equable West-European type and the extreme continental interior type. Again, if we study a map showing actual average temperatures, instead of sea-level isotherms, we shall see that there is not a great deal of difference between northern and southern Germany, the reason being that in southern Germany the increase of temperature due to a more southerly latitude is counteracted by the greater elevation. The deep valleys, such as that of the Rhine and the Main, are, however, sheltered from cold winds, and consequently enjoy a much warmer climate than the rest of Germany.

THE SOUTHERN HIGHLANDS AND BASINS

Southern and central Germany is a complex region which was formerly divided into several separate states.

The *Bavarian Plateau*, situated between the Alps and the Danube, corresponds in structure to the Swiss Plateau between the Alps and the Rhine. Both plateaus were built by sediments laid down in the inland sea which once extended round the northern side of the Alps from the Rhône valley to the plains of Austria and Hungary. The Bavarian Plateau is, however, much less fertile than the corresponding Swiss Plateau, for much of the surface is covered with marsh, peat-bogs, and coarse gravel. Pastoral farming predominates, though rye, oats, and wheat are grown, while certain districts are specially noted for the cultivation of hops.

Munich, the capital of Bavaria, is situated on a patch of gravel between marshes to the north and forest to the south. It is almost in the centre of the plateau, and so has become the chief railway centre of southern Germany, being situated at the junction of the Brenner Pass route from Italy and the main route from Paris to south-eastern Europe.

Munich is essentially a modern city, with fine wide streets and handsome public buildings which emphasize its status as a regional metropolis. Hydro-electricity, generated at the foot of the Alps, has enabled the city to become a great industrial centre, specializing in the manufacture of scientific apparatus, motors, glass, and leather goods. Another staple industry is the brewing of beer from hops grown in the surrounding district.

Nürnberg (Nuremberg) is situated in a broad gap in the hills and at the head of navigation of a small tributary of the Main; in the Middle Ages it was the chief road centre of southern Germany, and in modern times has become one of the principal railway centres of the region. It is noted as the centre of many industries whose products are characterized by high value in proportion to their bulk, e.g. toys, glassware, and electrical apparatus.

Regensberg (Ratisbon) is situated at the limit of barge navi-

gation on the Danube and first became important as the point
where goods left that river to be transported overland to the
navigable tributaries of the Main.   In the nineteenth century
a small barge canal was built from Ratisbon to Bamberg on the
Main, and several locks are now being constructed, to
enable 1,500-ton vessels to ply between the Rhine and the
Danube.

The Black Forest and the *Neckar Valley*.   Formerly nearly
the whole of Germany, like most of northern and central
Europe, was covered with trees; but while the lowlands have
generally been cleared, the forests have been preserved on
the highlands.   The German Government takes great care of
the forests, and whenever a tree is cut down another is planted
to take its place, so that the supply of timber is maintained.
Nearly all the woodland of the Black Forest is State-owned,
and is kept in order by a corps of State foresters.   At frequent
intervals are well-marked paths linking up the villages, providing 'hiking' routes for picnickers and tourists.

Lumbering is one of the chief industries of the region.
'The pines are sawn a little above the roots and then con-
veyed to the nearest stream.   Here they are pierced and tied
together with willow roots, in rows from four to ten at a time,
thus forming a raft.   When thirty or forty lengths of pine trees
have been so added, a hollowed tree trunk is fixed to the foremost to act as a bow, and the last section of the raft is fitted
with a rudder.   Then the unique craft is launched to float
down the stream.   Long before it reaches the Rhine, however,
other rafts have been added, so that it becomes a floating
village, with huts built upon it.   In the early stages of the voyage it is navigated by men with long poles, but when it comes to
the Rhine a tug is attached.'—C. Marlowe, *The Black Forest*.

In spite of the predominance of forest, there are many large
clearings with pleasant villages situated in the midst of fertile
fields.   The picturesque farm-houses are usually built of wood,
with wide overhanging roofs enclosing both dwelling-house
and farm buildings.   The ground floor is usually reserved for

the stock, but in the poorer farms the animals frequently share the living quarters of the family during the cold winter.

The Black Forest peasants have long been famous for their domestic industries, and the manufacture of clocks of various types is still carried on at Triberg, though the work is now done in factories instead of in the home as formerly. The manufacture of mouth-organs is another important industry, and near the Swiss border are many textile factories run by hydro-electric power. The valley of the *Neckar* is a fertile, densely peopled district, in which both agriculture and industry are highly developed. Factories run by hydro-electricity are frequently to be seen among the fertile fields and vineyards, and many of the factory workers are also small-holders. The valley also forms an important highway, linking the Rhine valley with the Danube; it is utilized by the main express route from Paris to south-eastern Europe.

Stuttgart owes its importance more to human factors than to great advantages of site. It is situated, not in the main valley of the Neckar, but in a side valley, and the line from Paris to Vienna has had to leave the Neckar valley and make a long loop in order to touch Stuttgart at all. Yet, because it was chosen as the capital of the State of Württemberg, it grew rapidly in importance, and has become the chief industrial and commercial centre of the Neckar basin. Partly because of the traditions of craftsmanship, and partly because of the distance from the coal-fields, Stuttgart, like many other cities of south Germany, specializes in the production of articles requiring much expenditure of skill and labour, rather than large quantities of raw materials, e.g. pianos, clocks, and optical instruments.

The Basin of the Main. The rocks in this region belong to the system which is known as the *Trias* since it is composed of three types of rock—sandstone, limestone, and clay. The sandstone generally forms forested ridges; the limestone, though suffering somewhat from lack of water, forms rich agricultural lowlands and hill slopes which are terraced for vines; the clay forms intensively cultivated basins producing hops, tobacco, flax, and fruit.

Bamberg is noteworthy as the terminus of the Main-Danube canal through Nürnberg to Regensberg.

Frankfurt owes its importance to its situation at the meeting-point of many routes. (See Fig. 62.) During the Middle

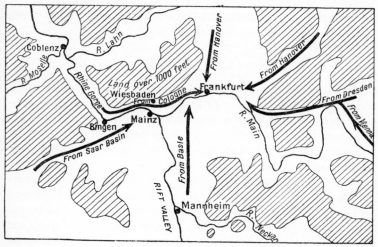

FIG. 62. THE POSITION OF FRANKFURT

Ages this convergence of routes made it the centre at which the Electors from all parts of Germany met to choose the Holy Roman Emperor. In modern times its situation at the focus of routes by road, rail, and river, and the productivity of the surrounding country, have made it one of the greatest industrial and commercial centres of Germany.

The Weser Basin. The upper part of the basin of the Weser, like that of the Main, is composed of Triassic rocks.

Numerous valleys, such as those of the Werra and Fulda, which unite to form the Weser, provide ways across the highlands, both from west to east and from north to south. In the Middle Ages many little states arose in this district, each centred on some castle which controlled a particular route. Even to-day the political map of this region is more confusing than that of any other part of Germany. As there is no outstanding route-centre, no one town has grown to be of preponderant importance.

KASSEL (Cassel) situated on the Fulda, not far from its confluence with the Werra, and where an east-to-west route along the edge of the highlands crosses the south-to-north valley route, is the largest town of the region.

Farm Life in Southern and Central Germany

Although Germany is one of the most highly industrialized countries in the world, nearly a quarter of her people earn their living on the land; and to understand the life of Germany we must think not only of the large towns, but also of the innumerable small towns and villages which are dotted over the face of the country.

A journey by road or rail through the country would show us one striking difference between farming in southern Germany and in England. In many districts we should see women working in the tiny, unfenced fields, sowing, weeding, reaping, or even driving the ox team. There are three main reasons for this difference: Many of the farms are too small to make machinery worth while; most of the cultivated crops require hand labour; and in some areas it is customary for the men to work in the near-by factories during the day. The farmers in southern and central Germany aim first at producing all the food required by their families and farm stock, and then at the production of a 'money' crop for sale. The almost universal food crops are rye, wheat, potatoes, oats, beans, lentils, etc., while the 'money' crop varies according to climatic and other conditions, e.g. vines on the sunny slopes of the river valleys, and hops on the richer lands of Bavaria.

The typical German farm-house, like the German farm, is self-contained. The first storey is usually built of stone, and contains stable, cowshed, store rooms, and the family living-room. Higher storeys resemble the old English frame house, as they are usually formed of a framework of wooden beams filled in with rubble, brick, or stone. Throughout southern and central Germany such farm-houses are to be found grouped in small villages, which form almost self-sufficing communities. Each village has its blacksmith, its butcher, its shoemaker, etc., and there are many small workshops specializing in the production of articles requiring the expenditure of much labour and skill on small amounts of raw material. Even large factories are often situated in country districts, and the employees may live in the family farm-house and assist in the farm work after their factory labour is over.

THE MARGINAL MINING AND MANUFACTURING BELT

The marginal zone between the Southern Highlands and the Northern Plain is one of the most densely peopled parts of Germany. Within this belt are many of the largest cities of Germany—Cologne, Hanover, Brunswick, Magdeburg, Halle, Leipzig, and Dresden. Such towns would naturally originate as markets for the exchange of the products of the hills and the plains, but in each case growth into a large city has been determined by special advantages. Thus Cologne owes much of its importance to its situation at the head of sea navigation on the Rhine; Hanover commands the Westphalian Gate; Leipzig is at the focus of many converging valley routes; Dresden lies on the navigable River Elbe, near the foot of the gorge by which the river leaves the Ore Mountains.

Again, nearly all the mining and manufacturing areas of Germany are situated in this marginal belt. Fig. 63 shows the position of the chief industrial areas of central and western Europe.

(1) *Saxony*. The great 'bay' of low land which lies to the north of the Ore Mountains and the Thuringian Forest (see Fig. 63) is one of the most densely peopled parts of Germany.

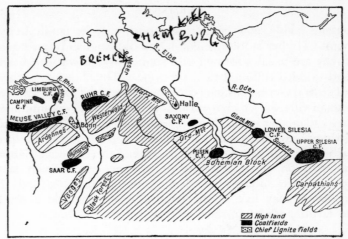

FIG. 63. THE COAL-FIELDS OF GERMANY AND NEIGHBOURING REGIONS
('The coal-fields of Europe are situated on the edge of the high land,
and near navigable waterways')

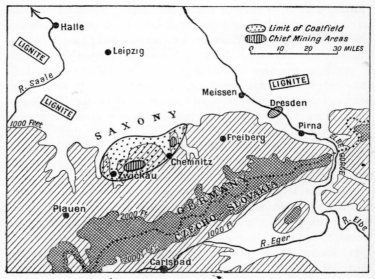

FIG. 64. THE SAXONY INDUSTRIAL REGION

Industries arose there at an early date, partly because the Ore Mountains were formerly very rich in silver and tin, and partly because the numerous sheep which were reared on the hillsides provided wool for domestic woollen manufactures. Though the Ore Mountains do not now yield minerals, and Saxony is not specially noteworthy as a sheep-rearing area, industries which were formerly based on the local supplies of raw materials continue to flourish.   One reason is that when the mines ceased to be productive the inhabitants of the mountain valleys were faced with a choice between starvation, migration, and the establishment of new industries.   Lacking raw materials, they turned their attention to industries in which skill would overcome this handicap, and began to manufacture such things as toys, clocks, lace, etc., whose value is great in proportion to the amount of raw material which they contain. In the lowlands of Saxony, on the other hand, modern industrial development has been based on the small coal-field near *Zwickau*.   Textiles, metal goods, glass, and chemicals are manufactured in a densely peopled belt which stretches along the foot of the hills from *Plauen* in the west to *Chemnitz* in the east.   (Fig. 64.)

In the north-western corner of Saxony are great deposits of brown coal or lignite.   Though the fuel value of lignite is low, it has two advantages: it occurs in great horizontal beds seven to ten feet thick, and only a few feet below the surface; and when heated it gives off much gas and oil, which can be used for the manufacture of ammonia, fertilizers, and other chemicals.   The lignite is not usually transported over long distances, but is used on the spot for the generation of electricity, which can be transmitted cheaply to distant towns and factories.   As Germany lost both the Saar basin coal-field and nearly all that of Upper Silesia as a result of the First World War, she had not enough coal left to supply both her own industries and the large amounts which she had to send to France and Italy as part of the war indemnity.   Her chemists, therefore, devised means of using her large deposits of lignite for industrial purposes, and were so successful that lignite is now one of the most important industrial resources of both West and East Germany.

Dresden is situated just below the gorge by which the Elbe breaks through the Ore Mountains. It was chosen as the capital of Saxony partly because of its strategic importance, and partly because of the scenic beauty of the surroundings. As the capital its commercial importance developed rapidly, and its industries, like those of most capitals, are concerned mainly with the manufacture of luxuries and articles of high quality, such as lace, clocks, porcelain, perfumes, gold and silver articles, and musical instruments.

Leipzig stands in the centre of a 'bay' of low land, at the point to which routes converge from all directions. Leipzig Fair, which is still of importance, is a survival from the days when exchange of goods was difficult, and it was necessary to arrange for them to be brought to some central market at a given date. The most notable industry of Leipzig, the printing of books, owes its origin to the fact that one of the earliest and most vigorous of the German universities was founded there.

(2) *The Harz region*. The Harz Mountains formerly yielded much copper, lead, and silver. Some copper is still obtained, and the region is important for various metal industries. The great steelworks of *Salzgitter* are based on local iron ore, which is smelted by coke brought by canal from the Ruhr.

Stassfurt is the centre for the mining of potash and other salts, which, though now covered by thousands of feet of rock, were formed millions of years ago by the drying up of inland seas. These salts have been of great service to both the agricultural and manufacturing industries in Germany. On the one hand they form valuable fertilizers, the extensive use of which has transformed the naturally barren German Plain into highly productive agricultural lands; and on the other hand they form the basis of great chemical industries which are centred in such towns as *Magdeburg* and *Halle*.

(3) *The Ruhr*. This area, with abundant supplies of coking coal and easy access to raw materials, has become the greatest industrial region on the continent. The Ruhr coal-field, which lies to the north of the Sauerland plateau and between the rivers Ruhr and Lippe, produced about three-quarters of Germany's total supplies of coal. Strange as it may seem, the chief coal-mining areas are not now within the coal-field as shown on a map of the rocks. The reason will be understood

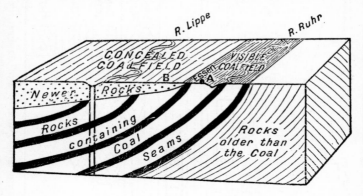

FIG. 65. BLOCK DIAGRAM SHOWING 'VISIBLE' AND 'CONCEALED' COAL-FIELDS

from Fig. 65. The coal-seams dip down towards the north, and the best seams are covered by newer rocks. The area over which the coal-seams come to the surface is called the 'visible' coal-field, and it is this which is shown on most maps. But to the north of this is the 'concealed' coal-field, where, although the seams do not come to the surface, coal can be obtained by boring down through the newer rocks. Coal-mining began in the Ruhr valley, since there the seams could be seen at the surface. But it was soon realized that shafts farther north, on the concealed coal-field, would pass through more and better seams, and so new pits were opened in that district. The chief coal-mining area is in the valley of the Emscher, which lies between the Ruhr and the Lippe, and

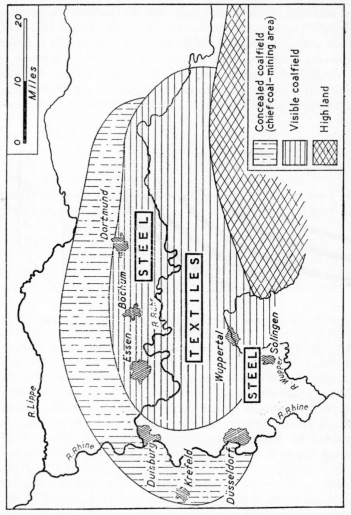

FIG. 66. THE RUHR: MINING AND MANUFACTURING

several deep pits have been opened in the latter valley. The situation is thus very similar to that in the South Yorkshire coal-field, where Doncaster, though lying far to the east of the visible coal-field, has recently become an important mining centre.

The iron industry of the Ruhr first arose on the basis of local ore, but this very soon became quite inadequate and modern industrial development was based on the local coal, iron ore from Lorraine, Sweden, and Spain, locally generated hydro-electricity, and various raw materials assembled by an intricate system of road, rail, and canal transport.

In the northern part of the region, between the rivers Ruhr and Lippe, is an almost continuous line of towns—Essen, Bochum, Dortmund, etc.—which are engaged in various types of engineering. To the south of the Ruhr, and outside the coal-mining area is the highly industrialized valley of the Wupper, where the twin towns of Elberfeld and Barmen (now united as one town under the name of Wuppertal) specialize in the manufacture of textiles. The industry owed its origin to local supplies of wool and water power, but modern industrial development has been based on imported raw materials, coal from the Ruhr, and hydro-electricity generated at dams on the Sauerland plateau. Farther down the valley of the Wupper is Solingen, which specializes in the manufacture of cutlery, an industry which first developed on the basis of local iron-ore, water power, timber for charcoal, and gritstone for grind-stones (cf. Sheffield).

The ports on the Rhine serving the industrial region are Düsseldorf and Duisburg, the latter being situated at the point where an important canal from the River Ems joins the Rhine.

K   E

THE NORTHERN PLAIN

Northern Germany owes many of its characteristic surface
features to the action of ice.   During the glacial period the ice
sheet advanced southward as far as the edge of the highlands.
When the climate improved the southern edge of the ice sheet
melted first, but there were long periods during which it was

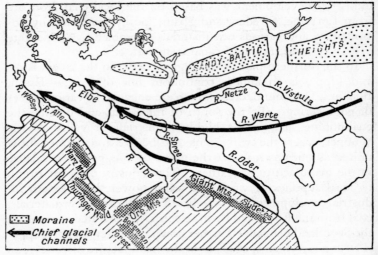

FIG. 67. THE GERMAN-POLISH PLAIN

more or less stationary, forming a great wall of ice across
central Germany.   The rivers could not flow northward over
this ice barrier, but were diverted towards the west.   When the
ice finally disappeared the channels which had been cut along
the successive edges of the ice sheet still remained, and are now
occupied by parts of the main rivers and by long tributaries
flowing from the east.   (See Fig. 67.)   These troughs have
always facilitated travel from west to east, and in modern times
they have been utilized for the construction of canals, linking
the great rivers of the plain.

The three most important barge-canals of Germany are the

Dortmund–Ems Canal, the Mittelland Canal, and the Hohen-zollern Canal. The first-named connects the Ruhr and Rhine waterways with the port of Emden. The Mittelland Canal, completed in 1938, takes off from the Dortmund–Ems Canal north of Münster and passes by the cities of Hanover and Brunswick to Berlin. The rivers Weser and Elbe are crossed by viaducts, but are also linked to the canal by locks, thus facilitating communication with the ports of Bremen and Hamburg.

From Berlin the waterway is continued eastward to the Oder by the Hohenzollern Canal. For the first sixty miles of its course this canal runs in a practically straight line without a lock, and is carried over marshes and valleys by great aqueducts, being at one point a hundred feet above the surrounding country. Before its junction with the Oder the canal drops a hundred and twenty feet by means of an electrically operated barge elevator—a tray of water into which the barges are floated and then lowered to the river level.

Another effect of the Ice Age is to be seen in the sandy hills of north Germany—the Baltic Heights, which run parallel to the Baltic coast, the Lüneberg Heath to the west of the Elbe, and the Bourtanger Moor on the borders of Holland. These hills are formed of moraine left by the ice sheet, or of sand deposited by streams which flowed from its melting edge.

The Baltic Heights are on the whole sandy and infertile, and large areas are occupied only by heath, woodland, and pine forests which have been planted by the Government. The most fertile areas lie on the northern slopes, in the province of Mecklenburg. Here the land is divided into large estates, and is devoted chiefly to the rearing of cattle, horses, and pigs, and to the cultivation of sugar beet and potatoes. In East Germany a considerable portion of the surface is occupied by lakes which have formed in the hollows of the moraine. Here the formerly privately owned estates have been turned into collective farms of the Russian type.

West of the Elbe the land is more intensively cultivated, and a much larger proportion of the area is in small farms.

In this western half of the plain four types of land surface may be distinguished, viz.:

(a) *The Geest*, forming dry, sandy, infertile uplands, such as the Lüneberg Heath. In recent years large areas, which were formerly desolate wastes, have been transformed into productive farm lands.

(b) *Peat moors*, such as the Bourtanger Moor on the borders of Holland. As in the latter country, large parts of these moors have been reclaimed by the digging of canals which serve for both drainage and transport, and by the removal of the lower layer of peat and the mixing of the sandy subsoil with the upper layer of peat and generous quantities of artificial manures.

(c) *The coastal lowlands*, which are protected from tidal floods by dykes. These lowlands are indeed very similar to the corresponding dyked lands of northern Holland.

(d) *The alluvial valleys*, such as those of the Ems, the Weser, and the Aller, which provide some of the most valuable farm land.

The main portion of the Great Plain, which centres on Berlin, is very varied in character. Some portions, such as those around Frankfurt and Magdeburg, consist of fertile loam, while other parts, such as those around Berlin, are sandy and infertile. Rye is the most widely grown cereal, but wheat and sugar beet are the chief crops of the fertile quadrant south-west of Berlin.

Berlin, like Gothenburg and Leningrad, owes its rise to the action of individuals, rather than to great natural advantages of situation. Built on an island, which facilitated the crossing of the River Spree, it enjoyed some prosperity as a trading centre, but was of little importance until, at the end of the fifteenth century, the elector of Brandenburg built a castle which he and his successors made their home. Even then its development was slow until, two hundred years later, the elector of Brandenburg became king of Prussia, and Berlin became the capital of a powerful country. No effort was spared to improve its connections with the rest of the country, and it became the centre of the canal, road, and railway system of Germany. In spite of difficulties caused by the partition of the country, Berlin is still one of the largest industrial centres of Germany, specializing in the processing of foodstuffs, the manufacture of clothing, furniture, and luxury articles, but above all in the production of electrical equipment and machinery.

Magdeburg, like so many other great cities of Europe, arose where islands in the river afforded facilities for crossing. During the time of Charlemagne, when the Elbe was the approximate boundary between the Germans and the Slavs, it was 'an extreme outpost of Germany'; later it became an important member of the Hanseatic League; and in modern times it has become one of the leading industrial cities. Sugar, the beet for which is supplied by the fertile plain around, and chemicals, for which the salts of Stassfurt are important raw materials, are its chief manufactures. Gloves, chocolate, glass, and pottery are also manufactured there.

Hanover grew up at the crossing of a tributary of the Weser by the great west-to-east route; in modern times it has become one of the chief railway centres of Germany, and the Mittelland Canal which passes through it has made it one of the chief inland ports. Its excellent system of communications and near-by deposits of coal, lignite, oil, and salts fostered the growth of engineering, chemical, and miscellaneous industries.

THE GERMAN COASTS

A curious feature of the **Baltic coast** of Germany is the existence of long, narrow peninsulas, which stretch out towards the north-east. These are sand-spits which were formed partly of sediment brought down by the rivers, and partly of sand which was washed eastward from the headlands by the prevailing westerly winds. Behind these sand-spits are large shallow lagoons, or 'haffs,' as they are called in Germany.

The largest of these, the Frisches Haff, like the Kurisches Haff in Poland, communicates with the sea by a narrow opening at the eastern end. In the course of time the haffs will be filled up with the sediment brought down by the rivers, and so the land will regain what it is now losing by the erosive action of the rivers and the sea.

The Baltic ports of Germany are only of minor importance, since they are somewhat remote from the great highways of world trade, and are often impeded by ice.

Kiel is noteworthy as the eastern terminus of the Kiel Canal. Though the canal is navigable by large ocean liners most vessels prefer to use the slightly longer but toll-free entrance to the Baltic via Copenhagen.

Lübeck, situated at the extreme south-western corner of the Baltic, was Germany's chief port prior to the discovery of America. Nowadays, although connected by canal to the Elbe, it is completely overshadowed by Hamburg, and ranks only as the tenth port of Germany.

The **North Sea coast** of Germany, though only one-third the length of the Baltic coast, is vastly more important, since it faces the busiest sea in the world, is never closed by ice, and is situated near Germany's busiest industrial centres.

Hamburg, despite its destruction in the later stages of the Second World War, has regained its pre-eminence as the chief port of Germany. It illustrates very clearly many of the causes which have led to the development of great commercial cities. (See Fig. 68.)

(1) It was the natural crossing-place and lowest bridge-point of the Elbe, for here firm sandy hills approach the river on both sides, while below this point the river flows through flat alluvial plains, which were formerly marshy and impassable.

(2) It is situated at the farthest point upstream which can be reached by ocean vessels. Above this point the river is split up into a number of small channels, none of which is navigable by ocean steamers.

(3) The small river Alster, which enters the Elbe on the

right bank, provided a safe anchorage for vessels, and in modern times has been utilized for the construction of commodious docks.

(4) The River Elbe forms the centre line of the country, and its south-east to north-west course directs traffic from central Germany and Czechoslovakia towards Hamburg. The post-war partition of Germany has, however, considerably reduced this traffic.

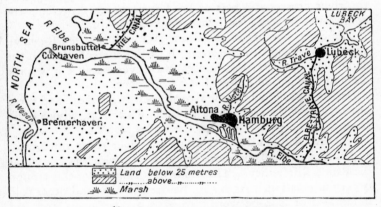

FIG. 68. THE POSITION OF HAMBURG

With all these advantages it is not surprising that Hamburg became the chief port of Germany, conducting, in fact, more than half her total trade.

Bremen on the estuary of the Weser, resembles Hamburg in that it is situated at the lowest bridge-point and at the head of ocean navigation. Though it has the advantage of being nearer the Ruhr than Hamburg, it suffers from the fact that the Weser does not bring down a great volume of trade, and from the shallowness of the lower part of the estuary. Though the channel has been deepened it cannot accommodate the largest ocean steamers, and an outport, Bremerhaven, has been constructed at the mouth of the river.

THE RHINE BASIN

(1) **The Swiss Section.** The Rhine rises near Mount St. Gothard and flows in a deep, picturesque valley north-eastward to Lake Constance. Some thirty miles beyond the exit from this lake the Falls of Schaffhausen mark the place where the river crosses the belt of hard rock which represents the connection between the Swiss and German Jura.

The Swiss portion of the Rhine is now little used for navigation on account of the strength of the current, though the name Schaffhausen (boat-houses) was given because it was the limit of navigation below Lake Constance.

Between Basle, where the river leaves Switzerland and turns northward, is the confluence with the River Aar, whose basin comprises the greater part of the Swiss plateau.

(2) **The Rift Valley.** At Basle the river turns northward and enters a broad, flat-bottomed trough, which is known as the Rhine Rift Valley. The mode of formation of this trough is very interesting. Ages ago, before the Alps and other fold mountains of Europe were formed, a great plateau stretched across the middle of Europe. There was then no Rhine valley, for the Vosges and the Black Forest were parts of a great dome of hard old rock. (See Fig. 69.) The crust of the earth wrinkled, forming the Alps and other ranges. As we saw in the study of Switzerland, tremendous forces were at work in the formation of these folds, and the dome of old rock could not stand the strains that were put upon it. Great cracks or faults were formed across it, and the middle portion sank, forming the great trench which we call the Rift Valley.

At first this 'valley' was an arm of the sea, and later an inland lake; even when it became dry land, the Rhine first flowed westward, between the Vosges and the Jura. Later the valley was tilted down towards the north, and the Rhine began to flow in its present direction. Towards the close of

A = *Campine C.F.*
B = *Limburg C.F.*

Zuyder Zee

Rotterdam *Lek* HOLLAND G E R M A N Y
Waal
Maas
Ruhr Coalfield
R. Ruhr
A
BELGIUM *Düsseldorf* *Sauerland*
B *R. Rhine* IRON
Franco-Belgian C.F. *Cologne*
Bonn *Sieg* *Westerwald*
R. Meuse *R. Lahn*
Coblenz *Taunus* *Frankfurt*
Ardennes *Eifel* *R. Moselle* *Mainz* *R. Main*
Hunsrück *Bingen* *Odenwald*
Saar C.F. *Mannheim*
Lorraine Iron Field *Hardt* *Heidelberg*
R. Rhine *Stuttgart*
Strasbourg *Black Forest* *R. Neckar*
FRANCE *Vosges* *POTASH* *L. of Constance*
Basle
JURA SWITZERLAND *Alps*

| Blocks | Iron | Folds | Coalfields |
0 Miles 40   80   120   160   200   240

FIG. 69. THE RHINE BASIN

*K   E

the Great Ice Age the rivers were swollen by the melting snow and ice, and the floods spread great masses of pebbles over the lowlands. Later, as the land dried out, wind-blown dust was deposited in many parts of the Rift Valley, forming a fertile soil similar to the loess of China. (See Fig. 81, page 290.)

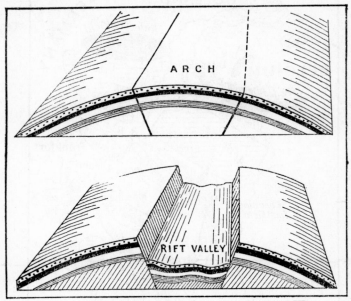

FIG. 70. FORMATION OF A RIFT VALLEY FROM AN ARCH

Each of these events in the physical history of the Rhine has its effect on the geography of the region to-day. The Vosges and the Black Forest fall steeply towards the Rhine, and gradually to France and Germany respectively; the former course of the Rhine westward, now known as the Burgundian or Belfort Gate, is one of the most important gateways into central Europe; the pebbly beds which were deposited at the end of the Ice Age form infertile, thinly peopled areas, while the loess districts are among the most productive areas in the world. (See page 289.)

THE RHINE GORGE, WITH TERRACED SLOPES

The towns in the Rift Valley are generally situated well away from the Rhine at the foot of the high land, so as to avoid the floods to which the valley floor was subject before preventive measures were adopted.

Mulhouse, at the foot of the Vosges, is one of the most important centres of the French textile industry, the power being derived from the rapid streams from the Vosges. In the neighbouring part of Alsace is one of the world's richest deposits of potash.

Freiburg, situated at the foot of the Black Forest where a small stream leaves the high land and enters the Rhine plain, is an ancient city which has also developed textile industries based on the local water power and on raw material brought up the Rhine.

Strasbourg (see page 292), situated at the junction of the River Ill with the Rhine and at the focus of canal, road, and rail communications, is the chief Rhine port of France.

Mannheim, situated at the confluence of the Neckar and the Rhine, was the head of barge navigation on the Rhine before the comparatively recent improvement of the channel as far as Strasbourg. It is still one of the most important of the Rhine ports, and its convenience for assembling raw materials has made it a great industrial centre. It specializes in the manufacture of agricultural machinery, textiles, and glassware.

Ludwigshafen, on the left bank of the Rhine opposite Mannheim, was Germany's chief centre for the manufacture of chemicals and dyes, using coal, potash, and salt assembled by barge and rail.

Mainz, situated near the confluence of the Main and the Rhine, seems to have a better position than many of the cities of the Rhine basin which far exceed it in population. The improvement of the channels of the rivers has, however, allowed water-borne traffic to pass it by, so that it is overshadowed by both Frankfurt and Mannheim.

The Rhine Gorge. Between the Rhine Rift Valley and the

plain of north-western Germany lies a great block of hard old rocks which forms the Lower Rhine Highlands.

The shape of this highland mass resembles that of a butterfly. The 'body' is formed by the deep Rhine Gorge between Bingen and Bonn; the wings are represented by the plateaus of the Hunsrück, Ardennes, Taunus, and Westerwald; and the divisions between the wings are marked by the deep valleys of the Moselle and the Lahn. The gorges through which the rivers Rhine, Moselle, and Lahn flow were not formed by the sinking of the land as in the case of the Rift Valley, but by the rivers cutting down through the hard rocks of the plateau. The Rhine Gorge, which stretches from Bingen to Bonn, is so narrow that in many places it has been difficult to construct road and railway along its sides, and the river itself, instead of meandering across a broad flood plain as it does in the Rift Valley, is often hemmed in between high banks of rock. Much of the charm of this portion of the river is due to the numerous ruined castles which crown the precipitous sides of the valley. Many of these castles were built by German nobles in the Middle Ages as places of refuge, or as strongholds from which they levied toll on passing boats. Among the best known of such castles are the Drachenfels, south of Bonn, the Rheinfels near St. Goar, and the Mouse Tower which guards the entrance to the gorge at Bingen. This last-named tower is the one associated with the legend of Bishop Hatto.

The steep sides of the gorges are frequently terraced for vine growing, while the plateaus consist largely of monotonous stretches of forest, barren moor, and poor pastures. Here the infrequent villages and small towns occupy specially favoured hollows and sheltered valleys, where the cultivation of such cool-weather crops as rye, oats, and potatoes can be carried on. Here and there the rivers have cut through the hard rocks of the plateau, and exposed mineral-bearing strata. The most important of such mining regions is the valley of the *Sieg* where iron ore is obtained. The basin of the *Main* has already been dealt with on page 212.

The *Moselle* is characterized by its deeply cut, narrow valley, and by the numerous S-shaped bends, which enclose spurs of high land. These features detract from the value of both river and valley as highways. There is, too, a great contrast between the forested north-facing slopes and the vine-covered south-facing slopes of the valley.

Coblenz, like Mainz, is a city whose size does not seem commensurate with its natural advantages of situation. But the Moselle is hardly navigable, while the Lahn has only recently been canalized, and even now can accommodate only small vessels.

Bonn, situated where the Rhine Gorge begins to open out to the lowland, is the capital of Western Germany.

Cologne, as its name implies, owes its origin to the establishment there of a Roman 'colonia' or military settlement. The same factors which led the Romans to choose this as the site of one of their most important fortresses have made it important in modern times. It is situated where the Rhine valley opens out to the plain, at the point where the east-to-west route along the edge of the highlands crosses the Rhine, and at the head of sea navigation of the river. It has, therefore, become one of the most important river-ports of Germany, having much trade in wheat, coal, and timber; it is also the market for the densely peopled region around; and, being within easy reach of Ruhr coal, it has developed great industries. These are, however, more concerned with the manufacture of luxuries—chocolate, tobacco, perfumes, etc.—than with the basic necessaries of life.

INDUSTRIAL DISTRICTS OF THE RHINE-MEUSE BASIN

The region drained by the Rhine and the Meuse and their tributaries contains the chief manufacturing districts of Europe. Industrial development has been based on the three great coalfields of the Ruhr, the Saar, and the Meuse valley, and on the iron-field of Lorraine and Luxembourg.

The iron and steel industries of these areas are now closely linked together in the European Coal and Steel Community, which was set up in 1952 to weld the separate industries of France, Luxembourg, Belgium, Netherlands, Western Germany, and Italy into one great organization which forshadowed the Common Market. (See p. 303.) It is, therefore, desirable that these mining regions, and the industrial areas based upon them, should be considered in relation to each other in preparation for more detailed treatment under the heading of the individual countries.

(1) *The Ruhr* (see page 219).

(2) *The Saar Basin.* This region, which takes its name from the Saar tributary of the Moselle, produces some ten million tons of coal per year, or about a quarter the annual output of the Yorkshire coal-field. Though the average density of population in the basin is over 1,000 per square mile there are few large towns, Saarbrücken being the only one with a population over 100,000. 'As in so many mining countries, the towns and villages seem to have congregated along the bottom of the valleys. One drives along the valley road for mile after mile through miners' dwellings, pit-heads, factory chimneys, and all the other signs of intensive industrialization, but the hills on each side are still unspoilt country, much of it woodland.'— B. T. Reynolds, *The Saar.*

The iron and steel industry first grew up on the basis of local ore and charcoal, but now depends on iron from Lorraine and Luxembourg and on coke produced from local coal or brought in from the Ruhr. The characteristic products of the region are the steel sheets, bars, and tubes which represent the 'raw material' of the engineering industries.

Other industries which arose on the basis of local raw materials are the manufacture of glass, pottery, and leather goods.

(3) *The Iron-field of Lorraine and Luxembourg.* This region, which lies almost entirely in the upper basin of the Moselle, is the foremost iron-mining district of Europe and the second largest in the world.

Most of the iron ore is smelted near the centres of production, since it is usually more economical to bring coke to the ore than to take the ore to the coal-field—modern blast furnaces smelt about three tons of ore with one ton of coke. Consequently the iron and steel industries of Lorraine and Luxembourg are dependent on the coke produced in the Ruhr, the Saar, and the Meuse valley coal-field of Belgium. These regions in their turn are among the chief markets for the pig iron and semi-finished iron and steel products of the iron-producing areas. Indeed, the industrial prosperity of the whole of western Europe is largely dependent on the free interchange of coal, coke, pig iron, and the semi-finished iron and steel products.

(4) *The Franco-Belgian Coal-field*. This coal-field lies on the northern edge of the Ardennes, in a similar situation to the Ruhr coal-field on the northern edge of the Sauerland plateau. The western half of the coal-field is in France and provides three-quarters of the total coal output of that country. The Belgian portion consists of a number of separate basins around Mons, Charleroi, and Liège. Modern industrial development in France and Belgium has been chiefly dependent on this coal-field. In the French section large supplies of good coking coal have led to the growth of iron and steel industries, though the iron has to be brought from Normandy and Lorraine. In Belgium the iron and steel industries first arose on the basis of local ore, but is now almost entirely dependent on imports from Lorraine, Luxembourg, Spain, and Sweden. Both the French and Belgian portions of the coal-field are also engaged in textile industries, e.g. cotton and linen at Lille and woollens at Verviers.

(5) *The Campine, Limburg, and Aix-la-Chapelle Coal-fields*. The coal seams which outcrop in the Meuse valley are continued beneath the surface in the Campine district of northeastern Belgium and the Limburg coal-field of south Holland, and reappear at the surface around Aix-la-Chapelle (Aachen). In the Campine and Limburg districts the existence of valuable

seams at a workable depth was known by the beginning of the present century, but mining operations were hindered because the coal is overlain by a great thickness of wet sand which flooded the shafts as they were bored. The difficulty was, however, overcome by artificially freezing the sand, and there are now several highly productive mines in both regions. The Campine coal-field actually contains more coal at a workable depth than does the Belgian part of the Meuse valley field, and will undoubtedly become, in course of time, the chief coal-producing area of Belgium. The Limburg field is the only coal-producing area of Holland, but as it is situated in the extreme south of the country the natural markets for coal are the neighbouring parts of Belgium and the Rhineland.

The Aix-la-Chapelle coal-field produces much good coking coal, which is normally sent to the iron-smelting areas of Lorraine: a further example of the interdependence of the industrial areas of western Europe.

THE RHINE AS A WATERWAY

The Rhine river and the Rhine valley have throughout the ages formed the great highway between the Mediterranean and north-western Europe, and in modern times the river has become the chief inland waterway of the continent.

One of its great advantages from the point of view of navigation is the remarkably small seasonal variation in level in the lower part of its course. The Alpine part of the Rhine from St. Gothard to Basle is fed mainly by melting snow in spring and by melting ice in summer; hence in this section high water occurs in spring and summer and low water in winter. The large tributaries of the middle course of the Rhine—the Neckar, the Main, and the Moselle—are fed chiefly by the winter rains of the highlands; their floods swell the Rhine in winter, just when least water is contributed by the upper Rhine, and in summer their smaller flow is counterbalanced by the greater contribution from the upper Rhine.

The absence of great fluctuations in depth in the lower part of the course, the freedom from ice, the great productivity of the region, and the fact that the river empties into the 'busiest corner of the busiest sea in the world' have all assisted in the development of transport on the Rhine.

Rotterdam, at the mouth of the most navigable distributary of the Rhine, is the greatest seaport of Europe, serving not only Holland and the Rhine basin but also a large part of central Europe. Sea-going steamers, as well as large steam barges, travel to the Ruhr ports of Duisburg and Düsseldorf, and beyond these to Cologne. Above this city traffic is conducted mainly by strings of barges drawn by powerful tugs, though small sea-going vessels can reach Mannheim, at the confluence of the Neckar. Beyond Mannheim navigation is hindered by low water in winter, and even in summer the depth may be as little as six feet; the Canal d'Alsace, from Strasbourg to Basle, now partially completed, will enable navigation to continue throughout the year and will make Basle an important terminal for the Rhine traffic.

Of the major tributaries of the Rhine the Neckar is navigable for 1,000-ton vessels as far as Heilbron, while the Main is navigable for large barges to the terminus of the Main–Danube canal at Bamberg. The Moselle is of minor importance as a highway because of the numerous wide loops of its lower course; but canalization, now in progress, may eventually make it of great importance for the transport of coal and iron ore between the Ruhr and Luxembourg.

THE NETHERLANDS (HOLLAND)

MUCH of the charm of Holland lies in the fact that it possesses so many characteristics which distinguish it from other countries. Thus, when we think of Holland we think also of windmills and canals, low-lying meadows and brightly coloured bulb fields, white-capped dairymaids, wide-trousered fishermen, and so on. Each of these mental pictures has much to tell us of the life of the people and of the way they have made use of Nature's gifts or triumphed over natural handicaps.

How Nature and Man made Holland

The Dutch have a saying, that 'God made the sea, but man made the land,' and we may indeed look upon Holland as a man-made country. When Nature made Holland she merely dumped down mud from the Rhine in the south and west, and sand from melting glaciers in the north and east, leaving one half of the land so swampy and the other half so infertile that man could hardly make any use of it. But Nature's handiwork was not good enough for the Dutch; they were not content to see good mud wasted; and by centuries of patient effort they have driven out the sea, confined the water within limits *they* have chosen, fertilized sterile sands, and made a homeland from Nature's rubbish dumps.

In Roman times practically all the land which is shown on our maps as 'below sea-level' was subject to frequent flooding by the rivers and the sea. Yet men had settled there, and learnt to make some kind of a living on the marshy lands; in times of flood they retired to 'terps' or mounds which they built as refuges. Then, as the marshes began to fill with mud and reeds, so that there was some prospect of making them into good farming land, dykes were built to keep out the high tides. Nature herself suggested the method by the protective barriers of sand dunes which wind and waves had formed along the whole length of the coast, and these dunes were made the basis of the dyke system. At first surplus water could be let out to sea at low tide through sluices in the dykes, but as time went on the land began to sink, so that the dykes had to be raised, and the water pumped out of the enclosed fields. Windmills have been used for this purpose since the fifteenth century, and are still the most striking feature of the Dutch landscape, though in general they have been replaced by more dependable oil- or petrol-driven pumps.

Though in the seventeenth century several fairly large lakes had been pumped dry by the use of windmills, it was not until the introduction of steam pumps in the nineteenth century that the largest lakes could be reclaimed. The most notable addition made to the area of Holland in that century was the former Haarlem Mere, which covered an area of seventy square miles. The work of reclamation was begun in 1848. A dyke was built round the mere, and outside this a high-level canal was constructed to carry off the water which was pumped from the lake by steam engines. In four years the lake was pumped dry; drainage ditches were dug, and pumps installed to prevent the reclaimed land from again becoming water-logged; then the land was ploughed by horses shod with broad pieces of wood to prevent their sinking in the mire; special plants were set to draw the salt out of the soil; and in a few years prosperous farms grew up where Dutch and Spanish fleets had fought three centuries before. The total cost of the scheme was a million pounds—a small fraction of the value of crops since reaped. During the last hundred years over four hundred square miles of land have been reclaimed, mainly by such 'dry makings' as that just described.

But it is not only the low-lying land which as been reclaimed. In the north-eastern provinces of Drenthe and Groningen are large stretches of peat bog and heather moors overlying sandy deposits which were left by the retreating ice sheet. In its natural condition this land is practically useless, but by a process involving almost as much labour as the reclamation of the polder land, large parts of it have been rendered fertile. The peat, which is often ten feet thick, occurs in two layers overlying the sand. In the process of reclamation canals are first dug to serve the double purpose of drainage and transport, then the upper layer of peat is removed and placed on one side; the lower layer, which is more combustible, is then cut up into blocks, dried, and taken away on barges to be sold as fuel; finally the sandy soil below is mixed with the upper layer of peat, and with chemical manures, and the land becomes capable of supporting colonies of small-holders. Canals are the only means of transport, and every house is built facing the canal, which thus becomes the village street.

In spite of all these reclamation schemes agricultural land is still scarce in Holland, and commands a higher price than in almost any other country in the world. Impelled by this demand for new land, and confident in the knowledge gained by centuries of successful strife with the sea, the Dutch Government has embarked on the most ambitious drainage scheme which has ever been attempted. A large part of the Zuyder Zee is being turned into fertile polders, which will provide over eight hundred and fifty square miles of arable land. As shown in Fig. 70, the reclaimed land will consist of four polders, enclosed by embankments. On the north is an enclosing dam, which impounds part of the Zuyder Zee, thus forming a lake which is known as Lake Yssel. The northwestern, the north-eastern, and part of the south-eastern polders have already been reclaimed and are under intensive cultivation. Lake Yssel is connected by locks and sluices to the outer portion of the Zuyder Zee, while a ship canal provides a 'back-door' entrance to Amsterdam. The surplus water from the polders is pumped into Lake Yssel, and from it discharged at low tide through sluices. The water of the lake is now free from salt, and the level is regulated so as to ensure that the neighbouring polders are neither dry nor water-logged. Freshwater fisheries have been developed to replace the former sea fisheries of the Zuyder Zee.

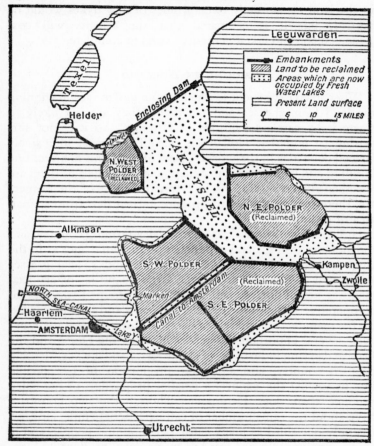

FIG. 71. THE RECLAMATION OF THE ZUYDER ZEE

In order to prevent a repetition of the catastrophe of 1953, when high tides engulfed 5,000 square miles of land, the Dutch are proposing to build dykes between, as well as round the islands, completely sealing off the mouths of the Rhine from the sea, and ensuring both greater security and an increase in the land area. Only twenty miles of new dykes would be needed, but it is estimated that the scheme will cost £200,000,000 and take twenty-five years to complete.

FARMING IN HOLLAND

Where men have spent so much labour and money in winning the land from the sea and the moor, they are not likely to waste it by careless methods of farming. So it is not surprising to find that Holland is one of the most intensively farmed countries in the world. Few of the farms are over one hundred and twenty acres in extent, and about half of them are less than fifteen acres. As in Denmark, most of the farmers are, therefore, compelled to produce a great deal from a small area of ground.

Holland, like Denmark, is a great dairy-farming country, and the industry is in general conducted on the same lines as in the latter country. In most districts roots and special grasses are grown as food for the cattle, large quantities of artificial manures are imported, and farmers are grouped together in co-operative societies for purchase of seeds and foodstuffs, and for the manufacture and sale of dairy produce. There are, however, several important differences between the Dutch and the Danish dairying industries. (1) Since Holland is a very densely peopled country, and a greater proportion of her people live in towns, she exports a smaller proportion of her dairy produce than does Denmark. Though the two countries have about the same number of cattle per square mile, Holland has only one-third as many cattle per thousand people, and is able to export only one-third as much dairy produce as Denmark. (2) A much larger part of the dairying land of the Netherlands is under grass than in Denmark, since much of the low-lying polder land is too wet to be ploughed. In the provinces of Holland and Friesland, for example, there are

HOLLAND, THE POLDERS: CULTIVATION AND A NEW FARM HOUSE

large dairy farms which grow nothing but grass. (3) While Denmark specializes in butter and bacon, the Netherlands produce more cheese and condensed milk, and these form the chief items of dairy produce which we import from that country.

Many of the most interesting Dutch towns are those connected with the cheese industry. *Alkmaar*, a picturesque little town in north Holland, is the principal centre for the manufacture and sale of the round Dutch cheeses with which we are so familiar in England. Upwards of half a million pounds weight of cheeses are sold in the market-place each week. *Edam*, situated at the dam on the River Y, is famous for its round red cheeses, while *Gouda* has given its name to the flat cheeses.

As there is a great deal of variety in farming methods in the Netherlands, there is also much difference in the types of farmhouses. One of the most interesting types is that of Friesland, in the extreme north. Here the farmstead is a four-square building, with low walls and high-pitched tiled or thatched roof. Barn, cowsheds, dairy, and living quarters are all included under the same roof. At the rear of the building the barn doors open on to a long threshing floor, on each side of which are the cow-stalls, so arranged that each cow faces a little window in the outer walls. 'In Holland the cow is the lady who pays the rent, and is, therefore, treated with respect. Nothing is more amusing than to see that to each window is generally a little linen blind, daintily finished off with a lace border.'—C. G. Harper, *On the Road to Holland*. At the front of the building, and connected with the cowsheds by a passage, are the living quarters. Formerly these were not separated by any partition from the cow-stalls; indeed, in some of the older farm-houses the living room is quite open on the side adjoining the cowsheds, and in any case it is customary for the farm labourers to sleep in the barn. The space below the rafters is utilized for storing hay and straw, though the uppermost portion is frequently used as a hen roost, which the fowls reach by means of an outside staircase. This 'is always daintily made, and may have brightly painted sides or equally gay-looking palisades. If it has solid sides, instead of palisading, the woodwork will often have little glazed windows.'

Horticulture and market gardening are specially characteristic of the belt of country stretching along the eastern edge of the coastal dunes, almost through the whole length of Holland. Here the sandy soil of the dunes has been mixed with the heavier soil of the polders, to produce a light fertile soil which is perfectly suited to the production of flowers, fruit, and vegetables. The Westland district, between The Hague and the Hook of Holland, is specially noted for its glass-houses, which produce large quantities of fruit and early vegetables. Between Haarlem and Alkmaar in North Holland is another market-gardening area, specializing in the production of strawberries, cauliflowers, and early potatoes. Between these two, around Haarlem and Leyden, is the chief area for the cultivation of bulbs. Bulb culture was a hobby of rich Dutch merchants in the sixteenth and seventeenth centuries, and very high prices were paid for new or rare specimens. The craze died suddenly, however, and many wealthy dealers were ruined, but the foundation of the industry had been laid, and the cultivation of bulbs began again on a basis of real value. The annual yield of bulbs is worth several millions of pounds.

Arable farming is specially characteristic of the heavy clay soils on the better-drained polders, where large quantities of sugar beet, potatoes, and cereals are produced. Though the yield of wheat *per acre* is more than twice that of Canada, and almost the highest of any country in the world, Holland cannot grow nearly enough cereals for her own needs. In fact, the wheat produced in the country would suffice only to provide her people with bread on one day per week.

Sheep rearing is of particular importance in the island of Texel, and on other dry sandy lands, such as the Veluwe, to the south-east of the Zuyder Zee, and the southern part of

Brabant. Formerly these sandy lands were largely waste, but in recent years the Government has encouraged the planting of forests and the establishment of small holdings.

FISHING

Every one is familiar with pictures of Dutch fishermen in wide trousers, tight waistcoats, and sabots, and many people assume that all Dutch fishermen dress in this way. As a matter of fact, it was only in the fishing villages along the shores of the Zuyder Zee that these picturesque costumes were ever seen. Indeed, they are now almost as much of a curiosity in Holland as they would be in England. Now that the Zuyder Zee has been transformed into a fresh-water lake, the fishermen there specialize in the catching of eels, and the only important fishing port is Ijmuiden, on the North Sea coast, which specializes in herrings.

THE MANUFACTURING INDUSTRIES OF HOLLAND

Although farming is so important in the Netherlands, only one-fifth of the working people are employed in the farming industries, and above half are engaged in commerce and manufacture. Although no coal-field is shown on a geological map of the Netherlands, there is a 'concealed' coal-field under the sandy deposits of the southern province of Limburg. Coal was mined here as early as the twelfth century, but it is only in recent years that the coal-field has been commercially developed. The seams are thin, and shafts have to be sunk through 300 to 1,000 feet of waterlogged strata, but in spite of these drawbacks the mines now produce almost as much coal as the country requires.

In recent years borings have revealed a huge reserve of *natural gas* in the province of Groningen in North Holland. Most of the gas now being produced is used for domestic purposes and space heating, but there is a considerable surplus for use in power stations and chemical works, and even for export.

As a manufacturing country Holland has the advantage of easy assembly of raw materials at her great ocean ports, and of a favourable situation for trade with densely peopled neighbouring countries. The manufactures of Holland may be divided into two classes, viz. those which owe their origin to local farm products, and those based on imports of coal and tropical produce. To the first class being the manufactures of dairy produce, 'hollands' gin (distilled from rye), and brown holland (linen). To the second class belong the great industries concentrated at the ports of Rotterdam and Amsterdam.

Perhaps the most interesting of the latter class of industries is the manufacture of margarine. This butter substitute was first made from animal fat and milk by a Frenchman named Mège-Mouries. As Holland produced large quantities of these materials she soon began to take a large share in the industry, and undoubtedly one of the chief causes of her success was the invention by Dutchmen of the machinery which is used in the industry. As the demand for margarine increased, substitutes for milk and animal fats were found in the vegetable oils obtained from the tropics, e.g. coco-nut oil, ground-nut oil, and palm-kernel oil. Large quantities of these oils were produced in the Dutch East Indies, so Holland was easily able to establish the industry on the new lines. Margarine forms one of the chief items of export from the Netherlands, and many Dutch factories have also been established in Britain, France, and other European countries.

The textile industry of Twente, in the extreme south-east of Holland, is somewhat exceptional. Its location was determined, not by any particular suitability of the district itself, but by historical causes. After the separation of Holland and Belgium in 1839, Dutch cotton manufacturers decided to build factories in their own country, and selected Twente, as this district had an old-established textile industry which provided plenty of skilled labour. Weaving schools were established, and an Englishman, Thomas Ainsworth, taught improved methods of manufacture, thus repaying some of the debt which the English textile industries owe to the Flemish and Dutch refugees of the sixteenth and seventeenth centuries.

Though much of the coal and most of the raw materials have to be imported, the industry has established itself as one of the foremost in the country.

THE PHYSICAL AND ECONOMIC DIVISIONS

Summing up what we have learnt from the foregoing descriptions, and from a study of the map, we may divide the Netherlands into three main regions, viz.:

(1) *The narrow strip of coastal dunes.* It is quite probable that much of the material which forms these dunes was derived from the 'land-bridge' which once stretched across the present Strait of Dover. To this has been added the material worn from the coasts of France and Belgium, and swept north-eastwards by the prevailing winds and tidal currents.

The chief value of the dunes is that they provide the basis of the main dyke system of Holland. In addition, they are also the chief source of the water supply for the towns of the Dutch lowland; and, as we have seen, on the eastern margins of the dunes, the drifted sand has mixed with the heavy clay of the polders to form one of the best horticultural soils in the world. Further drifting inland has, however, been prevented by the planting of special grasses, whose long roots bind the sand.

(2) *The land below sea-level.* This is the richest, the most productive, and the most densely peopled part of the Netherlands. It is this section, with its windmills, canals, and dyke-protected polders, which we think of when we call up a mental picture of Holland. It is here that the most intensive agriculture and dairying are practised, though, as we have seen, there is considerable specialization in the farming industries of different parts of the region.

(3) *The land above sea-level.* This is composed mainly of sand washed out from the ice sheet which covered northern Europe in the Ice Age. In spite of reclamation schemes, such as those described on a previous page, these sandy moorlands remain the least densely peopled parts of the country. The province of Drenthe, for example, is described by a recent writer as 'an immense sandy heath, that has almost defied even Dutch industry. After the fertility of Groningen and Friesland these wastes of moorland appear barren and desolate. Not that there is any lack of farms, villages, and cultivated fields, but these are all scattered about the endless flat moors, and have a lonely look. The farms are comparatively untidy, the dress of the people comparatively poor and negligent, and the hard-won acres, with difficulty won from the arid stretches of heath, do not bloom with the luxuriance of the neighbouring provinces. . . . The lack of trees, windmills, old towns, canals, and waterways gives a great part of Drenthe a monotony beyond that of any other part of the Netherlands.'—M. Bowen, *The Netherlands Displayed.*

The lack of fertility of the eastern and southern portions of the country is to some extent counterbalanced by industrial development in the Twenthe district, and by the coal-mining of the Limburg province.

TRANSPORT IN THE NETHERLANDS

As might be expected, rivers and canals provide the chief means of internal transport in Holland. The cheapness of this form of transport discouraged the early development of railways, and even at the present day Holland has fewer miles of railway in proportion to its population than any other country in Europe. In exceptionally hard winters, when the canals are frozen, so much extra traffic is thrown on the railways that they are unable to deal with it, and much confusion and loss may ensue.

The Great Cities of Holland

Rotterdam is situated on the New Maas, the most navigable distributary of the Rhine. It is not only the chief port of Holland, but also the most important port on the continent, being second only to London among European ports in respect of the volume of its trade. Its history, like that of other ports of the Rhine delta; has been one of constant struggle to keep open the connection with the sea. Towards the end of the nineteenth century it was found that the approach to the port by the natural waterway had become inadequate for the needs of modern steamers; so the New Waterway was constructed, linking the port to the Hook of Holland by a channel deep enough for the largest ocean-going steamers. Thus was another of Nature's mistakes rectified by the Dutch.

Rotterdam is the natural outlet for the whole of the Rhine basin, and is also linked by canals to the Meuse and the Scheldt, as well as to every part of the country. It has, therefore, a vast hinterland, and serves not only its own country, but also Germany, Switzerland, and large parts of central Europe, France, and Belgium.

About three-quarters of the goods imported at Rotterdam are, in normal times, sent on to other countries, either with or without transhipment. It is, therefore, primarily a transit port. Most of the imports consist of bulk goods, such as coal, iron ore, wheat, and petroleum, while the exports are chiefly foodstuffs and manufactured goods. As has already been stated, Rotterdam is an important industrial centre, being concerned chiefly with shipbuilding, engineering, oil-refining, and the preparation of foodstuffs.

Amsterdam, the second port and the capital of the Netherlands, first figures in history as 'Amstel dam'—the dam or dyke built round an island where the River Amstel enters the Zuyder Zee. In the Middle Ages, when ships were small enough to navigate the Zuyder Zee and the channels which then connected it with the Rhine, Amsterdam was the chief port of the country.   In the sixteenth century it was the great depot in north-western Europe for spices and silks, which it received from the East via Lisbon.   The Spaniards, however, stopped this trade during their temporary conquest of Portugal at the end of that century.   Faced with the alternatives of ruin or enterprising action, the Dutch, as always during their history, chose the latter course, and began to send out their own fleets to the East Indies.   Thus they laid the foundation of the Dutch Empire in the East, and of the great trade with the East which is still characteristic of Amsterdam.

In later times, when vessels became too large to navigate the Zuyder Zee, the port again lost its pre-eminence, but with characteristic resource the Dutch, who, centuries before, had created Amsterdam by shutting out the sea, re-created it by bringing the sea to the city in the form of ship canals.   The first canal to be made was the North Holland Canal to the Helder, and some years later the North Sea Canal running westward to Ijmuiden was built.   This latter canal has been repeatedly enlarged to cope with the ever-increasing size of vessels, and the locks at Ijmuiden have been reconstructed so as to accommodate not only the largest vessels afloat, but any that are likely to be built for many years to come.   The Merwede Canal, recently extended and enlarged, runs through Utrecht to the Rhine; and, as we have seen, the scheme for reclaiming the Zuyder Zee provides for a deep-water channel between the two polders.

The city itself is semicircular in shape, and is intersected by so many canals that, like Stockholm, it has been called 'the Venice of the North.'   Most of the heavy transport is conducted by water, and many of the principal streets are hardly more than banks to the canals, some being so narrow that they will accommodate only one-way traffic.   As in Venice, the land is too marshy to provide a firm foundation for building, so the city is built on piles driven deep into the ground.   It was this which caused Erasmus, the great Dutch scholar of the Renaissance, to call Amsterdam 'a city where the inhabitants perch upon the tops of trees.' Nowadays, however, columns of concrete are used instead of piles.

Amsterdam, in contrast to Rotterdam, is concerned chiefly with trade in tropical produce, while most of the vessels entering it fly the Dutch flag. Whereas many vessels pass through Rotterdam without unloading, few vessels leave Amsterdam without discharging their cargo, although a large part of the imports are re-exported after repacking or manufacture. Characteristic imports are tobacco, tin, coffee, tea, rubber, cocoa, rice, copra, cinchona, and spices—all of which are products of the East Indies. Amsterdam is also the chief diamond market of the world.

The Hague, though not the capital of the country, is the seat of the Government, and the administrative centre. The town originally grew up around a castle or 'haag,' built by a count or 'grave' of Holland. From this it received its Dutch name, 'S Graven Haag (Count's Park); though, as the possessive's in Dutch is placed in front of the word, perhaps we should say ''S Count Park'! The city is very different in appearance from other Dutch cities, since it has no canals except on the outskirts. Although it is not a port, and has few industries, it is the richest city in the Netherlands, and is noted for its stately mansions and magnificent public buildings.

Utrecht was originally a Roman fortress guarding the lowest crossing place of the Rhine. It is situated where the old Rhine divides, sending one branch to the Zuyder Zee, and another direct to the North Sea. These streams are now almost silted up, but they were formerly the chief branches of the Rhine, and Utrecht was an important Roman port.

The modern importance of the city is due to the following factors:

(1) It is situated at the junction of two different types of country—the polders on the west, and the higher sandy country on the east; hence it has become the market for the sale and exchange of the agricultural produce of these regions.

(2) It is the chief railway centre of the Netherlands, since the lines between western Holland and Germany naturally converge on the narrow neck of land between the Zuyder Zee and the Rhine.

(3) It is also an important centre of navigable waterways, being served by the Merwede Canal and by many minor barge canals. The facilities for the collection of raw materials have made it an important manufacturing centre.

Haarlem, like The Hague, grew up around a royal residence. It is to-day the chief centre of the bulb industry, and the pure water from the sand dunes to the west of the city has favoured the development of such industries as brewing and bleaching. It is also the natural market for the agricultural produce of the rich polders of the Haarlem Mere. A branch of the North Sea Canal has helped its commercial development and given it facilities for the assembly of raw materials which form the basis of miscellaneous industries.

Groningen is the chief city of the northern Netherlands. It is situated at the junction of the polders of the coastal region with the sandy lands of the interior, and at the meeting point of many canals. It has, therefore, become important as a local market, and as it is connected to the mouth of the Ems by a small ship canal it has some export of dairy produce.

Dordrecht, on one of the branches of the Rhine, was once the chief port of the Netherlands, and was given by law a monopoly of the Rhine trade. But in the seventeenth century Rotterdam compelled her to relinquish this, and as the channel silted up about the same period, Dordrecht became a 'dead' port. Recently, however, the port has begun to regain some of its former importance. Modern docks have been built, and a channel cut to the New Waterway, and it is hoped thereby to short-circuit some of the Rhine traffic which now goes to Rotterdam.

Flushing and *Hook of Holland* are packet stations which, in contrast to the commercial port of Rotterdam, are situated as far out to sea as possible, so as to expedite the transport of passengers, mails, and perishable goods such as fruit and vegetables.

Ijmuiden, besides being the ocean terminus of the North Sea Canal, is the chief fishing port of Holland.

Leyden is famous for the siege of 1574, which epitomizes those struggles with Spain through which the Dutch became a united people. At this period Holland was divided into seventeen states, each practically independent, though nominally part of the Holy Roman Empire. Philip II of Spain, who had inherited the Netherlands, set out to crush Protestantism, and unite the states under his own autocratic rule. For a time he carried everything before him, but in 1572 the 'Sea Beggars' began a series of counter-attacks which encouraged the provinces of Holland and Zeeland to rebel. The Dutch were no match for the Spanish armies led by the cruel Duke of Alva, but they had two defences—the sea and their city walls. Thus the War of Independence was notable chiefly for a series of sieges, of which that of Leyden is the most famous. William the Silent, the leader of the Dutch forces, knew that his forces were inadequate to relieve Leyden by land, so he ordered the dykes to be cut in order that his fleet might sail up to the walls of the city. The war ended in 1609 in the victory of the Dutch States, who banded themselves together in the first federal government of modern times. Then followed a period of great prosperity, during which Holland was mistress of the seas, and had almost a monopoly of trade with the East.

When the political map of Europe was redrawn after the defeat of Napleon at Waterloo, Holland and Belgium were united to form the kingdom of the Netherlands, under the rule of the king of Holland. But the Belgians had been so long separated from the Dutch that, although the language of *northern* Belgium is very similar to Dutch, they felt themselves a separate people, and found the union very irksome. Consequently, in 1830, they rebelled, and set up the modern kingdom of Belgium.

L   E

EXERCISES

1. 'Amsterdam is one of the chief air-ports of Europe.' On an outline map of Europe show the following lines:

        Amsterdam—Rotterdam—London.

        Amsterdam—Rotterdam—Brussels—Paris.

        Amsterdam—Hull—Liverpool.

        Amsterdam—Hamburg—Copenhagen—Oslo.

        Amsterdam—Cologne—Frankfort—Basle—Zürich.

2. Show on a sketch-map the following passenger routes between Britain and the Netherlands:

    Leith to Rotterdam.   Hull to Rotterdam.

    Harwich to Hook of Holland.   Harwich to Flushing.

          London to Rotterdam.

3. Of the total area of the Netherlands 37 per cent is under grass, and 30 per cent is arable. What does this suggest concerning differences in dairy-farming methods between that country and Denmark?

4. The Netherlands imports large quantities of the following vegetable oils and oil-seeds: copra, linseed, ground-nuts, palm-oil, palm-kernels, soya beans.

(*a*) Say why the Dutch need these commodities.

(*b*) In each case name one part of the world which is particularly important for the production of the commodity.

5. Draw diagrams to show that:

(*a*) 58 per cent of the Dutch people live in towns and 42 per cent in the rural areas.

(*b*) 20 per cent of the working people of Holland are engaged in manufacturing, while 25 per cent are engaged in agriculture.

6. The chief minerals imported by the Netherlands are coal, petroleum, and iron ore. In each case name the principal sources of supply.

7. Holland exports 50 per cent of its total production of the following commodities: butter, cheese, fish.

Show this by means of diagrams.

8. Collect newspaper cuttings and illustrations of interesting aspects of Dutch life and scenery.

BELGIUM

THE kingdom of Belgium is in many ways a 'two-sided' country. It is composed of two physical divisions, the northern plain and the southern plateau; it is not only one of the most intensively farmed countries in the world, but also one of the chief manufacturing countries; politically it is a 'buffer' state between France and Germany; and the Flemings who live in the north of the country speak a different language from the Walloons who live in the south.

The Walloons are descended from Celtic tribes known as the Belgae, who inhabited this region when it was part of the Roman Empire. France and Belgium then formed one country (Gaul), throughout which language, laws, and customs were very similar. The Flemings, on the other hand, belong to the Nordic group, and are descended from 'barbarian' tribes who came from districts round the mouth of the Rhine, and conquered the northern part of Belgium about the same time that the Anglo-Saxons settled in England. Just as in England the Celts were driven into the mountains and came to be called Welsh (foreigners), so the Celts of Belgium were driven southward into the forests and mountains, and received the name 'Walloons' which is essentially the same word as 'Welsh.' The Walloons still speak French, while the Flemish language is very similar to Dutch, and belongs to the same group of languages as English.

Though a large proportion of the people in the capital speak French, the division between the Flemish-speaking and the French-speaking peoples is an almost straight line running across the country a little south of Brussels. The peoples north and south of this line differ in other matters besides speech. The Flemings are laborious cultivators of the soil, but they have also a natural bent towards city life, craftsmanship, and commerce. The Walloons, on the other hand, do not take kindly to city life, and there are fewer large towns in the Walloon portion than in the Flemish portion.

FARMING IN BELGIUM

Though Belgium is, next to England, the most densely populated 'white' country in the world, farming is so highly developed that she is able to produce between 80 and 90 per cent of the total foodstuffs she requires. Very little of the soil is naturally fertile; yet it is made to yield large crops by careful cultivation, by the laborious mixing of soils, and by liberal applications of manure. The productivity of Belgium represents, indeed, one of the greatest of man's triumphs over Nature.

As in most other European countries, women and children undertake a considerable share of the farm work, and are frequently to be seen in the fields weeding, hoeing, or harvesting. This is especially the case in the industrial districts, where the men often work in the factories during the day, and in western Flanders, where it is the custom for the men to go to work in France during the summer, while the women are left to look after the farms. Taking the country as a whole, the chief crops are oats, rye, potatoes, wheat, and beet, in order of acreage. Though the yield of wheat per acre is almost as high as in Denmark, the total production is only about half the country's requirements.

The surface and soils of Belgium are so varied that there are very great differences in the types of farming. If we were to travel south-eastward through the country from Ostend, through Brussels to the Ardennes, we should pass through the following widely differing belts of country. (See Fig. 72.)

(1) Along the coast is a belt of sand dunes, a mile or more in width. Though these are an added attraction to such holiday resorts as Ostend and Knocke, from the farming point of view they are useful only as sheep pastures.

(2) Behind these, and to some extent protected by them, are low-lying polders, drained by canals, and protected from floods by dykes. This region is very similar to the Dutch polder land, and its heavy clay soils produce good crops of grass,

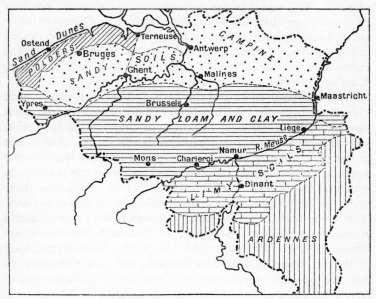

FIG. 72. THE SOILS AND FARMING DISTRICTS OF BELGIUM

barley, and sugar beet, while dairy farming is also important. An interesting feature of the older farm-houses of this district is that they are nearly all surrounded by deep moats.

(3) Between the polders and the River Lys is the sandy plain of Flanders. Though in its natural condition this was one of the most barren parts of Europe, it has been transformed, by careful cultivation and the lavish use of manures, into one of the most productive areas in the world. The farms are only a few acres in extent, and nearly all the work is done by the spade or with the hands. Here almost all the crops of western

Europe may be seen crowded together on a few acres of ground, and it is a common sight to see a line of women and children working their way, often on hands and knees, through a small patch of ground, weeding or tying up the plants. 'The aspect of the country is very different from that of the average agricultural region in Britain. There are many small villages, and far and near among the fields are dotted cottages, often whitewashed and with red roofs, in which the cultivators live close to their work.'—B. Seebohm Rowntree, *Land and Labour*.

(4) Between the Lys and the Meuse the sand is mixed with clay, forming a loamy soil, though there are also large areas covered with heavy clay. Conditions here are more suitable for the large-scale cultivation of cereals and roots. Sugar beet is the most important crop, and this in its turn leads to the keeping of dairy cattle, which are fed partly on the waste pulp returned from the sugar factories. In this region too there are many large farms, though small holdings are also numerous. The farm buildings are usually grouped in a quadrilateral round a central yard, and four or five such farmsteads are often seen clustered round a common pool. Market gardening is of great importance around Brussels, and on the outskirts of the city are to be seen many square miles of glass-houses, in which grapes and other fruits are cultivated.

(5) To the south of the Meuse the land rises sharply to the plateau region of the Ardennes.

The northern part of the plateau, where the land does not rise much above one thousand feet, and where the soil is a fertile clay, is the chief cattle-rearing and dairy-farming district of Belgium. In the higher Ardennes district there are large areas of forest and poor mountain pastures, though in recent years there has been considerable increase in the production of such crops as rye, oats, and potatoes.

Two other districts, which have not been crossed in this imaginary journey through Belgium, are:

(6) West Flanders, around Ypres, which is a clay plain,

somewhat similar to region (4), except that flax is the chief 'money' crop.

(7) The Campine, an undulating sandy plain, the lower portions of which are occupied by marsh and bogs, while the higher parts are barren sandy wastes. Agriculturally, this is the poorest part of Belgium, but for many years small-holders have been settling there, and patiently improving small areas. Industrially, however, this region has a great future, for coal seams occur deep down below the sand, and many mines are now being worked (see p. 235). New towns have been built in the midst of the heathland to accommodate the influx of miners, many of them from Italy, and the Campine as a whole is rapidly developing as one of the chief industrial districts of Belgium.

BELGIUM AS A MANUFACTURING COUNTRY

Though agriculture is of such great importance in Belgium, only about one-eighth of the working people of the country are regularly engaged in farming. Mining, manufacturing, and commerce account for the greater part of the remainder.

The origins of Belgian industries are to be found in the distant past. During the Middle Ages the Flemings were the most skilful weavers in the world, while the Walloons were using the local iron ore and charcoal for making iron and steel goods. In modern times the factors which have enabled her to become one of the foremost manufacturing countries of the world are:

(1) The skill of the workpeople, which has been passed on from generation to generation.

(2) Abundant supplies of coal, and former supplies of iron and other metals.

(3) Excellent systems of transport by rail, river, and canal.

(4) The cultivation of such crops as flax and sugar beet, which form the basis of manufacturing industries.

Coal is mined chiefly along the southern edge of the plain, in the valleys of the Meuse and its tributary, the Sambre.

(See Fig. 73.) The chief mining centres are Mons and Charleroi in the west, and Liège in the east. This coal-field now produces only about two-thirds of the coal required by

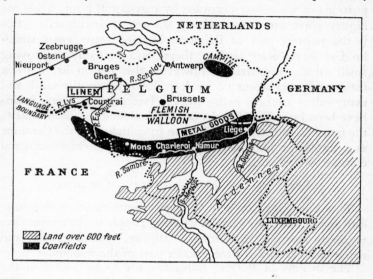

FIG. 73. BELGIUM

the country, the rest being supplied by the newly developed Campine coal-field.

The metal industries of Belgium are of outstanding importance, the chief centres being Liège and Charleroi. The iron and steel industries grew up here on the basis of local ore, but though some still exists, it is not worked, as it is found cheaper to import it from France, Luxembourg, and Sweden. Liège has also important zinc works. Here again the industry developed because zinc ore was obtained locally, but this is now almost exhausted, and large quantities are imported from Australia, India, and Mexico. Other metal industries of Liège are the smelting of copper and tin, the ores of which are imported mainly from the Belgian Congo.

The chemical industry is also of great importance in the Liège district, partly because the zinc sulphide which is imported for smelting is the chief source of sulphuric acid, which, in its turn, is the basis of many chemicals used in industry.

Glass manufacture is carried on mainly in Charleroi, since the coal mined there is specially suitable for the industry. Sand, which is the chief raw material, is obtained from Fontainebleau in France, and from the Campine district. Since the new coal-field in this latter region produces coal which is very suitable for heating glass furnaces, it is likely that the industry will soon grow up there, probably to the detriment of that in Charleroi.

The textile industries. Linen goods are made chiefly in the provinces of East and West Flanders. The prosperity of the industry is due to the local cultivation of flax, the special suitability of the waters of the Lys for the retting of flax, the modern use of electrical power, and the experience and skill of the workpeople. The towns most noted for the manufacture of linen are Ghent, Roulers, and Courtrai.

Cotton manufacturing is centred chiefly in Ghent, while Verviers, a few miles east of Liège, is the chief centre of the woollen industry. This latter industry forms almost the only exception to the general rule that the distribution of manufactures in modern Belgium is similar to that of the Middle Ages, viz. spinning and weaving in the north, and metal industries in the south.

Paper making is carried on chiefly in the country districts south of Brussels. Here numerous small streams supply pure water, which is so necessary for the success of the industry, while barge canals provide cheap transport for the raw material, which is imported mainly from Scandinavia.

TRANSPORT IN BELGIUM

Belgium is one of the natural foci of European trade, since it is situated where the European plain narrows as it approaches

*L   E

the Strait of Dover, and where the routes from the Mediterranean via the Rhine valley splay out fan-wise to the North Sea. In the Middle Ages the prosperity of Flanders was due very largely to the traffic along these routes; and in modern times excellent systems of transport by rail, river, and canal have done much to aid the industrial and agricultural development of the country.

Rail

These great natural highways are followed by main lines of railway. Belgium was the first country on the continent to build railways, and she is noteworthy as having a greater length of railway in proportion to her area than any other country in the world.

The close network of transport by road and rail has greatly assisted the development of small holdings in Belgium, for not only does it facilitate the marketing of produce, but it also enables men whose farms are too small to occupy their whole time to work in the factory during the day and travel back to their farm at night. Possibly, too, it accounts for the fact that Belgian manufacturers can find markets abroad for heavy, partly-manufactured articles, while countries with high transport charges can export only articles which are of great value in proportion to their weight.

The Belgian inland waterways are also of great importance. The mouth of the Scheldt is navigable for the largest ocean steamers as far as Antwerp, while the river itself and its tributaries, such as the Escaut and the Lys, are canalized. The Meuse, with its tributary, the Sambre, forms another great waterway, and canals have been constructed over the low watershed to connect with the Scheldt basin. Brussels is connected with Antwerp by a canal capable of accommodating vessels of two thousand tons; Ghent has a ship canal to Terneuzen on the Scheldt estuary; and Bruges, which was one of the great ports of the Middle Ages, but was cut off from the sea by the deposition of sediment, has again been made a port by the construction of a ship canal to Zeebrugge ('Sea Bruges').

The *Albert Canal*, which connects Antwerp with Liège, was opened to traffic in May 1939. Vessels of up to 2,000 tons burden can now reach Liège from Antwerp in two to three days, and the canal is proving of great importance in the continued development of the port of Antwerp, the new Campine coalfield, and the industrial district of Liège.

Antwerp is the only natural deep-water port of Belgium. Situated on the Scheldt estuary fifty miles from the open sea, it is the nearest port to Brussels and to the industrial district of the Meuse valley. It is also conveniently situated for tapping the Rhine traffic, and is one of the chief ports of call for ocean vessels passing through the Strait of Dover. It is not surprising, therefore, that it has become, not only the greatest port of Belgium, but also one of the greatest ports in the world. Its docks and quays stretch for nearly four miles along the right bank of the Scheldt, where a convex curve of the river brings the main channel close to the shore. Here may be seen vessels of all the maritime nations of the world, though British and French and Dutch vessels outnumber those belonging to Belgium. One reason why so many vessels call at Antwerp is that there is a great variety of cargo to be picked up there, e.g. metal goods from the Ruhr district of Germany, textiles from Flanders, iron ore and potash from Lorraine.

The competition of many different lines of steamers has kept ocean freights very low, and this in its turn has brought additional traffic to the port. The hinterland of Antwerp (i.e. the region served by the port) extends far beyond the boundaries of Belgium; in fact, nearly half the goods handled are exports from, or imports to Germany, France, and other neighbouring countries.

Brussels is situated in the centre of the oval plain of Belgium, midway between the coast and the industrial centres of the Meuse valley; it is practically on the line dividing the areas of Flemish and Walloon speech; and it is the natural focus of routes from France, Holland, Germany, and the North Sea coast. Yet it was none of these advantages which caused the original growth of the city, but merely the fact that the ruling princes in the Middle Ages chose that site for a country residence. The city grew up around their castle, and as the advantages of its central situation came to be realized, it became the capital of the country.

To-day Brussels is one of the finest cities of the world. The 'inner town' is surrounded by boulevards, which have replaced the former city walls, and is divided into lower and upper portions. The former is the business quarter of the city, and the home of most of the industries and of the working people; the latter is the fashionable quarter, with numerous mansions and magnificent public buildings. Outside the boulevards, especially on the healthier hill slopes to the south, have grown up large suburbs, which now contain more than half the population of Brussels.

Brussels has also considerable importance as a port, and the converging canals and railways have assisted the development of industries. Like most capital cities it specializes in the manufacture of foodstuffs, clothing, jewellery, and luxury articles of all kinds.

Ghent is an ancient city, which grew up round a fortress built on an island at the confluence of the Lys and the Scheldt. This 'Castle of the Counts' is one of the finest existing examples of a medieval fortress. From its towers one may see the city spread out like a map. In the foreground is the medieval city, with its picturesque red-tiled and gabled houses, and narrow streets intersected by innumerable canals. Beyond are the modern commercial and industrial quarters, for Ghent is to-day the 'Manchester of Belgium'—the centre of the cotton industry, and a great port.

Bruges grew up round a bridge ('brug') situated where the coastal road crossed the river Zwin. In the Middle Ages it was the chief centre of the cloth trade of Flanders and one of the chief ports of Europe, but with the silting up of the estuary which gave it access to the sea, it became a 'dead' city. Such it remained for three hundred years, until the ship canal to Zeebrugge, built in 1907, again gave it access to the sea. In spite of some industrial development, however, Bruges, with its narrow cobbled streets, ancient gabled houses, numerous canals and historic buildings, still remains 'a fossilized city of the Middle Ages.'

Ostend is the only large town on the Belgian coast. It is situated where a break in the sand dunes, partly natural and partly artificial, provides a harbour for sea-going vessels. As it is the nearest port of Belgium to the English coast, it has become the chief packet station of the country, with regular services to Dover. It has also considerable exports of fruit and vegetables.

EXERCISES

1. For every 1,000 people Denmark has 750 cattle, Holland 300, and Belgium 250. Suggest some reasons why the proportion of cattle is lowest in Belgium, and say what the effect is on the foreign trade of the country, as compared with that of Holland and Denmark.

2. 'At Antwerp the tonnage of cargo arriving or dispatched by total inland crafts is as important as by rail. About 50 per cent of the total inland water-traffic of Belgium is concentrated around the port.' Draw a sketch map to show the waterways converging on the port.

3. 'Belgium produces all the milk and butter she requires, four-fifths of all her foodstuffs, but only three-quarters of the meat, and one-quarter of the wheat.' Comment on this statement from the knowledge you have gained of the farming industries of Belgium.

4. Cotton goods and iron and steel are both imported from and exported to Great Britain by Belgium. Can you explain this?

LUXEMBOURG

THIS Grand Duchy is a small independent state which grew up around the natural fortress of the city of the same name. This city is situated on an easily defended site at the convergence of three great routes, viz.: westward to Paris around the south-eastern corner of the Ardennes; eastward to Germany along the Moselle valley; and northward across the plateau to Liège.

Though inhabited by a people who are determined to remain independent, the state is too weak to stand entirely by itself. At different times in its history it has been joined to France, Belgium, or Germany. After the Franco-German War of 1870–1 Luxembourg, though still retaining its political independence, entered into close commercial relations with Germany; but since the First World War, though most of the people speak German, it has had an almost complete union with Belgium in matters of trade.

Small as the state is, two physical divisions may easily be distinguished on the map; the northern half is part of the high, bleak, and barren plateau of the Ardennes, while the lower southern half, which is known as 'Goodland,' is composed of softer, more fertile rock.

Much of the northern part is sandy heath and forest, cultivable land is restricted to the more fertile valleys, and the population is scanty. In the south, however, there are large tracts of fertile pasture and agricultural land; wheat and sugar beet are important crops, and vines are cultivated in the valley of the Moselle.

In the extreme south of the duchy is a narrow strip which forms an extension of the Lorraine iron-field of France. Much iron ore is mined, most of it being smelted within the duchy and exported as pig iron to Belgium and Germany.

FRANCE

How Nature built France

WE have seen (page 3) that when the earth was young Nature 'shrugged her shoulders' and heaved up the rocks to form a great range of mountains which stretched across the region

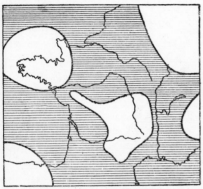

FIG. 74. THE SEAS IN WHICH THE NEWER ROCKS, FORMING THE LOWLANDS OF FRANCE, WERE DEPOSITED

Sea ▤

Islands of hard, old rock left white.

now occupied by the south-western part of the British Isles, France, and central highlands of Europe.

Having formed the range, Nature destroyed it. During the course of hundreds of millions of years some parts subsided to form hollows, like those of Paris and Aquitaine (see Figs. 74, 75), in which water-borne sediments accumulated to form limestone, chalk, sandstone, and clay; in other parts, like Brittany, the range was worn down to a skeleton, so that only the hard old 'ribs' project above the general level; still other parts were raised up again to form plateaus, such as the Ardennes and the Central Plateau of France.

Having destroyed or remoulded one range of mountains, Nature again caused the rocks to be folded and crumpled, so forming the moutains which belong to the Alpine system, e.g. the Pyrenees, the Alps, the Jura. During the hundreds of millions of years which have elapsed since these mountain ranges were upheaved, Nature, aided for a very brief period

267

by man, has been busy binding together the fragments which
she had strewn upon this corner of Europe. Rivers have
opened up ways into the highlands and carried alluvium down
to the lowlands; the gateways formed by Nature have helped
man to link the varied regions together by a network of roads,
railways, and canals; and a central government so unified the
country that it became one of the strongest political units of
the continent.

Just as Nature may be said to have moulded France around
the nucleus of the Cen-
tral Plateau, so the Paris
Basin has been the centre
round which modern
France grew. Turning
over the pages of an his-
torical atlas we see many
parts which from time to
time have been indepen-
dent states, or subject
to foreign rulers, e.g.
Burgundy,   Aquitaine,
Savoy; but always the
Paris Basin has been only
French. (Fig. 76.)

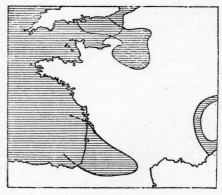

FIG. 75

The last parts of France to rise from
the sea

Here were laid down the newest rocks

The territory we now
call France was united
under the rule of the
Romans, and again under Charlemagne. We have seen
(p. 204) that it was from the western third of Charlemagne's
empire that modern France was formed, but it was not till the
end of the fifteenth century that the whole country was united
under one ruler. At first the duchy of France was merely one
of several independent states which acknowledged the nominal
overlordship of the king of the West Franks. Towards the
end of the tenth century, however, Hugh Capet, duke of
Paris, was elected king of the Franks, and during the next

five hundred years his successors gradually gained possession of the dominions of their vassals, until the whole area of modern France was under their rule.

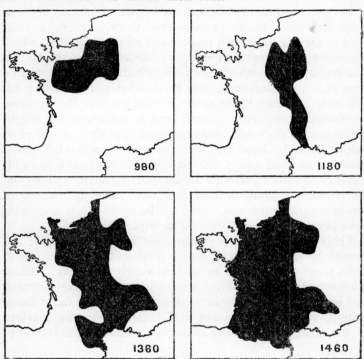

FIG. 76

The country of France grew up around the Paris Basin

RURAL LIFE

Although France has many busy manufacturing centres, it is predominantly a farming country. More than a quarter of the working people are engaged in agriculture, and there are only seven towns with a population of over 200,000. This is in marked contrast to our own country, where only one person

in forty is a farmer, and where there are more than a score
of towns of over 200,000, although our population is little
larger than that of France.

In France a third of the farms are less than ten acres; most of
them are owned by the peasants who work on them, and the
land of each farm is often made up of many small plots which
are situated far apart.   This great subdivision of the land is
due mainly to the inheritance laws, which decree that when a
man dies his possessions must be divided equally among his
children.   Further, though most French peasants choose wives
who own, or expect to inherit, land in the immediate neighbourhood, it does not usually happen that the various plots
belonging to husband and wife are next to each other, and a
man may have to walk a mile or so from his wheat field to his
meadow, another half-mile to his potato patch, and so on.
This wastes a good deal of time, and prevents the use of
modern agricultural machinery, so in many places the fields
have been regrouped by mutual arrangement.

The French peasant is passionately fond of the land; but
though he toils incessantly on his own small farm, he seldom
seeks to own more than he and his family can work.   There
are comparatively few large landowners, few tenant farmers,
and few agricultural labourers in France, though the *métayage*
system, whereby landowner and tenant share the produce
of the farm, still survives in some districts.   (Cf. Italy, pp.
153–4.)

Though there are several districts where the farms are large,
well equipped, and run on modern lines, the average output
of the French farmer is only two-thirds that of an English
farmer.

The French countryside often lacks much of the beauty
and variety of English rural scenery.   In spite of great differences due to climate, relief, and methods of cultivation, the
dominant feature of the French landscape is monotony.   In
contrast to the shady lanes and winding country roads of
England, the typical French roads are straight and dreary, with

few hedges, and practically no isolated dwellings. Nearly all the farm-houses are grouped in small villages. One reason for this may be that in former times the unsettled state of the country made it advisable for the farmers to dwell together for mutual protection. More probably it is because the houses are necessarily grouped round the common water supply, and because the village is the most convenient centre from which a farmer can reach his scattered plots.

The villages themselves are usually much less picturesque than English rural hamlets, and the farm-houses, which are ranged on each side of the village street, either turn their backs to it or are separated from it by outbuildings. Flower gardens are rarely seen, though vegetable gardens are attached to most farm-houses and cottages.

The farmyards, round which the main buildings are grouped, are hidden from view by large wooden or iron gates, suggestive both of the former need for defence and of the strong individualism of the French peasant. The living accommodation and the household furniture do not suggest a high degree of prosperity. 'The dominant note in the rural home is work. . . . They say, if they know a little about Britain, that comfort is our god, while the soil is theirs, or was theirs until the drift away from the countryside became serious and the effects of the declining birth-rate were seen on every hand.'—H. J. Fleure.

THE NATURAL REGIONS OF FRANCE

The physical map shows us that France is a country of very varied relief. Climatically, too, there are great differences between the mild, moist, north-western parts, the sunny south-east with its 'Mediterranean' climate, and the continental eastern section with its cold winters and rather extreme climate. Variety is, indeed, the keynote of the geography of France, and it is impossible to understand the country as a whole without considering separately the various natural regions of which it is composed. (See Fig. 77.)

(1) The Central Plateau (Fig. 78)

This elevated region is composed mainly of granite and other hard old rocks. The soil is generally thin and infertile, and the winters long and cold. Wheat will not ripen, conse-

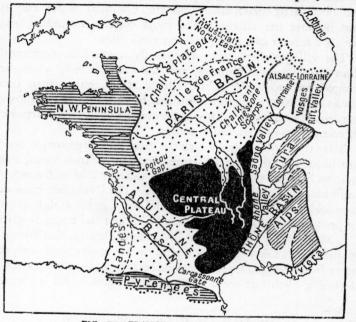

FIG. 77. FRANCE: NATURAL REGIONS

quently sheep rearing is the chief means of livelihood. Cattle are kept mainly as draught animals; and as there is not suffi- cient winter food for large numbers, the young stock are sold at great autumn cattle fairs.

In spite of the general infertility the land supports a moder- ately dense population. The farms are generally small, and every tiny patch of fertile alluvial soil is carefully cultivated to yield such cool-weather crops as rye, oats, and potatoes. Though the peasant and his family work hard from dawn to

dark they cannot wring a sufficient livelihood from their
farms alone. Neither can they supplement their income by
manufacture. With the exception of china clay, which has
given rise to the pottery industry of Limoges, the granite

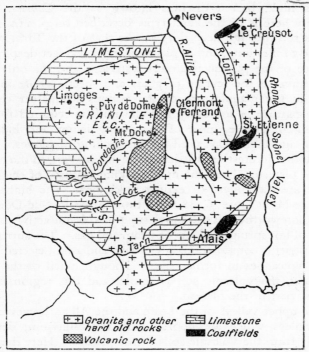

FIG. 78. ROCKS FORMING THE CENTRAL PLATEAU OF FRANCE

rocks bear no minerals; there is little water-power available,
as the contours of the land are remarkably regular; and there
are few forests to provide the basis of home industries as in
the Black Forest. Consequently many of the men find it
necessary to emigrate temporarily to Paris and other large
cities, so as to earn money to supplement the produce of
the farm.

Though the granite forms the greater part of the surface of the plateau, there are parts where other kinds of rock cause widely different types of scenery and human activity. In the south-west the plateau is fringed by a belt of limestone, which forms high, barren districts known as the *Causses*. The scenery here is of the karst type, described on p. 114. The rivers run through deep gorges, like that of the Tarn, which is thirty miles long, and in places nearly 2,000 feet deep. The surface of the plateau is almost waterless, and the only type of farming is the rearing of goats and sheep, whose milk is used in the manufacture of the famous Roquefort cheese. Since pasture is so scanty and the milk is required for the making of cheese, most of the young lambs and kids are killed, and their skins used for the making of gloves.

Another interesting district is that of *Auvergne*, in the centre of the plateau. Here the most striking features of the landscape are the 'puys' or extinct volcanoes. The highest of these is Mont Dore (6,188 feet), though the Puy-de-Dôme is more noteworthy as it still shows signs of volcanic activity in the form of hot springs and jets of steam and gas. The surrounding district is composed mainly of lava and ashes, ejected from these volcanoes in former ages. Though much of the land is stony, the volcanic soil is fertile, and this region is the richest part of the plateau.

The upper valleys of the Loire and the Allier, however, are rift valleys which are floored with rich alluvium, derived mainly from the volcanic soils of the plateau. Here the land is intensively cultivated, and supports a large population of peasants who grow a great variety of crops in their tiny fields. The chief town of the region is *Clermont-Ferrand* (101,000). As its name implies, the town was originally noted for its iron industry, which was based on local supplies of ore. These are not now worked, and the modern prosperity of the town depends on its rubber industry, e.g. Michelin tyres. There is, however, no geographical reason why the industry arose there rather than elsewhere, and the town is not specially well situated for receiving supplies of fuel or raw material. It just happened that one of the first Frenchmen to be interested in the rubber industry was a native of Clermont-Ferrand.

At a few places on the edges of the plateau coal seams have been preserved, e.g. Le Creusot, St. Etienne, and Alès. As these are situated along the eastern edge of the plateau they are more closely connected with the Rhône valley than with the plateau, and are, therefore, considered below.

(2) The Rhône-Saône Basin (Fig. 79)

The Rhône *basin* is, of course, a much larger region than the Rhône *valley*. It includes all the land drained by the Rhône and its tributaries, and may be divided into several sub-regions.

The lowlands adjacent to the delta, though not all included within the river basin, belong to the same natural region as the lower valley.

The Jura Mountains have already been considered when dealing with Switzerland (pages 191, 197). The French portion of these mountains is very similar to the Swiss section. Sheep and goats are kept in large numbers, and much gruyère cheese is made from their milk. There are also numerous small industries, such as the manufacture of clocks, watches, and optical instruments.

The French Alps are also similar to those of Switzerland, though as the pastures are poorer, sheep and goats are more numerous than cattle. The Rhône and its alpine tributaries are the chief source of hydro-electricity in France. The chief generating stations are Génissiat and Donzère, both on the upper Rhône. Subsidiary benefits are improved facilities for navigation and irrigation.

The valley of the Isère is highly industrialized, being especially important for the smelting of aluminium by locally generated hydro-electricity. Grenoble is noted for the manufacture of gloves and has one of the foremost French universities.

The Rhône-Saône Valley was formed, like a rift valley, by the sinking of the land between the Central Plateau and the

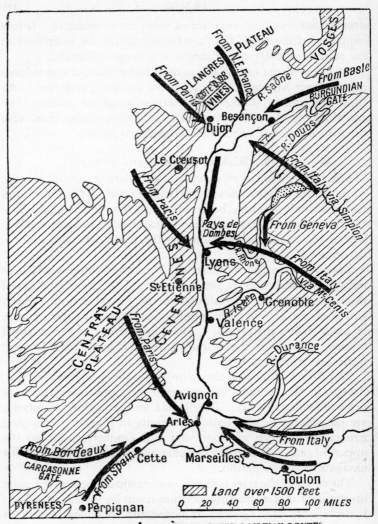

FIG. 79. THE RHÔNE VALLEY: CHIEF RAILWAY ROUTES

Alpine folds. The French speak of it as a *couloir*, and from the dawn of history it has been a corridor leading from the Mediterranean to north-western and central Europe.

Although on the physical map the Rhône-Saône valley seems such a clearly marked unity, there are strong human and economic contrasts between various parts of the valley. The part north of Valence has a continental type of climate, with cold winters and more rain in summer than in winter. Wheat and vines are grown along the whole valley, but dairy farming is almost restricted to the northern part, while olives, mulberries, and walnuts flourish only in the south.

The Côte d'Or is a limestone escarpment, specially noted for the production of wine. The best vines are grown on small terraces on the lower slopes of the hills. 'Higher up the ground is too stony; you will see a rough wall overgrown with brambles dividing worthless brake from vines most carefully tended. Lower down, on the level, the soil is too moist. Yet vines grow there; you will see them stretching out a mile or so. . . . But these vines are of a different kind, hardier, more productive, easier to cultivate, but producing poorer quality of wine.'—S. Gwynn, *Burgundy*.

Nearly all the villages of this region are situated at the foot of the steep scarp slope, near the best vinelands, and where pure water is obtainable from springs.

Dijon owes its importance largely to its situation at the focus of routes. It stands some distance west of the Saône, at the mouth of a gap in the Côte-d'Or, which has from earliest times been used by the main highways (road, canal, and railway) between the Mediterranean and northern France. In Roman times it was the centre of the system of roads, and in the Middle Ages it was the capital of the dukedom of Burgundy. To-day, though completely overshadowed by Paris and Lyons, it is noteworthy as a great railway junction, and as a centre for the preparation of various foodstuffs.

The Pays de Dombes in the angle between the Rhône and the Saône, is a barren, thinly peopled, marshy region, formed of clay and pebbles deposited by a glacier which formerly extended from the Alps into the Rhône valley.

Lyons, situated almost midway along the Rhône-Saône corridor, at the confluence of the two rivers, and in the centre of a fertile region, has become, with the exception of Marseilles, the largest town of the basin. Its world-famous silk industry owes its origin partly to the introduction of silk-worms by the crusaders and partly to the immigration of Italian silk weavers in the thirteenth and sixteenth centuries. Though the locally grown silk has long been quite inadequate for the needs of the industry, and a great deal has to be imported from Italy, China, and Japan, Lyons has maintained its lead among the silk-manufacturing cities of the world. A large part of the manufacture is, however, carried on in the homes of the people, and in small factories on the outskirts of the city. Hydro-electric power is largely used in these small factories, which are thus enabled to compete with the large factories in other countries. In recent years, however, there have been in Lyons itself large developments in the manufacture of artificial fibres, and this district produces about three-quarters of the French output.

Le Creusot, situated on a small coal-field on the edge of the Central Plateau, is noteworthy as the chief French centre for the manufacture of ordnance. Formerly its iron ore was obtained locally, but this supply is now quite inadequate, and has to be supplemented by ore brought from Lorraine.

Saint Etienne, situated on the edge of the Central Plateau, is another industrial city whose prosperity is based on local coal. Its chief manufactures are silk ribbons and steel goods.

Below Valence the Rhône valley opens out to the funnel-shaped lowland which is the typical 'Mediterranean' region of France. It was in this area that Roman influence was strongest, and there are many interesting remains of Roman temples, aqueducts, and amphitheatres. Arles, Nîmes, and Avignon are particularly rich in such remains, while Aigues-Mortes, a 'dead' port, to the west of the delta, is said to be the most perfect medieval town in existence. Built to serve as the base from which the crusaders set out in the eleventh and twelfth centuries, it has never been taken except by treachery, and its walls and towers still rise from the mud flats whose accumulation has destroyed its importance as a port.

The human activities of Provence and Languedoc are typically 'Mediterranean.' The laboriously cultivated fields and terraced hillsides yield the crops of olives, beans, vegetables, wheat, maize, and vines which form the staple foods of the people. Temperamentally the people are distinguished by their gaiety, vivacity, and love of poetry and song.

One of the trials of life in this region is the *mistral*, a cold north-westerly wind which is drawn down the Alpine valleys by the depressions which frequently pass over the Mediterranean in winter. This wind is so harmful to growing crops that wind-breaks are planted round the fields. 'It matters very little what the size of the field, however small, it will probably be held in by cypress trees, which bend away from the north-west, showing clearly the presence of the mistral; and if more evidence were needed of the bitter strength of that wind, you can see that on the mistral side of the trees the foliage is thin and blanched, while on the opposite side it is thick and green. Frequently the lower parts of the cypress stems are latticed with cane stalks as still further protection.'— Roy Elston, *Off the Beaten Track in Southern France*.

The *Île de Camargue*, between the arms of the Rhône delta, is a region of saline swamps on which black bulls are reared for the bull rings of Provence. Some parts have now been transformed into productive rice-fields. The *Plaine de la Crau*, to the east of the delta, is an arid, stone-strewn area which provides winter pasture for sheep which are summered in the Alps.

Arles is an ancient Roman city and modern market town at the head of the delta, and *Les Baux* is a picturesque ruined city which gave its name to bauxite, the ore of aluminium.

The distributaries themselves are not easily navigable, so the

great port of the region, *Marseilles*, has grown up a little to the
east of the delta, on a harbour which is within easy access of
the Rhône valley, but away from the silt brought down by the
river.   The port was founded by the Phoenicians, and ever
since it has been the chief point of contact between France and

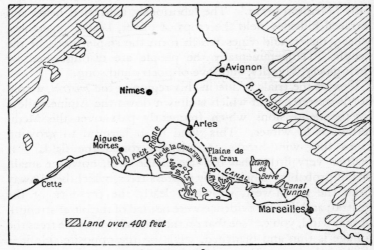

FIG. 80.   THE RHÔNE DELTA

the Mediterranean world.   In modern times it has gained
enormously by the opening of the Suez Canal, and by the
development of French colonies in northern Africa and in the
Far East.   Besides being the chief port of France, it is a great
industrial centre.   Local supplies of olive oil, and facilities
for the importation of vegetable oils from the tropics, have
enabled it to become one of the world's greatest centres for
the manufacture of soap, margarine, and candles.   Petroleum,
which now represents half the total tonnage of imports, is the
basis of the petro-chemical industry.

The port will benefit greatly by the scheme for the canalization of the Rhône, which is now in progress.   The first section

of the work has linked Marseilles by a tunnel to the Étang de Berre, which has thus become a great inner harbour for the port of Marseilles.

Future stages in the development of this great scheme will be directed towards the improvement of navigation on the Rhône and the Saône, the deepening of the Rhône-Saône Canal, the generation of hydro-electricity by the building of dams, and the provision of water for the irrigation of about 1,000 square miles of land. Two of the great hydro-electric stations have already been built, one at Génissiat on the upper Rhône and the other at Donzère-Mondragon, near Avignon.

Toulon is the chief French naval station in the Mediterranean. It is situated on a deep, land-locked harbour, and is easily defended from the landward side by forts on the hills which rise up steeply on all sides.

The coastlands to the eastern and western sides of the Rhône delta show very marked contrasts. To the east is the narrow belt known as the *Riviera*. Here the mountains, rising up sharply from the shore, reflect the sun's rays and protect the coastlands from cold northerly winds, thus causing the warm winters which make Cannes, Nice, Monaco, etc., so famous as holiday resorts.

On the western side of the Gulf of Lions the coast is low and sandy and lagoon-fringed. One of the industries of this district is the preparation of salt by the evaporation of sea-water. Cette, or Sète as it is now called, is situated at the Mediterranean terminus of the Canal du Midi, which runs through the Carcassonne Gate to the Garonne River. It is the chief port for the sardine and tunny fisheries of the Gulf of Lions, and as it is the centre of the largest vine-growing district of France it has some export of wine.

(3) Corsica

Like Sardinia, this island is a remnant of an old land-mass, and is formed chiefly of hard old rock. Nearly all the island is mountainous, and the only parts at all densely peopled are the northern and south-western corners.

Difficulties of communication largely account for the simple and rather primitive mode of life of the people.   Much of the land is covered with *maquis*, which consists of a thick mass of sweet-smelling plants, such as myrtle, heather, lavender, rosemary, and broom.   It is the maquis which gives Corsican scenery its characteristic beauty and has earned for it the name of the Scented Isle.

The people are almost self-supporting, living mainly on the grain, fruit, wine, olive oil, and chestnuts which they produce. In addition olive oil, cork, walnuts, charcoal, and bruyère (the root of a heath plant, used for making 'briar' pipes) are produced for export.   It might have been expected that the infertility of the land, and the presence of numerous harbours on the indented coast, would have led to the development of fishing.   But the Corsican does not readily take to the sea, and the fishing industry is comparatively unimportant.   Neither has Corsica developed overseas trade, in spite of its excellent position between France, Italy, and Spain.

Ajaccio, the capital, is beautifully situated on a broad, mountain-girt bay in the south-west of the island.   *Bastia* is the largest town and chief port of the island.

(4) The Pyrenees

Although the Pyrenees are neither as high nor as broad as the Alps, they form a more effective barrier.   The striking differences in the climate on opposite sides of the range— mild, moist, 'European' type to the north, and arid 'steppe' type to the south—support the statement that 'Africa begins at the Pyrenees.'   Physically, too, the Pyrenees are a well-defined boundary between France and Spain, since there are few passes through the range, and until recently no railway crossed the mountains.   Yet even this range has never formed a complete barrier to human intercourse.   At various periods in history French power has spread over to the Spanish side, and vice versa (see, for example, Fig. 58); and even to-day the widespread seasonal movements of sheep are quite independent of the political boundaries.

The only low pass across the Pyrenees is the Col de Perthus in the east, which carries the main tourist route from France to Spain. Another route much used by tourists crosses the tiny independent state of ANDORRA.

In the steep valleys on the northern side of the range are many hydro-electric stations which supply power to the electrified railways and to various small-scale industries.

Natural gas is produced in great quantity at Lacq near the western end of the Pyrenees, and stored in underground layers of porous sand-stone and pumped as required through pipe-lines to Paris and other cities.

(5) The Aquitaine Basin

This is the region lying between the Central Plateau, the Pyrenees, and the shores of the Bay of Biscay. The basin is composed of strata lying one upon the other like a nest of saucers. As might be expected from its position, the climatic characteristics are midway between those of north-western Europe and those of the Mediterranean region. Consequently the type of farming, and the crops produced, resemble to some extent those of both these regions. Wheat and maize are the chief cereals, but small quantities of oats, rye, and millet are also grown. The climate is not warm enough for the typical 'Mediterranean' fruits, olives and oranges, but chestnuts and walnuts can be grown.

The chief 'money' crop of the region is wine, particularly in the Médoc peninsula, north-west of Bordeaux. In this region the vines are grown on large farms, worked by hired labour, instead of in small vineyards worked by the peasant and his family, which is the system obtaining elsewhere in

France. The valley of the Charente is noted for the brandy which is prepared in the district around Cognac by distilling wine. Armagnac is another brandy region.

Bordeaux is the chief city and commercial centre of the whole region. It is situated at the head of ocean navigation of the Gironde at the lowest bridge-point and at the natural focus of the main routes of the region—from Marseilles through the Carcassonne Gate, from Paris via the Poitou Gate, and from Spain via the coastal gap at the western end of the Pyrenees. It is interesting to see how each of these gateways has been of importance in military history.

In the Poitou Gate lies *Poitiers*, famous for the battle in which the Black Prince defeated the French in 1356. *Bayonne* is a fortress town guarding the point where the coastal route from Spain crosses the River Adour.

At the western end of the Carcassonne Gate is the ancient city of *Carcassonne*, which rivals Aigues-Mortes in the perfection of its medieval defences. On the Aquitaine side of the gap is the modern city of *Toulouse*, situated where a number of tributary valleys converge upon the Garonne. It has thus become the chief route-centre and market-town of the surrounding region, but the convergence of so many valleys upon it causes it to suffer occasionally from disastrous floods.

The Landes. This term is used by the French to designate sandy, barren lands in general, and the coastal region between the Gironde and the Adour in particular. The long straight coast, which is so noticeable on the maps, is formed by lines of sand dunes; behind these are shallow salt lagoons or *étangs*, similar to those around Cette; inland again are extensive marshes and great expanses of barren sandy plain.

Formerly the only occupation open to the people was the rearing of sheep, by shepherds mounted on stilts, with a third stilt for a rest. But in modern times the landes have been made productive by the planting of pine trees which are tapped for turpentine, or cut down for export as pit props.

'By undaunted perseverance the seed was made to take
root in the shifting sand, and thus dune after dune was fixed.
It was one of those long battles with the forces of nature in
which human purpose, often discouraged, but never turned
from its object, triumphs at last over seemingly insurmount-
able obstacles.   Before the dunes were covered with pines
they were constantly changing their shape and place, ebbing
and flowing like the sea; but always gaining in the sum of
years upon the mainland.' [1]

A recently developed oil-field at Parentis now produces
about a million tons of oil a year.

(6) The North-western Peninsula

The north-western corner of France, which includes the
western half of Normandy and all Brittany, is very different
from the rest of the country.   The greater part of the surface
is composed of ridges of hard old rocks, the last remnants of
the Hercynian range which, hundreds of millions of years
ago, stretched from south-western Ireland, through South
Wales, Cornwall and Devon, and Brittany, to the Central
Plateau of France.   In Brittany, as in Cornwall, these granite
ridges form the barren moorlands between which are situated
deep fertile valleys and secluded basins.

Standing on one of these landes, or moorland wastes, we
should see no sign of human habitation, though in many
districts we should see great circles and avenues of stone which
were set up by the pagan inhabitants of thousands of years
ago.   One such avenue, at Carnac, contains more than 1,200
huge single blocks standing upright in parallel lines.   Why,
and how, they were reared we can only guess, though, like
the similar stone circles and avenues in Britain, they certainly
have some connection with the religious ceremonies of the
pre-Christian inhabitants.

All the villages, and even the single farms, are snugly
hidden in the deep valleys where Nature, relenting of her

[1] E. H. Barker, *Wayfaring in France.*

M E

niggardliness, has left patches of fertile soil. Even here
granite is much in evidence, for it is the only building material;
the single-story houses, the low-spired village church, the
calvaire or crucifix at the cross-roads, even the garden fences,
are all constructed of this same grey stone.

Near the church we may see the 'Bone House,' a gruesome
reminder of the scarcity of good land; for it was built as the
permanent repository of bones dug from old graves in order
to make room for other burials, thus avoiding the necessity
of taking good land from the living in order to accommodate
the dead.

The scanty farm-land surrounding the village is divided into
numerous little fields surrounded by high walls of granite or
turf, above which rise straggly wind-clipped trees and bushes
which shelter the crops from the full force of the Atlantic
gales. Grass is the chief field crop, for the westerly winds
from the Atlantic make the climate mild and moist; here and
there are small fields of rye and buckwheat, which provide
the people with their chief food. The characteristic drink of
the people, cider, is represented by numerous apple orchards
which, particularly in spring, add great charm to the rural
scene. The chief 'money' crops are vegetables which the
peasant has found he can sell at a good price, since the mild
winters and early springs enable him to produce them many
months earlier than we can in England.

The coastal regions of Brittany are more fertile than the
inland valleys; indeed the southern margin of the peninsula
is so productive that it is sometimes called the 'belt of gold.'
From both the northern and the southern coastal plains dairy
produce, early vegetables, and small fruits—especially strawberries—are exported, in normal times, to England.

The coast itself is deeply indented by many *rias*, formed by
the subsidence of the land in bygone ages. As in many other
countries where fertile land is scarce and there are many good
harbours, fishing has become an important industry, though
nearly every fisherman also possesses a plot of land which he

cultivates in his spare time.   The chief fish caught in the home
waters are sardines, which are canned for export.   Many Breton
fishermen also participate in the cod and herring fisheries of
Iceland and Newfoundland.

The rugged character of the peninsula and its remoteness
from the main routes have caused Brittany to be always
somewhat isolated from the rest of France.   At the dawn of
history it was peopled by Celtic tribes similar to the Ancient
Britons.   It was conquered by Julius Caesar in 56 B.C. and
remained under Roman rule until the fifth century.   After the
withdrawal of the Romans it became, like Wales, Cornwall, and
Ireland, a refuge from invading 'barbarians,' and for three
hundred years it had more in common with the Celtic parts
of our own islands than with France.   Welsh and Irish missionaries converted the people to Christianity, and many of the
towns and villages in both Brittany and Cornwall were named
after these saints; also the syllables 'tre,' 'pol,' 'pen,' etc.,
occur very frequently in the place-names of both peninsulas.

During succeeding centuries Brittany has remained somewhat aloof from the main currents of French life.   The Breton
language, which is similar to Welsh, is still spoken by some
of the peasants, and ancient customs, festivals, and styles of
dress still linger in the remoter districts, giving the people the
quaintness which is so attractive to tourists.

Normandy comprises two physical divisions.   The western
half, including the Cotentin Peninsula, is composed of hard
old rocks, and so resembles Brittany.   The eastern half is
composed of newer and softer rocks, like those of the Paris
basin.   It is, indeed, a part of the latter region, and is considered under that heading.

The Lower Loire.   The Loire basin does not constitute one
natural region, but is shared between three such regions.   The
upper portion, as already noted, is part of the Central Plateau
region; the middle portion is part of the Paris basin, and will
be considered with that natural region; the lower portion of
the basin, which is formed of hard old rocks, is really part of

the North-western Peninsula. Here, as in Brittany, market-gardening, fruit-growing, dairying, and fishing are the chief occupations.

The Towns of the North-western Peninsula

Saint-Malo, the chief port of northern Brittany, is a picturesque town which sums up a good deal of the history and modern activities of the peninsula. It grew up around a monastery which was founded by the Welsh missionary, St. Malo, on a small island near the mainland. As the country became more settled the island became a trading centre and fortress-port. In modern times the island has been joined to the mainland by a broad embankment, but the city walls still remain to remind us of the former need for defence. To-day Saint-Malo is a busy fishing port, an attractive holiday resort, and a centre for the exportation of the typical products of Brittany—butter, cheese, and early fruits and vegetables. The harbour has recently been improved to make it capable of accommodating, at any state of the tide, passenger steamers which ply from Southampton. On the nearby estuary of the Rance the exceptionally high and powerful tides are now being harnessed to generate electricity.

Brest, situated on a fine ria harbour at the extremity of the peninsula, is comparable with Falmouth in Cornwall. It is a naval station, guarding the western entrance to the Channel, but suffers as a commercial port from the fact that it is much cheaper for transatlantic vessels to take their cargo to ports like Havre and Rouen than to land them at Brest and send them forward by rail.

Rennes, the capital of Brittany, is situated in the fertile valley of the Vilaine. It is chiefly noteworthy as the market town of the surrounding dairying and market-gardening area.

Cherbourg, at the extreme northern end of the Cotentin Peninsula, is a naval station guarding the Channel routes and the entrance to the Seine. It is also a calling station for transatlantic liners.

E. N. A.

A Shepherd on the Meseta of Spain

E. N. A.

A Farm Yard in Brittany

Nantes grew up at the head of sea navigation of the Loire, where tributaries join the main river on either bank, and where islands facilitate crossing. Though it cannot be reached by the largest ocean vessels, it is connected with the sea by a ship canal, and ranks as the sixth port of France. Its facilities for the importation of raw materials have led to the development of miscellaneous industries, such as flour-milling, the canning of fish and fruit, and the making of biscuits and chocolate.

Saint-Nazaire is the outport for Nantes, and *Lorient* is an important fishing station.

(7) Alsace-Lorraine

After the Franco-German War of 1870 these two provinces were annexed by Germany, but were returned to France by the Peace Treaty following the First World War.

Physically Alsace consists of the faulted block of the Vosges and the western half of the Rhine Rift Valley (see pp. 226–9), while Lorraine consists of alternating layers of hard and soft rocks which dip westwards towards the Paris basin.

A magic-carpet flight across these two provinces would show us the following features. (See Fig. 81.)

(*a*) On each side of the Rhine is a waterlogged, infertile flood-plain. South of Strasbourg the river is in some places too shallow, in others too rapid for navigation; consequently there are few towns or villages in this section.

(*b*) West of the marshes and extending as far as the River Ill is a narrow belt, forested in some places, and bare in others, but everywhere thinly peopled. This belt of land was formed by the pebbles which were deposited at the close of the Ice Age. (See p. 228.)

(*c*) The western half of the plain, between the River Ill and the Vosges, has large areas which are covered with fertile loess soil. This region is, therefore, one of the most densely peopled and intensively cultivated farming regions of Europe. Market gardening, fruit-growing, and the cultivation of tobacco and hops are of great importance, while wheat, maize, sugar beet, and flax are also widely grown. The foothills of the Vosges form one of the chief vine-growing districts of France. The vineyards are situated on the fertile loess-covered slopes, above the mists and frosts of the plain, and facing south-east so as to obtain the maximum amount of sunshine.

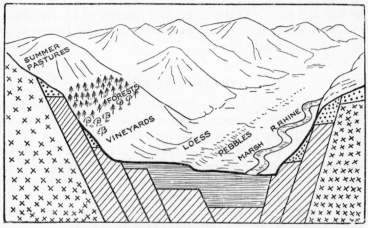

FIG. 81. BLOCK DIAGRAM OF THE RHINE RIFT VALLEY

(d) The steep slopes of the Vosges are covered with forests except at the base and the summit. The lower slopes are devoted to the cultivation of cereals, tobacco, vines, etc. The rounded grassy summits, or 'chaumes,' are bare of trees, and form excellent summer pastures. Cattle are driven up to the chaumes in May, and remain there under the charge of herdsmen until the end of September. As in Switzerland, cheese is made from the milk.

The forests of the middle slopes furnish much timber, which is usually transported to the valleys on sledges which run over 'corduroy' roads made of trunks of trees.

(e) The Lorraine Plateau, sloping westward from the summit of the Vosges towards the Paris basin. This plateau is composed

CHAVMS

of the Triassic series of rocks, like the uplands of central
Germany mentioned on p. 213. The most easterly and highest
belt is a forested ridge of sandstone, then comes a rather
more fertile belt of limestone, and finally a very productive
belt of clay. (Fig. 82.)

Westward again we come to the scarped edges of the limestone rocks which underlie the Paris basin. In these rocks
occur great deposits of iron ore, forming the Lorraine iron-
fields, which are dealt with in a later paragraph.

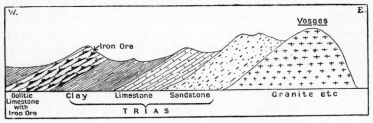

FIG. 82. DIAGRAM SECTION ACROSS LORRAINE

The plateau is drained by the rivers Meuse and Moselle,
which flow northward along clay vales between the eastward-
facing scarps. The upper Moselle was formerly a tributary
of the Meuse, but was captured by the lower Moselle; the low
gap between Toul and the Meuse marks the former course of
the upper Moselle.

The hilly regions are for the most part forested, but the clay
vales between form good agricultural land. About half the
total area is arable land, the chief 'money' crops being wheat
and hops. Lorraine is, however, more famous for its mining
and manufacturing industries than for agriculture.

Towns and Industries of the Rift Valley

Belfort is situated in the Belfort or Burgundian Gate, between
the Vosges and the Jura, and on the most direct route between
the Rhône and the Rhine valleys. Its chief industries are the
manufacture of textiles and electrical machinery.

Mulhouse, now a manufacturing town of 100,000 inhabitants, was founded more than two thousand years ago on a small island in the River Ill. Its textile industry was begun by Huguenots, who found safety in Alsace when it was part of Germany. To-day it is still an important centre for the manufacture of cottons, woollens, and silk. Some distance to the north of the town is one of the world's chief deposits of potash and common salt. These minerals have given rise to a large chemical industry, besides providing valuable manures and a considerable surplus for export. Many of the textile factories are now run by hydro-electricity, derived from the rapid streams of the Vosges. The city is at the junction of several railways, and is served by the Rhine-Rhône Canal. It will also benefit considerably by the completion of the Grand Canal of Alsace, which will provide increased facilities for transport, and large supplies of hydro-electricity.

Colmar is another ancient city which has developed modern textile industries.

Strasbourg first grew up on an island between two branches of the River Ill, near to the confluence with the Rhine. Historically it first became important as the 'street-burg,' or fortress, on the Roman road across the Rhine. The factors which have assisted its development into a large city are: (*a*) It is the natural market centre of a rich loess-covered plain. (*b*) The Saverne or Lorraine Gate, which leads from Strasbourg around the northern end of the Vosges, provides the most direct route from Paris to the upper Rhine and central Europe. This gap is followed by the Orient Express route from Paris to Vienna, and by the Rhine-Marne Canal. (*c*) The Rhine has been deepened so as to enable barges and steamers to reach the city, and the Rhine-Rhône Canal gives it connection with the Mediterranean. It has thus become one of the chief ports of France. Its chief imports are coal, cereals, and petroleum, and its exports iron ore from Lorraine and potash from Alsace. It has also many miscellaneous industries, such as the manufacture of machinery, chemicals, and beer. The manufacture of *pâté de foie gras*, for which the city is specially noted, owes its origin to the invention of this delicacy by a Strasbourg cook in the eighteenth century.

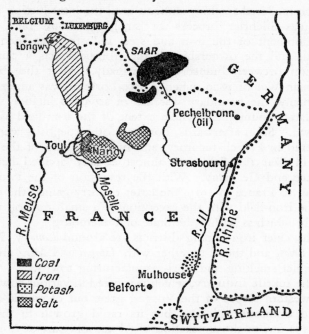

FIG. 83. ALSACE-LORRAINE: MINERALS

Towns and Industries of Lorraine

The Lorraine iron-field has already been mentioned as the chief iron- and steel-producing district in Europe (see page 234).

As in the iron-mining districts of Cleveland and the English Midlands the ore occurs in beds of Oolitic limestone, which form an escarpment running from south to north. (See Fig. 82.) In most districts the beds of ore lie so near the surface that they can be worked by merely stripping off the

*M E

'over-burden' of soil and digging out the ore by mechanical
excavators which load it directly into railway trucks.

The Lorraine ore contains a certain amount of phosphorus,
which rendered smelting difficult until the introduction of the
Thomas-Gilchrist process of smelting about 1880. The
development of the iron and steel industry was then very
rapid, and the ownership of the iron-field was a cause of
friction between France and Germany. After the Franco-
German War of 1870, when Alsace-Lorraine was annexed by
Germany, the boundary was drawn so as to include within
the latter country the whole extent of the iron-field as then
known. Soon afterwards, however, other deposits were discovered in French territory, and up to the end of the First
World War the field was almost equally divided between
France and Germany. With the reversion of the two provinces to France in 1919, the latter country gained the whole
of the iron-field with the exception of a small portion in the
north, which is within the State of Luxemburg.

The chief iron-mining districts are around *Longwy*, *Nancy*,
and *Briey*, and these, together with *Epinal* and *Metz* are also
the chief smelting and steel-manufacturing towns.

The textile industry, which is centred in various towns on
the western slopes of the Vosges, grew out of an old-established domestic industry, but its rapid growth in modern
times is due to the annexation of Alsace and part of Lorraine
by Germany in 1871. When this took place many French
manufacturers abandoned their works at Mulhouse, Colmar,
etc., and built new ones on French territory at such towns as
Epinal and Saint-Dié. Though practically all the raw materials
have to be imported, coal is near at hand in the Saar basin, and
the industry has increased more rapidly than that of Alsace,
to which coal has to be brought from a distance.

Glass making is one of the oldest industries of this region,
having developed here because of the supplies of sand and
of wood for fuel. Nowadays, of course, coal is used in place
of wood, but the industry continues to flourish in a line of

towns situated where the Vosges sink to the Lorraine Plateau. Specialities include the manufacture of crystal glass, watch glasses, and lenses.

Cutlery is manufactured at various centres on the Langres Plateau. The industry is carried on chiefly in the homes of the people, and the recent introduction of hydro-electricity has enabled this domestic industry to hold its own in competition with the large-scale factory products.

Chemicals are manufactured at Nancy and other towns, the industry being based on local supplies of potash and rock salt and gypsum.

(8) The Paris Basin

This is an almost circular lowland, the north-eastern half of which is drained by the Somme and the Seine, while the south-eastern portion is drained by the middle Loire. Structurally it is a great hollow, filled by successive layers of rock which lie upon one another like saucers. The lowest 'saucer' is of limestone, and its edges crop out to form the rim of the 'basin' round the headwaters of the Seine and its tributaries. Another 'saucer-edge' is represented by the chalk escarpments of Champagne and Picardy, and by the chalk hills on each side of the mouth of the Seine. Between the 'saucer-edges' are layers of clay, which form the district known as the 'Wet' Champagne, in distinction to the 'Dry' Champagne of the Chalk Scarp. (Fig. 84.)

The chalk saucer itself is filled with a variety of rocks— limestone, sandstone, and clay—which make up the country immediately around Paris.

These different types of rock affect the mode of life of the people so profoundly that it is necessary to divide the Paris basin into several minor natural regions, viz.:

(a) *Île-de-France* is the region of newer rocks filling the 'saucer' of chalk. The French distinguish several districts or 'pays,' each characterized by particular types of rock, soil, and cultivation. Thus Beauce is a low plateau between the Seine and the Loire, formed of limestone overlain by a fertile soil called *limon*. This is a great wheat and sheep land, the animals being turned into the fields after the harvest to feed on the stubble. Brie is the district between the Seine and the Marne. Here the soil is a heavy rich clay, devoted largely to the cultivation of sugar beet.

FIG. 84. ESCARPMENTS EAST OF PARIS

Where the surface is very sandy, as around Fontainebleau, large stretches of forest still remain. The Fontainebleau sand is so pure that it is in great demand for glass making, and large quantities are shipped to England for this purpose.

Paris. Before Julius Caesar conquered Gaul a semi-civilized tribe, known as the Parisii, lived in the middle part of the Seine basin. They chose as their stronghold in time of war a group of little islands in the Seine, and it is around the site of this early fortress that the modern city of Paris has grown up. After the Roman conquest the primitive fort was replaced by a strong encampment, and gradually a Roman city grew up around it. Bridges were built from the island to both banks of the river, and Roman roads from west and east were made to converge on the city. For nearly five hundred years the city enjoyed peace and prosperity under Roman rule, until at the end of the fifth century it was taken by Clovis and his barbarian host, and became the capital city of the conquerors.

In succeeding centuries certain natural advantages of the site of Paris considerably assisted the development of the city. It is situated where the easiest route from Belgium to south-western France, via the Poitou Gate, crosses the Seine; the Seine itself, and its tributary, the Yonne, form natural routes

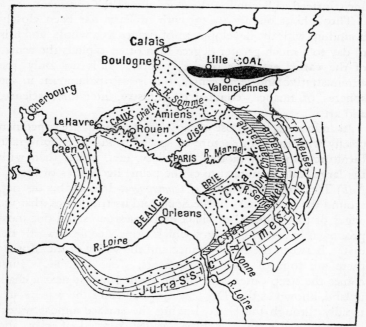

FIG. 85. THE PARIS BASIN

from the Rhône-Saône basin to the Channel coast. The valleys of the Marne and the upper Loire also direct traffic to Paris, while breaks in the limestone and chalk rim surrounding the Paris basin make the city the natural focus of routes from the east. Paris is, moreover, at the head of sea navigation of the Seine, and has always had some importance as a port. But closely interwoven with these purely geographical factors are personal and historical factors. In A.D. 987, for example,

Hugh Capet, the count of Paris, was chosen as overlord of
the region which is now northern France. Had some other
nobleman been chosen, and had the little realm of Île-de-
France not been ruled by a succession of able and ambitious
men, Paris might have remained a city of secondary importance, instead of becoming the chief city of the continent.

Throughout history the growth of Paris has been closely
bound up with the development of France as a whole, and it is
to-day to a much greater degree than other capitals the centre
of the varied activities of the country. It is not only the
administrative and legal centre, but is also paramount in the
spheres of finance, commerce, industry, literature, science,
and art.

Its industries, like those of most great capitals, are concerned
chiefly with the manufacture of special foodstuffs, high-grade
furniture, clothing, motors, jewellery, etc., rather than with
the large-scale manufacture of the prime necessities of life.

(b) *The Scarps and Valleys of Champagne*. It is in this district,
around the headwaters of the Seine and its tributaries, that the
edges of the 'saucers' of chalk and limestone stand out most
prominently, forming ridges which slope steeply towards the
east.   Between the Île-de-France and the valley of the Moselle
there are four of these escarpments. (See Fig. 84.) First
comes the steep outer edge of the Île-de-France; next a chalk
upland, known as the 'Dry Champagne,' since the water soaks
rapidly through the chalk, leaving the surface almost waterless; eastward again is a broad valley formed of clay, and
known as 'Wet Champagne'; beyond this are limestone
escarpments separated by wet clay vales.   The uplands of the
'Dry Champagne' and of the limestone escarpments are largely
given up to sheep rearing, but the scarp slopes are terraced
with vineyards which produce the wine known as champagne.
The moist clay vales between the scarps form a marked contrast with the limestone and chalk uplands; streams and ponds
are numerous; the population is evenly distributed in villages
and picturesque hamlets; dairy cattle graze on the rich moist

pastures, and a large proportion of the land is under the plough. Most of the towns have grown up at the foot of the scarp, where the two rivers make gaps through the hills, e.g. Epernay and Troyes. Rheims, situated between the Aisne and the Marne, is the centre of the champagne country, and has also some textile manufactures.

(c) *The Middle Loire.* The River Loire is somewhat peculiar, as in both its upper and lower courses it flows through areas of hard old rock (the Central Plateau and Brittany respectively), while its middle course is through the newer rocks of the Paris basin. In this part of its basin, the districts between the rivers (e.g. the Sologne district, between the Cher and the Loire) are rather barren and thinly peopled, but the alluvial valleys themselves are among the most intensively cultivated and densely peopled agricultural regions of France.

The district of the middle Loire is often called 'the château country' because of the remarkable number of famous châteaux, such as Chaumont and Blois. The châteaux were built as country mansions during the eighteenth century, usually on the site of some former fortress overlooking the Loire. Orleans grew up where the great right-angle bend of the Loire brings it nearest to Paris. It is, therefore, the natural route-centre and market-town of the region. Tours is somewhat similarly situated where the Paris-to-Bordeaux route crosses the Loire and turns southward towards the Poitou Gate.

(d *The Lower Seine.* The chalk in the district on either side of the estuary of the Seine is covered with *limon*. It is, therefore, more fertile and more densely peopled than the corresponding 'Dry Champagne.' Eastern Normandy, including the Caux district between the lower Seine and the sea, with its apple orchards, rich pastures, and thatched cottages is, indeed, very similar to Kent.

Caen, notable as the birthplace of William the Conqueror, has iron mines in the vicinity. Much of the ore is smelted locally to supply steel to shipyards on the estuary of the Seine.

Rouen is the lowest bridge-point and head of ocean navigation of the Seine. As a port it ranks next to Marseilles and Le Havre, and is also one of the greatest centres of the cotton industry, which arose there for the following reasons: (*a*) The people had long been accustomed to making woollen and linen cloth in their own homes, and were, therefore, able to supply the skilled labour needed in the factories. (*b*) The Seine provides cheap transport of raw material and finished products. This was a very important factor in the early days of the industry when land transport was slow and costly. (*c*) The Seine and smaller streams provided water-power which, though not much used to-day, was of great importance in former times.

Le Havre, at the mouth of the Seine, is the chief transatlantic passenger port of France, and its second most important commercial port. Its chief imports are petroleum, cotton, timber, and oil-seeds.

The chief industries of the port, and of the many small towns on the banks of the lower Seine, are shipbuilding, engineering, oil-refining, and the manufacture of paper and chemicals.

Boulogne is one of the chief packet stations for cross-Channel traffic.

(*e*) *The Industrial North-east.* The provinces of Artois and Picardy are composed, like south-eastern England, of chalk and limestone hills, with intervening alluvial valleys. The soil is, however, deeper than on our chalk and limestone hills, and so the region is one of great fertility. The chief speciality is the production of sugar beet, but flax, hops, and grain are also grown in large quantities.

This region ranks first among the industrial regions of France, its prosperity being based largely on the continuation of the Meuse valley coal-field, which extends into France around Valenciennes, Lens, and Béthune. Many of the mines were badly damaged during the First World War, but they have been re-equipped with the most up-to-date machinery.

Lille is the largest town of the region, and specializes in the manufacture of linen goods, cotton goods, machinery, and sugar. Most of the factories are on the outskirts of the town.

Other towns which are engaged principally in the textile industries are *Roubaix*, *Tourcoing*, and *Armentières*. *Cambrai* and *Saint-Quentin* are noteworthy chiefly as markets for the linen cloth which is woven in the surrounding districts. *Valenciennes* and *Arras*, though formerly textile towns, are now centres of miscellaneous industries, such as the manufacture of machinery, chemicals, glass, sugar, and alcohol.

Dunkirk is the chief commercial port of the region, and *Calais* is an important packet station for cross-Channel traffic.

THE COUNTRY AS A WHOLE

We have seen from the above studies of the natural regions that France is a very varied country; indeed, hardly any other country in Europe contains so many diverse physical units, and, in consequence, such a diversity of interests among its people. Yet the essential unity of France ensures her a dominant position in Europe and the world.

In the early days of her history the diversity of France was a source of weakness and disunity; but by the accidents of history, by the action of the instincts of common nationality, and by the deliberate design of the rulers, the diverse elements in the population have been united to form one nation, and the various natural regions have been welded together to form an economic whole. In order to achieve this unity the Government has for centuries adopted the policy of centralization, which means that the affairs of every part of the country are controlled from one centre—Paris. The various departments do not enjoy the same degree of self-government as do our English counties and municipalities; and Paris is much more the centre of France than London is of Britain. It is this policy of centralization which explains, for example, the remarkable convergence of all the main roads, railways, and canals upon Paris. The systems of transport, like the system of government, were designed to increase the dependence of outlying parts of the country upon the capital.

Again, because of her diversity, France is more self-sufficing and less dependent on foreign trade than most other highly

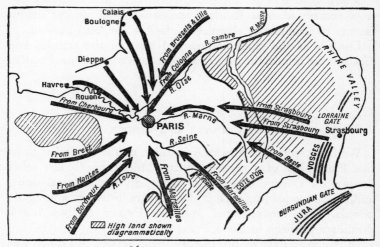

FIG. 86. PARIS AS A ROUTE-CENTRE

civilized countries. Her foreign trade per head is, indeed, little more than half that of Britain. In normal years, in spite of the rather low yield per acre, she is able to produce much more wheat than she requires, and has a sufficiency of other staple foodstuffs. The chief commodities she has to buy from other countries are wool, cotton, coal, and silk, and tropical products; while the chief exports are manufactured goods such as silk and cotton, chemicals, clothing, iron and steel, motor cars, and wine.

THE COMMON MARKET

For a thousand years and more Western Europe was divided into several countries in rivalry with one another and often at war. Though this diversity has had some beneficial results, it became clear after the disaster of the Second World War

FIG. 87. THE COMMON MARKET

that unity and not rivalry was the necessary condition for the revival and continued growth of the prosperity of the region. Accordingly in 1958 the six countries of France, Western Germany, Belgium, the Netherlands, Luxembourg, and Italy joined together to form the Common Market, thus restoring by voluntary action the unity which had been forced upon the region by Charlemagne. (Compare Fig. 87 with Fig. 58, p. 205.)

The object of the organization is to create in Western Europe a unified region within which farming, manufacturing, and trading may develop as freely and fully as in a single large country.

Among the means by which this objective is being achieved are:

(1) The abolition of all tariff and other barriers to trade between the member countries.

(2) The development of a unified system of transport so that goods and people can move freely across the former frontiers.

(3) The co-ordination of production in various parts of the Community, so that each district may make its maximum contribution to the welfare of the region as a whole.

(4) The development of the more backward areas within the Community and its partners overseas.

These policies have been so successful that in the first five years of its existence the Community increased its industrial production by 40 per cent, its trade between its member countries by 50 per cent, and its trade with the rest of the world by 25 per cent.

The following statistics show how closely Western Europe as a whole compares in population and productivity with the other two 'giant' powers of the world—the United States and the Soviet Union.

	Western Europe		U.S.A.	U.S.S.R.
	'The Six'	U.K.		
Population (millions)	170	52	180	215
Coal (million tons)	350	200	500	500
Steel (million tons)	73	22	89	71
Wheat (million tons)	26	3	31	70
Imports (million dols.)	20	13	15	6
Exports (million dols.)	20	10	20	6

INDEX